Managing and Evaluating Healthcare Intervention Programs

Ian Duncan, FSA, FIA, FCIA, MAAA

Manufactured in the United States of America

10 9 8 7 6 5 4 3 2 1

Cover design by Christine Phelps

Library of Congress Cataloging-in-Publication Data

Duncan, Ian G., 1950-
Managing and evaluating healthcare intervention programs / Ian Duncan.
p. ; cm.
Includes bibliographical references and index.
ISBN 978-1-56698-656-4 (alk. paper)
1. Managed care plans (Medical care)--United States--Finance. 2. Managed care plans (Medical care)--United States--Evaluation. 3. Disease management--United States. I. Title.
[DNLM: 1. Managed Care Programs--economics--United States. 2. Actuarial Analysis--United States. 3. Disease Management--United States. 4. Health Care Costs--United States. 5. Program Evaluation--economics--United States. 6. Treatment Outcome--United States. W 130 AA1 D911m 2008]
RA413.D86 2008
338.4'3362104258--dc22

2008038456

ISBN: 978-1-56698-656-4

CONTENTS

PART 1
AN INTRODUCTION TO CARE MANAGEMENT INTERVENTIONS

PART 2
ACTUARIAL ISSUES IN CARE MANAGEMENT INTERVENTIONS

PART 3
PRACTICAL APPLICATIONS

PART 4
WELLNESS, INTEGRATED PROGRAMS AND OTHER NEW DEVELOPMENTS IN CARE MANAGEMENT PROGRAMS

PART 5
CONCLUSION

PREFACE

This book grew out of a series of papers that was developed with grants from the Society of Actuaries Health Section and the Society of Actuaries Council for Knowledge Extension and Research, together with additions from other actuaries and researchers in the field of measurement of chronic care and other care programs. The author is grateful for the peer review and valuable input on the original papers by the project oversight group:

Bryan Miller, FSA, MAAA, Blue Cross Blue Shield of Kansas City (Chairman)
John Cookson, FSA, MAAA, Milliman USA
Stacey Lampkin, FSA, MAAA, Anthem, Inc.
John Stark, FSA, MAAA, Anthem Inc.
Margie Rosenberg, PhD, FSA, MAAA, University of Wisconsin-Madison
Ronora Stryker, ASA, MAAA, Society of Actuaries
Stephen Siegel, ASA, MAAA, Society of Actuaries

We are also grateful to the Society of Actuaries for their permission to use the original copyrighted papers as the foundation for this book.

The valuable assistance, support and input from the Society of Actuaries Health Section (Karl Volkmar, FSA, MAAAA, Chairman) and the Committee on Knowledge Extension Research (Curtis Huntington, JD, FSA, MAAA, University of Michigan, Chairman) is also acknowledged. Also, a number of reviewers have read earlier drafts of the manuscript and their suggestions are gratefully acknowledged.

Sheryl Coughlin, PhD
Henry Dove, PhD
J. Ramsay Farah, MD, MPH, FAAP, FACPM, CPE, CMRO,
Stephen Siegel, ASA, MAAA

One reviewer deserves special thanks. Iver Juster, MD, ActiveHealth Management Inc., diligently reviewed the entire text and his thoughtful contributions are reflected throughout.

A number of co-authors and research assistants have contributed to different chapters.

Chapters 2-4: Henry Dove, PhD, Yale University, Division of Health Policy and Administration

Chapter 4: Koren Odierna, Yale University, Division of Health Policy Research and Administration Assistants Elizabeth Heckinger, UCLA

Chapter 9: Mita Lodh, MBA, PhD, FSA, MAAA Schrammraleigh Health Strategy, Gregory Berg, PhD, and David Mattingly, BA, McKesson Health Solutions.

Chapter 10: Thomas Messer PhD, ASA, MAAA, Solucia Inc., J. Ramsay Farah, MD, MPH, FAAP, FACPM, FASAM, CPE, CMRO, Kyahn Kamali, MHS, CPHIMS and Jeffrey Harner, MS, Nationwide Better Health Inc.

Chapter 11: Robert Bachler, FSA, FCAS, MAAA, Munich Re Healthcare and Iver Juster, MD, ActiveHealth Management Inc.

Chapter 12: Rebecca Owen, FSA, MAAA, Solucia Inc. Henry Dove, PhD Yale University, Division of Health Policy and Administration

Chapters 13-14: Sheryl Coughlin, PhD MHA, B. App. Sci., Solucia Inc.

Chapter 15: Christian Birkmeyer, MS, Solucia Inc.
Manjula Singh, MA, PhD, Solucia Inc.
Appendix: Vincent Kane, FSA, MAAA, DxCG Inc.
Anju Joglekar, PhD, DxCG Inc.

Gail Hall, FSA, MAAA of ACTEX Publications should be commended for taking a risk on an unknown author and a topic that is still outside the actuarial mainstream. I am grateful to Marilyn Baleshiski for her help in editing and laying out the manuscript.

Readers familiar with the Society of Actuaries papers will recognize that they form the basis for Chapters 2 through 12. Chapters 5 and 10 are, however, entirely new material. We have added new material on wellness and employer worksite health programs, a growing, related, area, in Chapters 13 and 14.

A note on terminology: this book purposely aims to cover the broad topic of Care Management Interventions. As discussed in Chapter 2, there are many different types of interventions that may be included under this broad title. Later in the book, we focus specifically on one type of intervention, Disease Management. This is for several reasons, including the significant interest on the part of actuaries and purchasers in this type of intervention. Despite this focus, the techniques and methods discussed in later chapters may be applied (with appropriate modifications for circumstances) to different types of interventions.

We also acknowledge the contributions of Munich Re Health Care, Highmark Inc., McKesson Corporation and Nationwide Better Health Inc., without whose support the analytical work would not have been completed.

A Guide To The Contents Of This Book

Our first two Chapters are essentially background reading for those with little prior exposure to the topic. Chapter 2 discusses different conventional care management intervention programs. In an appendix to this chapter we address specifically care management interventions within Medicaid Programs, an area of growing interest and importance. In Chapter 3 we discuss specific actuarial topics that arise in program evaluation, including study design and the importance of understanding and accounting for risk. Chapter 4 is a review of the published literature about the financial outcomes of different types of programs.

Chapter 5 deviates a little from the remainder of the book, being more operational than financial in nature. Nevertheless, if the reader is to be able to assess financial and other results, it is important that he or she understand the underlying mechanics of programs. And the technique discussed – Value Chain analysis – is worth considering for its potential contribution to understanding the components of a program.

Chapter 6 discusses the economics of Disease Management. Chapters 7 and 8 discuss principles for designing a study to assess financial results of a program, and the practical implementation of those principles in a particular study design, the adjusted historical control methodology. These principles are discussed further in Chapter 9 where we examine the issue of changes in the risk profile of the intervention population, its potential effect on the measured outcomes of a program, and methods for mitigating this effect. Chapter 10 contains an extended discussion of the topic of sample size and the difficulties inherent in measuring outcomes in small populations.

Chapter 11 examines what is arguably the most important single factor in program evaluations – healthcare cost trend. This chapter, a re-print of an article that appeared in the North American Actuarial Journal in 2006, examines both theoretically and practically the potential measurement bias that can arise in measuring trend under different assumptions. Chapter 12 is a practical test of the effect that varying different assumptions has on the measured outcomes of a program.

Chapter 13 defines wellness programs, a relatively new concept of growing interest. Chapter 14 reviews the published literature on outcomes and savings, and Chapter 15 looks at the possible savings from a program in a commercial population, using one measurement methodology.

Finally, in Chapter 16, we look again at the state of financial management of the industry and where it may be headed in the next few years.

Introduction

Howard Bolnick, FSA , MAAA, HONFIA

Health actuarial practice has been a growing and dynamic part of the profession for many decades. When I began working in the area in the 1970s, indemnity insurance was the only game in town: data were quite limited, and actuarial tools were basic. All this changed with the advent and growth of managed care. There were new types of insurance arrangements that required more robust data, and, new actuarial tools were needed to successfully manage a growing variety of managed care plans, each with its own distinct characteristics and its own distinct health actuarial needs. The profession successfully responded to these changes. Health actuaries broadened their scope of practice and developed the tools and analyses needed to successfully support this new environment. Health actuaries remained leaders in a changing environment by using our background, unique skills, and creativity to become a key resource in the success of managed care plans.

Throughout its existence, managed care has continued to evolve. Older prescriptive approaches to care management are being replaced with newer supportive approaches to population health management such as disease management programs and wellness programs. As these new types of care management evolve, they clearly pose a new challenge to health actuaries. To sustain our leadership role, health actuarial practice will need to continue to broaden its scope and create new tools to support the changing environment.

Ian Duncan's new book, *Managing and Evaluating Healthcare Intervention Programs,* continues this tradition of actuaries responding to a changing environment. This book is a thoughtful, well written, and well-researched study that provides actuaries, senior managers, financial managers, and others interested in the topic with a wealth of information, careful analyses, and a strong intellectual basis for expanding actuarial and financial leadership to population health management.

This book is dedicated to

my wife Janet,

who has had to share me with the book

for the past 5 years.

Part 1

An introduction to Care Management Interventions

1 INTRODUCTION

This book covers the developing topic of care management interventions. Originally written for actuaries (the financial engineers of the healthcare payment system) it will be of value to anyone interested in the financial management of healthcare intervention programs. While it may address operational topics from time to time (such as the organizational structure and management of a disease management program), the focus (appropriately for actuaries) is generally on cost, outcomes and other financial issues.

The text is for the most part analytical, objective and based on research. When I began the research in 2003 that led to this book, I had little idea of the scope and duration of the work that it would require. Five years is a long time in which to be engaged in a single project, albeit part-time and with the assistance of many volunteers, co-authors, reviewers, and others along the way. In total the study generated eight papers for the Society of Actuaries, to which as much material again have been added for this book. Many practitioners, both actuaries and non-actuaries, have downloaded one or more of the papers from the Society of Actuaries Web site, and have used some of the principles we have developed in their work. Some of the terms that we have coined in the course of the study, ("migration bias" for example) have found their way into day-to-day discussion of disease management (DM) outcomes. The popularity of the papers vindicates the Society of Actuaries Health Section's and the Committee on Knowledge Extension Research's decisions to support the research, and confirms the increasing role that actuaries are playing in this new and exciting area of managed care.

1.1 THE STATE OF THE UNION

In Chapter 4 we provide a detailed review of the literature on financial outcomes of different care management programs. Over the years that we have been engaged in the study, however, the world of DM has not stood still. Others have researched and written on similar topics. It is interesting to consider what has been achieved and what has *not* been achieved in the last few years. In 2004, the Disease Management Association of America (DMAA) published "Principles for Assessing Disease Management Outcomes [61]" Far from establishing once and for all methodology and principles to be followed by practitioners, it is widely-agreed, including I believe by DMAA, that the guide fell short of the needs of the industry in this area. Accordingly, DMAA convened another work group in 2006 to tackle the subject again. The findings of this workgroup, entitled "DMAA Outcome Guidelines Report" [154] were published in December 2006. Because it is an industry consensus document, the DMAA workgroup report made a number of recommendations with which readers of this book may be familiar. In addition, the guidelines identified a number of potentially controversial issues, many of which were deferred for future consideration. Accordingly, DMAA convened a third series of work groups in 2007, which led to the publication of a second edition of Outcomes Guidelines [155] in the same year. The second edition addressed some of the gaps left by the first – for example, DMAA now recommends a particular method of selecting members for inclusion in a study population (which we discuss in greater detail in Chapter 11, and refer to as a re-qualification standard) when applying the adjusted historical control methodology, to overcome one of the more glaring areas of potential difference between comparison populations. The Guidelines also identify, but do not make recommendations for, the issue of minimum sample size for credible measurement. This and other topics are due to be covered in the 2008 volume of DMAA's guidelines. We have provided guidance in this book (see Chapter 10) that may assist users in this area.

While its guidelines may help practitioners, DMAA, as the industry trade association, will always be perceived by purchasers as representing an industry viewpoint, and at least somewhat suspect. The professional North American actuarial associations[1], Society of Actuaries, Canadian Institute of Actuaries and American Academy of Actuaries, on the other hand, have a reputation for being objective. Recommendations from these professional actuarial bodies, therefore, will carry more weight, particularly given the increasing involvement of actuaries in the performance and review of studies.

The American Academy of Actuaries released its paper "Disease Management Programs: What's the Cost?" [43] in 2005, and has been working for several years on a Practice Note for actuaries practicing in the field. This document was released early in 2008. It is the nature of actuarial practice notes to be descriptive, rather than prescriptive, providing a compendium of acceptable approaches taken by actuaries in tackling a particular problem, rather than choosing a particular approach as the "best practice." Actuarial best practices in DM will be published in a Standard of Practice for DM, but, given the lack of maturity of actuarial practice in this area, publication is some years away,

Some peer-reviewed papers have been published since we began this study. Ariel Linden, a well-known researcher in this field, has published a paper that has attracted considerable attention [119]. This paper addresses what the author calls "number needed to treat," and which may also be called (as we do in Chapter 6 of this book) the economics of DM. In addition, this paper draws attention to the need for identification of a causal relationship between any savings estimated or measured, and the underlying inpatient admission experience of the population (where the major portion of savings are to be found). Soeren Mattke, MD, and others from RAND published a paper with a provocative title: "Evidence for the Effect of Disease Management: Is $1 Billion a Year a Good Investment?" [130] The authors' conclusions will be familiar to those who have read the literature review in Chapter 4, namely that there is some evidence that DM improves quality of care but that there is little reliable evidence of financial improvement. With the exception of these papers, the literature has not seen many peer-reviewed publications. What is particularly puzzling is the absence of practical papers that examine the biases in measurement and the impact that these have on outcomes, as, for example, we have done in Chapter 12 of this book.

---

[1] The Society of Actuaries mission is to provide education and research for North American Life, Health, Pensions and Investment Actuaries. The American Academy of Actuaries is the U.S. profession's interface with regulators, and is responsible for professional standards and accreditation. The Canadian Institute of Actuaries combines both educational and regulatory roles in Canada.

Chapter 4, which was written and published early in the life of the SOA project, has not been revised to take account of newly-published articles. The good news, however, is that (as suggested above) little relevant research has been published in the past four years, so the "state of the union" four years after completing the primary research for this book is not materially different to what it was when I began this project in 2003.

The last four years have seen considerable increase in actuarial involvement in DM outcomes studies and audits. The fundamental building blocks of studies – rigorous reconciliation of data and understanding of Per Member Per Month (PMPM) costs and trends – lend themselves to analysis by actuaries. We also suggest in Chapter 10 that a relatively new technique in the actuarial arsenal, but one gaining wide acceptance – risk adjustment – also has a role to play in ensuring equivalence between populations.

To the extent that actuaries enter what was previously an area dominated by other health professionals, this study will have made a contribution.

1.2 WHAT HAVE WE LEARNED FROM OUR RESEARCH?

The key conclusions from the research can be summarized as follows:

1. The most important objective in any care management outcomes study is to ensure comparability between the intervention and comparison populations. The existing DM literature tends to encourage a belief that there are two "threats to validity" in studies: selection bias, which will be observed when participants are compared with non-participants, and regression to the mean. But as we show in Chapter 3, regression to the mean is an *individual,* not population concept (except in the default case of a population comprising similar individuals). As discussion throughout our research suggests, the identification and correction of regression to the mean is a much larger and more complicated issue than some of the literature suggests, particularly when definitions of who is included in a population may not be clear.

2. Chapter 6 presents an important concept – the economics of DM. (While this chapter addresses DM, the techniques are general and may be applied to any type of intervention program.) One of the questions often asked is whether DM savings outcomes are plausible. Application of a simple economic model to the underlying population data allows users to estimate a range of likely outcomes, as well as test the sensitivity of those outcomes to different program components. More importantly, understanding the key variables of the financial model and their contribution to the overall savings calculation will allow analysis of individual variables that can be directly measured (the enrollment rate, for example).

3. Population studies, the most common study design in DM evaluation, may achieve comparability if the populations being studied do not change much from period to period. A major challenge for actuaries is to demonstrate this stability. Fortunately, actuaries understand the issues involved in ensuring comparability over time and the implication for PMPM costs when comparability is not achieved. Actuarial tools such as risk-adjustment exist that make assessment of risk profiles over time and demonstration of equivalence simpler.

4. As discussed in Chapter 7, the actuarially-adjusted historic (pre-post) design, which is the most prevalent in the industry, offers a reasonable compromise between validity and practicality. Many would wish to use more scientifically-pure methods, but, as we discuss, these are seldom achievable. Instead, the popularity of the actuarially-adjusted historical control method in the industry is testament to the fact that a well-executed study is viewed as being reasonably reliable. The work that we and other researchers have done attempts to address some of the areas of sensitivity in outcomes, for example the identification of patients for different populations.

5. While the fundamental methodology does not vary much between practitioners, the assumptions and methods used to deal with data issues do vary considerably. Definitions matter. We cover in Chapter 8 many of the issues that are usually considered in a study – exclusions, inclusions, timing, and so on.

6. In several chapters, we discuss some of the issues that arise in measurement. We recognize that the methodology we use is not perfect. With more research into its biases and publication of actual results, we would perform better and more accurate studies.

7. Chapter 11, published in stand-alone form in the North *American Actuarial Journal* in October 2006, highlights the issue of chronic identification and its impact on chronic prevalence and trends. In a population study, the issues of *what* claims codes identify a chronic population, *when* those codes have to be observed, how frequently and over what time period, are crucial. As an industry we have only begun to scratch the surface of these issues, but it is probably the single most important issue for the industry to focus on in the future.

8. It is important to understand the impact or "value" of different assumptions on the final results of a study. It is surprising to me that most of the discussion in the DM literature remains at a theoretical level when many practitioners have access to data sets and could simply test out some of the issues that they debate. The industry would benefit from it. It would make the current methodology more robust and would reduce the need for the industry to search for alternative methodologies. In Chapter 12 we examine some of the sensitivities of the results calculated using one such methodology for one client, under different assumptions. Much more of this type of analysis needs to be published, to gain knowledge about the methodology.

The DM industry continues to expand. One area of growth is Wellness and Worksite Health. Recognizing this, DMAA (formerly the Disease Management Association of America) renamed itself "DMAA-The Care Continuum Alliance" in 2007. DMAA now covers the new, broader spectrum of interventions. Consistent with this focus we have added chapters to the original SOA study that address some of the issues of Wellness and Worksite Health programs.

1.3 A CHANGE IN EMPHASIS?

Traditionally, actuaries have worked with aggregate data, often at a category of service level. Work with different populations has changed this emphasis, however. Dealing with chronic populations, for example, requires that one have a more detailed knowledge of the underlying services (and the claims that they generate) that a particular chronic member requires. This, in turn, requires actuaries to have more clinical knowledge than was the case in the past. It also turns the old "financial" analytical paradigm around, with the condition-population becoming the unit of interest and analysis. We have much to learn, still, about the behavior of traditional actuarial measures (for example cost PMPM and trend) when applied to sub-populations with common characteristics, such as a health condition. And because our clinical colleagues have barely begun to scratch the surface of what constitutes "clinical best practice" for members with conditions, we have a long way to go before we can begin to benchmark utilization and cost for these populations. Nevertheless, for the actuary interested in pursuing this area of practice, the techniques and tools described in this book are a place to start.

2 Care Management Programs and Interventions

2.1 Introduction

Early insurance approaches to the financing of health care focused on hospital reimbursement and were characterized by two key assumptions. The first assumption was that providers would exercise reasonable professional judgment in the provision of services to patients. The second was that patients would tend to be conservative regarding their use of services (since these services often involved both discomfort and uncertain outcomes).

Insurance companies, of course, have a role in the healthcare system as major funders of the care provided. Medicare and state Medicaid programs are similarly major funders of care, and also have a role in directing medical management for those programs. Historically, (at least until the development of HMOs and their growth in the 1980s) the insurance company's role was limited to "traditional" insurance functions such as underwriting and pricing, verification of insurance eligibility and claim payment. Cost was restrained through these means as well as through traditional insurance product features such as deductibles and coinsurance. Intervention by the insurer – either with the patient or the provider – was unthinkable in this era.

Over time, the traditional insurance model failed to contain costs and was replaced by a more interventionist model in which the entity financing the services began to exert influence over the demand for and access to medical resources and services. The "insurance" model gave way to the "managed care" model. The chart below, taken from OECD data[1], illustrates how costs have increased in the United States since 1970 (the "heyday" of the indemnity insurance model).

	1970	1980	1990	2003
US Healthcare expenditure per person	$352	$1,072	$2,752	$5,711
GDP per person	$5,065	$12,249	$23,200	$37,654
Health expenditure/GDP per person	7.0%	8.8%	11.9%	15.2%

Since managed care became commonplace in the United States in the mid-1980s, managed care organizations (MCOs) have tried a multitude of methods to influence the resource con-

[1] Source: Organization for Economic Co-operation and Development. *OECD Health Data 2006*, from the OECD Internet subscription database updated October 10, 2006. Copyright OECD 2006, Reported at the Kaiser Family Foundation web-site. GDP data are from the National Accounts; population data are from the Census (author's calculation of GDP per person).

sumption behavior of health care providers and patients. These methods are known as **Interventions.** Early managed care models focused on physicians and hospitals, using a variety of administrative, regulatory or legal tactics. These included a formal peer review process to reduce unnecessary hospital admissions and inappropriately long hospital stays, and a formal regulatory and planning process aimed at gradually reducing the number of unneeded hospital beds. Other tactics included a requirement that physicians obtain approval for hospitalizations prior to admitting a patient (except in emergency situations), as well as various contracting models with "preferred providers."

The use of preferred provider (discounted) networks (PPOs) accounted for much of the "value" of managed care, at least in the 1990s when commercial health plan health care cost trend[2] moderated in the U.S. As costs began to increase again at the end of the decade, health plans and other payers became interested in methods of managing care, rather than simply managing costs.

More recent evolutions of care management have aimed to include the patient as well as the provider. New attempts to "manage care" continue as MCOs experiment with different interventions, try to determine which interventions have proven to be cost-effective, and respond to patients' and providers' complaints about their intrusiveness.

Many supporters of managed care advocate the clinical benefits of intervention. Our interest, however, is in the financial value of care management, such as whether interventions bring financial value to the organization that sponsors them and the extent to which they contain costs. The over-arching question is whether cost savings are greater than the implementation and ongoing costs of the interventions themselves.

Seven Care Management Methods

The subject of managed care covers a substantial body of techniques. The interested reader can consult one of a number of textbooks, including, Kongstvedt [110a]. In addition to the discussion in this chapter, Chapter 4 includes a selective review of the literature on care management program evaluation. More recently, wellness interventions have developed, often outside the health plan (payer) setting. Chapter 14 contains a similar literature review of wellness interventions. The focus of this current chapter is to briefly introduce the reader to care management techniques commonly used in managed care plans as background to a discussion of their implications for actuaries and other financial managers.

The purpose of managed care plans is to control the utilization of their members' services through methods usually known as "utilization management." We prefer the broader phrase "care management" because the former term includes methods that focus primarily on providers and has acquired a very negative image. "Care management" is a broader term that includes recent approaches that foster more patient participation and include healthcare professionals who often are not physicians. As a term, it is also consistent with the development that has taken place in the industry to focus more on "upstream" prevention of illness and improving the quality of care delivered, in contrast to what was essentially "downstream" management of utilization through review and pre-authorization. Terminology in this field is not precise, has not been standardized, and continues to expand.

---

[2] Technically, what is referred to as "trend" is actually "Healthcare Cost Trend." Consistent with the rest of the healthcare industry we will refer to this as "trend" throughout this book.

This Chapter describes seven methods used in care management in the order of their historical development:

1. Pre-Authorization
2. Concurrent Review
3. Case Management
4. Demand Management
5. Disease Management
6. Specialty Case Management
7. Population Health Management

Finally, because of a considerable current interest in a new form of program, the Medical Home, we have added a discussion on the Medical Home model.

2.2 PRE-AUTHORIZATION

Pre-authorization requires that a physician or hospital obtain approval from a Managed Care Organization (MCO) before performing a diagnostic procedure or surgical intervention on a health plan member. Pre-authorization is generally applied to inpatient procedures, although its use has been growing for certain outpatient procedures (Imaging Services) and most recently certain high-cost outpatient drugs. In cases where an admission occurs without a pre-authorization, such as an emergency admission, a retrospective "pre-authorization" may still be required because the approval is necessary for claim payment and to initiate the discharge planning process.

MCOs determined the procedures that required authorization based on the price, volume, or total dollar expenditures on procedures or certain areas of care. Researchers found that certain procedures (such as hysterectomy, prostate surgery or carotid endarterectomy[3]) were frequently performed on patients lacking clinical indications, and so pre-authorization reviews were performed, not only for economic reasons, but also for patient safety/quality[4] (when the risks of a procedure outweighed its benefits). The classic research on supplier-induced demand for medical procedures is the work of Jack Wennberg, MD of Dartmouth University [211 & 212].

Physicians and managed care reviewers frequently struggled with each other in the authorization process as they discussed certain diagnoses, symptoms, and other patient characteristics. Over time, physicians and MCOs gradually reached an equilibrium in which both parties knew what to expect from each other in the pre-authorization process.

[3] An operation to remove an obstruction in the carotid artery – a main blood supply to the brain – to reduce the risk of stroke, sometimes performed with a catheter and stent.

[4] Quality" is a term used frequently in managed care. Several organizations, for example NCQA (National Council on Quality Assessment), URAC (Utilization Review Accreditation Commission), JCAHO (Joint Commission on Accreditation of Healthcare Organizations) and other accrediting organizations exist to set standards for managed care quality, and do so by evaluating outcomes and measures (quality indicators) within an insured population. Examples of quality indicators include tests and screening for certain conditions, rates of compliance with certain treatment protocols, etc.

2.3 CONCURRENT REVIEW

Concurrent Review involves monitoring a health plan member's care while the member is still receiving care in an acute hospital or nursing home. This process is most commonly performed by a utilization review nurse who may request information about a hospitalized patient and discuss the case with the responsible clinician via telephone. As the provision of services within the hospital has become more complex and multidisciplinary, services may be performed by a "**hospitalist**," a physician located in the hospital (but paid by either the hospital or the health plan). The hospitalist's function is to coordinate the different disciplines directed to an individual patient, eliminating overlaps or gaps in care and ensuring better outcomes and lower cost [207].

Concurrent Review was initially annoying to physicians, in part because communications between nurses and physicians were awkward and threatened the autonomy of physicians. As clinicians became more experienced with diagnosis-related groups[5] and as hospitals and MCOs developed practice guidelines and clinical pathways, this form of intervention became routine and was one factor that helped to reduce hospitals' average length of stay. An example of an analysis of the effect of DRGs on inpatient stays can be found in Kahn, Keeler et al. [103].

2.4 CASE MANAGEMENT

Case Management typically involves a health care professional who coordinates the care of a patient with a serious disease or illness (such as a stroke, multiple sclerosis, AIDS, some cancers, or lupus). The complexity of diseases that necessitate a case manager usually results in medical care that involves multiple medical specialties, institutions, a wide array of possible diagnostic and therapeutic tools, and a significant social or community-based welfare element. Case Management often begins during an inpatient hospital stay with the planning of the patient's post-hospital care (Discharge Planning) and continues once the patient returns home.

Case Management has a number of common features. The case manager is usually a nursing professional (Registered Nurse or Licensed Practical Nurse). The work of the case manager often involves services outside the acute hospital setting. Because of the intensity of services, caseloads are small (a typical average will be 100 or fewer patients concurrently) and the duration of services will be extensive (six months on average). Case managers often have the authority to approve extra-contractual benefits for members.

Case managers have found it difficult to perform their activities consistently and uniformly. In some instances, a case manager is not empowered to control access to resources, but may only suggest alternatives to a patient or a physician. Essentially, case managers view their role as that of *coordination* of care: ensuring that the many different providers of services, treatments, community-based resources, therapies (drug and non-drug) and equipment are appropriate, non-duplicative and efficacious (that is, producing an improvement in the patient's condition). Case Managers often have the authority to order alternative treatments or

[5] Diagnosis Related Groups (DRGs). Under the Medicare Prospective Payment System, discharges are classified into Diagnosis Related Groups. A specific payment rate is established on a geographic basis by DRG.

equipment outside of the plan (extra-contractual benefits) when these are indicated and may save the payer money in the long-run. The progression of the member's condition may result in a wide range of outcomes (from recovery to death), as may a patient's response to various therapies, which makes development and strict adherence to clinical guidelines difficult. In many communities, the medical resources available to patients may vary considerably both in quantity and quality, further complicating the work of case managers. Finally, many diseases may have new, untested (and often expensive) treatments that can be difficult for MCOs to deny in the face of determined patients and physicians. In reality, the Case Manager runs the risk of becoming a patient advocate rather than a resource working in both the patient and the payer's interests.

2.5 Demand Management

Demand Management refers to certain passive forms of informational intervention, often provided by clinical staff over the telephone. One form of Demand Management is Nurse Advice Lines, which address episodic, often acute, illnesses. One objective of these services is "triage," or the process of determining whether a medical condition or event requires immediate intervention, such as an emergency room visit. Another example of Demand Management is Shared Decision Making. Nurses give patients facing a significant medical decision (such as major surgery) the most current information on alternatives to surgery. In some models, nurses also provide the patient with coaching to ask physicians crucial questions, and provide a framework for informed decision-making based on the patient's personal preferences [202].

One objective of Demand Management is to ensure that the initial diagnosis (triage) and provision of information to the patient is done at the lowest professional level consistent with quality standards. The Demand Management movement has helped to systematize the collection of information and response to key symptoms. A new, similar development is the growth of "Minute Clinics," often in pharmacies, staffed by Registered Nurses. Minute Clinics provide some of the same initial diagnostic and triage services as the Nurse Lines, together with other routine clinical services, such as inoculations. They are evolving to include screenings and preventive services, and to include personal health records that *may* be linked back to the patient's primary care physician, thus integrating into the continuum of care.

2.6 Disease Management

The focus of *Disease Management* (DM) is on chronic conditions with certain characteristics that make them suitable for clinical intervention. Some of these factors are:

- Once contracted, the disease remains with the patient for the rest of the patient's life.
- The disease is often manageable with a combination of pharmaceutical therapy and lifestyle change.
- The patient can take responsibility for their own condition in a meaningful way.

- The average annual cost of some chronic patients is sufficiently high to warrant the expenditure of resources by the health plan or employer to manage the condition.

DM is a "system of coordinated health care interventions and communications for populations with conditions in which patient self-care efforts are significant. DM supports the physician or practitioner/patient relationship and plan of care. It emphasizes prevention of exacerbations and complications using evidence-based practice guidelines and patient empowerment strategies. DM evaluates clinical, humanistic and economic outcomes on an ongoing basis with the goal of improving overall health."[6]

Traditionally, DM has focused on the "big five" chronic diseases: ischemic heart disease (also called Coronary Artery Disease), diabetes, chronic obstructive pulmonary disease, asthma, and heart failure. Some companies add other conditions to this list, particularly diseases of the kidneys and endocrine system, musculoskeletal (often lower-back) problems, and depression. (The identification of depression and related privacy issues make this a difficult condition to treat except as it occurs together with another chronic condition.) Chronic disease costs matter because they are manageable, and are often self-manageable. The greater the percentage of total expenditures represented by manageable chronic disease, the greater the savings opportunity for DM. Healthcare costs associated with health plan members who have a chronic condition can be a significant percentage of all costs of a health plan. This percentage is different in commercial and Medicare populations. Estimates of the percentage of total health expenditures represented by members with chronic conditions differ; some authors estimate that more than one-half of all medical expenditures are incurred by individuals with chronic conditions. There is another well-publicized estimate that this percentage is 78 percent of all medical expenditures [21]. Another estimate of chronic medical expenditures made in 1990 was $425 billion [98]. The National Medical Expenditure Survey estimated total medical expenditures of $800 billion in 1996, implying that expenditure by chronic persons represents more than 50 percent of all expenditures [138]. Estimates of the number of individuals with chronic diseases ranged between 80 and 100 million in the earlier 1990s. The Centers for Disease Control estimates that there were 90 million Americans with chronic diseases in 1995, representing a total cost of one trillion dollars, 75% of all medical expenditures, or about $12,000 per person. In addition to the inclusion of conditions that are not among those that are traditionally managed by Disease Management programs (for example, HIV, pregnancy, arthritis, and stroke) the costs probably include all costs associated with individuals who have one of the specific conditions, rather than just the costs of treating the conditions themselves.

As with many issues in DM, the questions of how many individuals have a chronic condition, and what the associated claims are, are confused by a lack of a consistent definition. There is no single agreed upon list of those conditions that are "chronic," nor are there agreed upon criteria for identifying the presence of the diseases. Some estimates may simply add the prevalence of different diseases (which double- or triple-counts some individuals with multiple conditions). Chronic prevalence may also be over-estimated if the same individual is covered by more than one study (as, for example, when an individual is dually-eligible, that is eligible for Medicare but with an income low enough to qualify the member for Medicaid benefits as well). Similar confusion exists around the amount of medical claims, which may be reported for a single chronic condition, all chronic conditions, or as all claims for the individual.

---

[6] Disease Management Association of America. Web-site www.dmaa.org. Accessed January 2, 2008.

Analysis of health plan data shows a different picture than that reported in some studies. In part, this may be because health plan (insured) populations are more likely to be younger, healthier (working individuals) and have fewer chronic conditions. (For example, the U.S. population as a whole contains more older and non-working individuals.) Our analysis of commercial health plan data shows net incurred claims of chronic condition individuals to be in the range of 20- to 25-percent of the total of all incurred claims. Medicare population expenditures amount to 50- to 55-percent of total claims. Costs associated with chronic conditions represent approximately 70 percent of these total expenditures. Although our estimates may be lower than those of other researchers, they still show the chronic condition population representing a significant source of total expenditure and savings opportunity.

DM programs are generally offered telephonically, involving interaction with a trained nursing professional, and require an extended series of interactions, including a strong educational component. Patients are expected to play an active role in the management of their disease. With the rise of the Internet in the 1990s and the access to medical information on free Web sites, many patients took greater interest in self-care and in learning about the latest available research on specific diseases. Many companies saw the Internet as providing an opportunity to reach a larger population and deliver DM services at lower cost. DM programs that rely solely on the Internet have largely been unsuccessful (although most DM companies offer ancillary Internet service) because successful DM requires strong outreach efforts to contact patients and generate enrollment, and change behavior. Discussion about the practical aspects of DM enrollment and outreach may be found in Chapters 5, 6 and 8.

DM vendors initially specialized in single diseases from the target list, and some vendors still do so. Because of the presence of co-morbidities or multiple conditions in many high-risk patients, this approach became operationally difficult to execute, with patients receiving care in more than one program. Over time, the industry has moved more towards a "whole person" model in which all the diseases a patient has are managed by a single DM program. Unlike Europe, where the financing of healthcare is different, DM has largely become an outsourced function performed over the telephone by a third-party. The relative efficiency of this method makes it attractive when there are large numbers of patients to manage and when the means exist (such as diet, exercise and drug therapy) for the patient to take responsibility for care. In Europe, by contrast, DM services are more frequently provided within the provider office by a physician or nurse. This type of model is also encountered in the U.S. within integrated systems such as the Kaiser Foundation Health plan. Because of system differences, it is important to keep in mind the characteristics of the system when evaluating outcomes studies.

Although DM interventions are largely patient focused, most programs contain a provider-focused element as well. This may range from providing the participating patient with information to be shared with the physician, through to a model that involves the provider in the patient's care by communicating critical issues such as gaps in the patient's care. Many commentators and physicians look forward to the day when physicians are more actively involved in Disease Management programs, and some pilots have been implemented. No physician-oriented model appears to have been successful enough to replace the nurse-telephonic model that is the industry staple.

2.7 SPECIALTY CASE MANAGEMENT

Specialty Case Management is performed by a care manager who has expertise in a particular area (such as mental health, organ transplantation, maternity, certain drug therapies, or oncology) and to whom the MCO has assigned primary responsibility for coordinating the patient's care. Patients referred for specialty care management have often developed difficult and potentially expensive diseases.

Typically, MCOs contract or "carve out" this intervention to a private company that has established networks of specialists or centers of excellence. Frequently, the financial responsibility is carved out of the overall plan liability and transferred, along with the service responsibility, to the Specialty Case Manager. Patients still need a case manager's assistance to help them negotiate through multiple sites and stages of treatment, often over an extended period of time.

Because the specialty management company must deal with a variety of illnesses and a wide spectrum of disease severity, it may rely on tools from concurrent review, case management, and disease management. For example, a firm that specializes in behavioral health may use concurrent review for a patient hospitalized for a bipolar disorder, case management for an adolescent with newly diagnosed schizophrenia, and disease management for a patient with an obsessive-compulsive disorder.

2.8 POPULATION HEALTH MANAGEMENT

Population Health Management is a recent intervention in which a broad set of medical conditions is addressed. Unlike disease management, the focus is not on patients with a specific disease. A broader approach is used in which the entire membership of a health plan is evaluated; using statistical tools such as predictive modeling or Health Risk Assessments[7]. Statistical models are constructed with the objective of identifying potential high-cost patients who can benefit from some kind of "softer" intervention that is voluntary for the patient, and information is provided to the member about conditions and self-care. Population Health Management programs deliver education and other information to the target population in an attempt to make members aware of and better managers of their conditions.

Firms specializing in population health management usually rely heavily on information technology to identify and then closely track patients using nurses or other clinical experts. The data sources used by predictive models are crucial and may differ among population management firms. In some instances, a health risk assessment instrument is used to identify specific diseases and risky behaviors of MCO enrollees. More frequently, medical claims are the main source of diagnostic data. Prescription data from pharmacy benefit management firms are another possible source of data.

The emphasis of population health management is usually on wellness, prevention, or early detection of disease through educational services or Health Risk Appraisals. We will discuss

[7] Surveys that collect member-supplied information about health and risk-factors.

these interventions in more detail later (see Chapters 13 and 14). They may also include population-wide programs, such as those aimed at inoculation for various diseases, smoking cessation, weight-loss or other lifestyle-improvement[8].

2.9 THE MEDICAL HOME: AN AREA OF GROWING INTEREST

All the above interventions have one thing in common: they are all delivered by a third-party (either the health plan or its surrogate, a vendor). There is a growing interest in and movement toward returning the responsibility for the management of the patient's care to the physician. Some see this as being accomplished through a financial mechanism – for example, "Pay for Performance" or "P4P" programs.

P4P programs work well in the context of chronic care member management because there are well-established clinical measures that may be relatively simply and cheaply measured from claims data. A representative example of these measures for chronic conditions may be found in the Appendix to Chapter 5 of this book. In P4P programs, clinical quality targets for a population are set for physicians and the program sponsor measures outcomes periodically, paying a bonus for achievement of the required absolute level of each clinical measure, or for improvement in the clinical measure over its baseline value. For example, the target level of blood sugar (Haemoglobin A1C) in a diabetic population is less than 7.0 mg/dl. In a specific physician's population in which only 20% of diabetics are controlled at this level, improvement to, say, 30% would result in a payment under the program. P4P programs provide targets and rewards, but do not lay down a mechanism by which the physician is expected to attain the goal, instead leaving this to the physician's professional judgment and experience.

A second type of provider-focused program that is receiving considerable attention is the "medical home." This type of program is actually not new: the American Academy of Pediatrics introduced such a model in 1967, referring to the central location for a child's medical records, particularly important for children with special health care needs, as the "medical home." The Medical Home (also called "Patient-centered Medical Home") movement takes a different approach to the P4P movement, but also places the responsibility for the patient's care management on the professional judgment of the physician. The physician is expected to organize the testing, education and overall care coordination of his or her panel of patients. The Medical Home movement relies on the primary care physicians, based on research such as those quoted by Thomas Bodenheimer [12].

> " ...studies have demonstrated that a primary care–based health care system has the potential to reduce costs while maintaining quality. The hospitalization rates for diagnoses that could be addressed in ambulatory care settings are higher in geographic areas where access to primary care physicians is more limited. States with a higher ratio of generalist to population have lower per-beneficiary Medicare expenditures and higher scores on 24 common performance measures than states with fewer generalist physicians and more specialists per capita."

[8] For more information about Population Health Management (and the role of predictive modeling in identifying and targeting patients) the reader is referred to Gomaa, Morrow et al. [85], Lynch, Forman et al. [128]], Forman [66] and Celebi [23].

Patient-centered Primary Care Collaborative has published a set of principles for establishing the patient-centered medical home.

Personal physician – each patient has an ongoing relationship with a personal physician trained to provide first contact, continuous, and comprehensive care.

Physician directed medical practice – a team of individuals taking responsibility for the patient's ongoing care.

Whole person orientation – appropriately arranging care with other qualified professionals for all stages of life; acute care, chronic care, preventive services, and end of life care.

Care coordinated and integrated across all elements of the health care system and the patient's community. Facilitated by registries, IT, and health information exchange.

Quality and safety – patient centered outcomes, evidence-based medicine, clinical decision-support tools, performance measurement, Continuous Quality Improvement, patient expectation measurement.

Enhanced access – open scheduling, expanded hours, E-visits and other options.

Reimbursement structure to support and encourage this model of care.

The National Committee for Quality Assurance (NCQA) has published standards for Medical Homes, covering 9 different areas:

1. Access and Communication.
2. Patient tracking and Registry.
3. Care Management.
4. Patient self-management support.
5. Electronic prescribing.
6. Test tracking.
7. Referral tracking.
8. Performance reporting and improvement.
9. Advanced electronic communications.

As this list shows, a physician or physician practice that wishes to operate a medical home model will require significant investments, both in terms of time and effort with patients, and in terms of the supporting infrastructure. The extent of the investment required points to why the traditional third-party models such as DM have been implemented by payers, and the medical home (which may make more sense clinically) has been slower to penetrate the healthcare system. Payers, too, have not been able to determine a way to find the necessary funds to increase the reimbursement of providers (except on a pilot basis).

Despite the interest in the Medical Home model, there is (as yet) little evidence on the model's effectiveness at achieving higher quality and lower cost of care. Many studies have been performed of related models (such as the Chronic Care Model of Ed Wagner, and the primary care movement). Results of these studies are somewhat mixed: some show reduced utilization and costs and others do not. A movement towards greater penetration of the medical home will also have to contend with multiple, conflicting programs. Most payers, for example, have implemented case management programs (that often address the needs of members with chronic conditions), disease management programs through an outside vendor, and wellness and coaching programs. An individual member with a chronic condition may also be eligible for management by a disability or workers compensation management program, and have their drug utilization managed by a Pharmacy Benefits Manager. In this environment the concept of patient management by a physician in the medical home appears rational, but we cannot underestimate the difficulty in actually implementing it.

Nevertheless, the interest in the model is growing and there is increasing involvement of some of the third-party care management program vendors and new entrants in providing the necessary infrastructure to physician practices. All these factors indicate that this form of program is likely to grow significantly in the future.

2.10 CONCLUSION

In this chapter, we have briefly surveyed common types of medical management directed at the member or patient. These interventions have certain common features:

- All rely heavily on identification of at-risk members, often through medical claims and sophisticated scoring algorithms;
- All rely on some form of standardized treatment or best-practice care. The at-risk patient is then encouraged to seek best-practice care and to comply with the guidelines, while the physician is practicing according to the care guidelines;
- All rely on clinical resources to perform evaluation of the patient's condition and to provide coaching for those members whose care deviates from best practice guidelines;
- All rely (to some degree) on participation by the member or patient in the member's own care;
- All have proven to be difficult (to a greater or lesser degree) to assess and justify financially.

The reliance on clinical resources, as we will see in Chapters 3 and 6, can be costly for the sponsoring organization. They are a resource to be used sparingly, to be applied to the most productive patients and functions. It is often possible to justify intervention programs based on the associated improvement in clinical outcomes or quality. As such programs become more widespread, however, and their cost increases, purchasers are looking for solid financial evidence of the value of programs and interventions. We will return to this topic in Chapter 4, when we undertake a selective review of existing literature on financial outcomes of intervention programs.

3 Actuarial Issues in Care Management Evaluations

3.1 Introduction

This chapter addresses specific details of measurement principles and practice that the actuary should consider when planning to conduct or review a study of care management interventions. Three major topics are covered: **Measurement Principles**, addressing basic principles that should be considered in any evaluation; **Study Design Issues**, exploring issues that arise when assessing or planning a study; and **Risk Factors**, covering factors that influence the inherent risk in a population being managed and which therefore influence the measured outcomes.

As managed care has evolved, actuaries have tended to perform their traditional roles (product development, pricing, rate filings, reserving and underwriting) while care management functions have been provided by professionals with a clinical background. Often, the two professions have operated in separate functional areas, coming together only at the most senior level of the health plan. One consequence of this separation of clinical and financial functions has been the establishment, in many health plans, of a separate informatics and evaluation function within the care management area, staffed by non-actuarial health professionals.

More recently, however, as health care costs continue to escalate despite many and varied clinical intervention programs, the senior financial managements of health plans have begun to look to the actuarial profession for counsel. Because the health care actuarial profession has traditionally been involved in rigorous financial calculations, actuaries understand health insurance and health claims data. Much of the debate in care management evaluation concerns methodology, but this is just one of a larger set of issues concerning the validation of financial outcomes.

We believe that in the future actuaries will be involved in three important areas: the economics of care management programs, risk adjustment and predictive modeling, and financial outcomes evaluation.

3.1.1 The Economics of Care Management Programs

One factor common to the seven care management programs described in the previous chapter is that they all involve, to different degrees, highly qualified and costly clinical resources. While considerable attention has been paid to evaluating outcomes and savings from these programs, (as will be discussed in detail in Chapter 4), fewer questions appear to be asked about the relationship between inputs and outputs, or the appropriateness of the level and volume of clinical resources and programs to the outcome. Rather than analyzing the economics of a particular care management opportunity, a health plan is more likely to determine its level of case management intervention by using industry norms or benchmarks from other plans, potentially replicating over- or under-resourcing mistakes made elsewhere in the industry. We will address this issue in more depth in Chapter 6.

3.1.2 Risk-Adjustment and Predictive Modeling

Risk-adjustment and predictive modeling are processes for comparing different populations, providing insights on where to devote clinical resources, how to evaluate programs, and how to profile and reimburse providers. Risk-adjustment and predictive modeling have been addressed elsewhere in the professional actuarial literature[1]. Predictive modeling is the convention used in Disease Management (DM) to identify, categorize or prioritize candidates for intervention programs. DM companies differ in the balance that they strike between "risk" and "impactibility." In this context, "risk" implies that a group of members are highly likely to experience high cost; "impactibility" introduces the idea of suitability for DM (for example, those members who exhibit signs that they are ready to change behavior, or who have a condition that, while less risky, is more amenable to self-management with the aid of telephonic intervention). Interest is growing in using risk adjustment or similar techniques (for example, propensity scoring) in the process of the assessment of outcomes. This topic is discussed in more detail in Chapter 7.

3.1.3 Financial Outcomes Evaluation

Program evaluations have generally tended to validate the savings of programs, despite continued escalating health plan costs. There are many issues with the methodologies chosen for these studies, which are discussed in detail in Chapter 7. As important as the choice of a methodology, however, are the adjustments made to achieve comparability between the reference and the intervention population. (Throughout this text the terms "reference population" and "comparison population" or "comparison group" are used interchangeably.) Many of the issues faced by researchers evaluating equivalence are the same issues faced by actuaries in pricing and underwriting different populations. Actuaries, using their background and training, can help to bridge the gap between program outcomes and the overall trend in health plan costs.

While there has been general acceptance of intervention programs clinically, the same is not true of financial results of interventions. The most significant ongoing issue for any form of intervention program is its ability to justify itself financially. A recent meta-analysis survey of *clinical* outcomes of disease management programs showed that these clinical outcomes were generally favorable (Weingarten et al. [209]). A similar survey of financial outcomes found mixed results (Krause [111]). Since it is an axiom of the managed care industry that "higher quality" leads to lower cost [2], the apparent inconsistency in these two studies should be of concern to all who work within the care management industry, and requires further analysis.

---

[1] See for example, Cumming et al. [35], Duncan, Dove et al. [47] and Duncan & Robb[53].

[2] See for example, IOM [34] and Gingrich [71].

Evaluating intervention programs has proved to be difficult. Unlike in clinical outcomes, where one can measure clinical improvement, what is being measured in financial outcomes is often something that did *not* occur. The objective way to measure the non-occurrence of a particular event is through a randomized control test. Health plans and other healthcare professionals generally believe that conducting randomized trials is impractical or even illegal, with the result that it is not considered to be feasible to design a study that withholds medical management services from an otherwise eligible health plan member, solely for the purpose of collecting information on equivalent patients who are not affected by intervention programs. Thus most studies that are conducted for business purposes use some form of non-randomized control methodology, or no control at all.

3.2 MEASUREMENT PRINCIPLES

Actuaries who deal with measurement of intervention outcomes should be familiar with the following six principles when constructing, reviewing or comparing a study. The first three of these principles were proposed in a paper by Wilson and MacDowell [219]. We have added three other principles of our own that we have found to be equally important in practical applications (numbers 3.2.4 through 3.2.6 below).

3.2.1 Reference Population

Any outcomes measurement requires a reference population against which to evaluate the statistic(s) of interest, even if that reference population is the intervention population at an earlier point in time (pre-program).

3.2.2 Equivalence

To ensure validity in outcomes measurement, the reference population should be equivalent to the intervention population. We discuss the meaning of "equivalence" in more detail later.

3.2.3 Consistent Statistics

The comparison needs to measure the same outcome variable(s) in the same way in the reference and intervention populations.

3.2.4 Appropriate Measurement

Avoid, if possible, extraneous, irrelevant or confounding variables (factors) in measurement. As an example, a DM program may be implemented to manage the medical admissions of chronic patients. The actuary could measure all admissions (medical and surgical) of all patients (chronic and non-chronic). The medical and surgical admissions of all patients will however, be affected by many different factors, some of which may be influenced by DM, while many will not. The chances of a broad analysis being confounded by these other factors and non-managed lives is far greater than a narrow study of medical admissions within the chronic population. We do not go so far as to recommend that the study follow only the members who enroll in a program, because that approach introduces other biases. By defining as narrow a population as possible, and as narrow a set of outcomes as possible, the effect of confounding will be reduced.

3.2.5 Exposure

As actuaries are well aware, the calculation of an actuarial statistic requires clear definition of the numerator and denominator. In actuarial calculations, the denominator is defined as "exposure." Accurate calculation of exposure requires similarly explicit definitions of categories of member, measurement time-periods, and eligibility in those periods. Those members who meet these definitions should be included in the appropriate group in the measurement period. In our (practical) experience performing care management evaluations, many of the problems that arise in studies do so because of difficulty in defining who is exposed, and when.

3.2.6 Reconcile the Results

DM companies frequently analyze only small (managed) sub-populations, and sometimes claim savings results that do not appear to be reasonable in the context of the entire population or health plan. The actuary should be prepared, therefore, to reconcile the outcomes of a small population and those of the entire health plan. More important, the actuary should be prepared to explain what factors are driving the health plan's overall trend upward, even when the outcomes from the DM program are favorable. Some in the industry refer to this process (and the specific factors that are recommended) as the application of "Plausibility Analysis."

3.3 STUDY DESIGN ISSUES

Outcomes are evaluated within the context of a study design. Examples of study designs are:

- Randomized;
- Historical control; or
- Observational.

The application of the study design raises many issues relating to methodology, measurement, data management, validity, treatment of chronic populations and claims.

In Chapter 7, we examine how some of these issues can affect measured patient outcomes and the estimated cost-effectiveness of interventions, as well as techniques that may be used to mitigate their influence on a study. First, we will introduce two concepts discussed in more detail in Chapter 7: the concepts of methodology and causality.

3.3.1 Causality

Causality is an important concept in both scientific and commercial studies of DM outcomes. Just because savings are associated with a program does not necessarily mean that the savings are a result of the program. Attributing causality to an intervention program is a difficult problem, and one that has not been much studied in the field of DM outcomes. The scientific community demands a demonstration that a particular outcome has resulted from a particular cause. This requires proof that the DM intervention "caused" the specific outcome. Research to date has been focused on attempts to obtain an accurate estimate of savings, no matter the source. Because of the difficulties inherent in proving causality, commercial purchasers of DM programs are usually satisfied with a weaker standard of proof: "demonstration" of savings, rather than proof of causality. Appendix 3.1 contains a more detailed discussion of causality for readers who are interested in studying the issue further. Business users, while demanding considerable rigor in other aspects of an evaluation, (such as validation and reconciliation of source data) may be satisfied with a "demonstration" standard, where "association" between cause and effect may be sufficient, rather than the stricter test of "causation."

3.3.2 What is a "Methodology?"

The dictionary definition of a methodology is: "a body of methods, rules, and postulates employed by a discipline: a particular procedure or set of procedures[3]". Methods on the other hand, are the tools, techniques and procedures that bring that vision to life. The calculation techniques or methods used by actuaries all contribute to the overall methodology. For example, a technique (such as an adjustment for age, or for trend) does not stand on its own but is rather an input to a methodology. In Chapter 7, we compare the characteristics, including validity, of 10 different methodologies for calculating savings results.

Methodological Issues in Study Design

Ensuring equivalence in the reference population is an important methodological issue. As discussed above, a good study methodology should include a reference population. Such populations are generally constructed by one of three methods: randomized selection from the overall population; non-random selection from the population, with or without adjustment; or by following patient experience over time (a methodology often referred to as "patient as their own control").

The practicality of the study design implementation is also a consideration. Although a randomized trial does not necessarily guarantee an equivalent population, it is considered to be the "gold standard" for clinical researchers. Even in a randomized trial, equivalence between the intervention population and control group still needs to be demonstrated. Achievement of randomization in DM evaluation studies is believed by health plans to be impractical or even, in some instances, to be forbidden by medical ethics or regulation. When randomization is not possible, every effort should be given to planning and executing a study in such a way that equivalence is demonstrated in the reference and intervention populations.

Individual versus population studies is the last methodological issue explored. Many studies that claim to employ a reference group use the patient (pre-intervention) experience as the reference and patient (post-intervention) experience as the intervention group. While this design may meet the criteria for a reference group, the reference group may not meet the criteria for equivalence.

3.3.3 Measurement Issues in Study Design

In this section we review questions such as what to measure and when to measure it.

Appropriate Outcome/Outcome Measure

Clinicians, patients, and researchers often disagree about what outcome measure is most suitable. Patient "outcomes" include medical costs, quality-adjusted life years, functional status, employment status, long-term clinical outcomes, prevention of high-cost events, number of

[3] Merriam-Webster Unabridged Dictionary On-line.

work- or school-days lost to illness-related absence, and patient satisfaction/quality of life measurement. The result of greatest interest to the actuary is the financial outcome measured either directly via claims, or indirectly via alternative measures such as admissions. Paid claims net of cost sharing are subject to a number of effects such as contractual arrangements, plan design features, primary/secondary payer responsibility, or new technology. Thus an alternative measure not affected by these factors (such as admissions, bed-days, or allowed charges) may be a more stable variable for the purpose of outcomes tracking.

Timing of the Study: Determining "End Points" and "Starting Points"

In most clinical trials, patient "exposure" to a particular treatment begins at a defined time and ends at a pre-determined time, based on risk profile. A population measurement involves a single start- and end-date for the entire population. During the period of measurement, different members will have different risk profiles—some will be recently diagnosed, diseases will have progressed; some members will have had recent "events" (such as a hospitalization) and others not. Measurement of exposure and risk are fundamental building blocks of actuarial science, so the appropriate classification of members over time is an area where actuaries may be able to make a contribution to outcomes measurement.

Total Medical Costs Versus Disease-Specific Medical Costs

Most care management strategies focus on specific diseases. It is challenging to separate the medical costs by disease entity, for two reasons. First, since there is not always consistent coding of the medical claims on which evaluations rely, and claims may be coded to maximize reimbursement rather than ensure comparable outcomes, isolating the costs related to a single disease may prove impossible.

Second, members enrolled in disease management programs often suffer from more than one chronic disease. Where a particular chronic member should be classified is a challenge: should the member be classified according to the primary diagnosis on a claim, or according to the most frequently encountered diagnosis, or the most expensive diagnosis? From a financial perspective, a DM program is usually implemented to reduce costs, not disease-specific costs, so measurement of overall cost savings is appropriate.

Data Issues

As actuaries are all-too aware, drawing financial conclusions from data requires attention to data quality and interpretation. Many of the measurement issues in study design concern sources and uses of data.

Three common sources for data are incurred claims data, medical records, and survey data. The source of the data can affect measurement reliability. One characteristic of many intervention programs is the limited availability of machine-analyzable data. This is in part due to clinical training, which emphasizes extensive note-taking, and is resistant to a program design that emphasizes automation and homogeneous definitions, as are required for machine-analyzable data.

The timing of data collection and evaluation is also an issue. The financial pressures on both for-profit, publicly traded health plans and not-for-profit plans demand very quick evaluation of outcomes. This constraint, together with high membership attrition rates limits a Managed Care Organization's (MCO's) ability to continue a program and to track outcomes for a period of months or years. It also argues for proxy methods of interim measurement, based for example on admission data, work volumes or clinical improvement measures. There is a hypothesis (not tested, as far as we are aware) of "recidivism" (the tendency of the measured outcome to reverse over the long-run) in case and disease management. An intervention program may appear to achieve cost savings over a six- to 12-month period, but in fact, costs are simply deferred to a later period.

The issue of definition or which members to track for evaluation purposes, will be covered in more detail later.

3.3.4 Measurement Issues Specific to Chronic Populations

This section discusses certain issues specific to chronic condition populations that affect Disease Management evaluations.

Regression to the Mean

Many before-and-after evaluations that use the patient as the unit measurement (so-called "patient as their own control" designs) ignore the phenomenon that the outcomes of patients in period $t+1$ (evaluation or measurement period) are very often influenced by their state in the prior period t. Specifically, a high percentage of high-cost patients in period t are no longer high-cost in period $t+1$.

The graph in Figure 3.1 illustrates the phenomenon of regression to the mean at the level of the individual member:

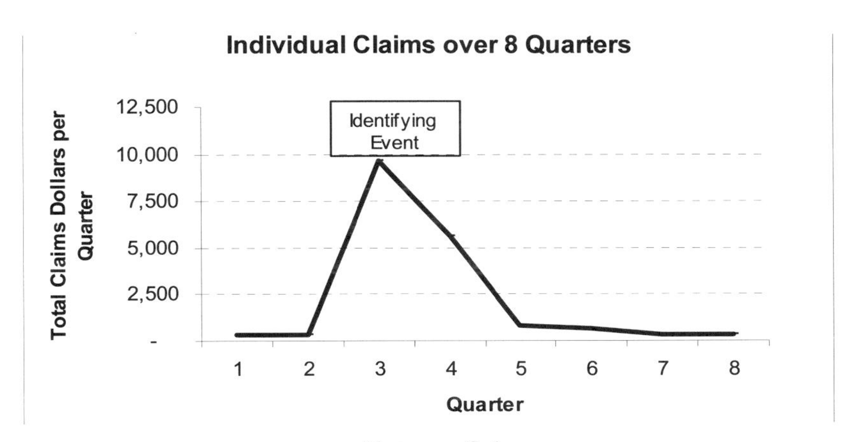

FIGURE 3.1

Depending on when this individual's experience begins to be tracked for the purpose of measurement, regression to the mean may be captured in the claims data. For example, if the identifying event for a DM program is the hospitalization claim that occurred in Quarter 3, and this claim is included before the start of the DM program, the tracking of the experience after the program start will show lower cost. The reduced cost may incorrectly be attributed to a DM program, when, in fact, the cost reduction is the natural course of the individual's illness and claims experience. This phenomenon is illustrated in Figure 3.2. In this example, an individual member is identified (through claims) and enrolled in a program. The experience before the member's enrollment (the enrollment is indicated by the vertical line) is included in the "Pre" experience; the experience after enrollment is included in the "Post" experience.

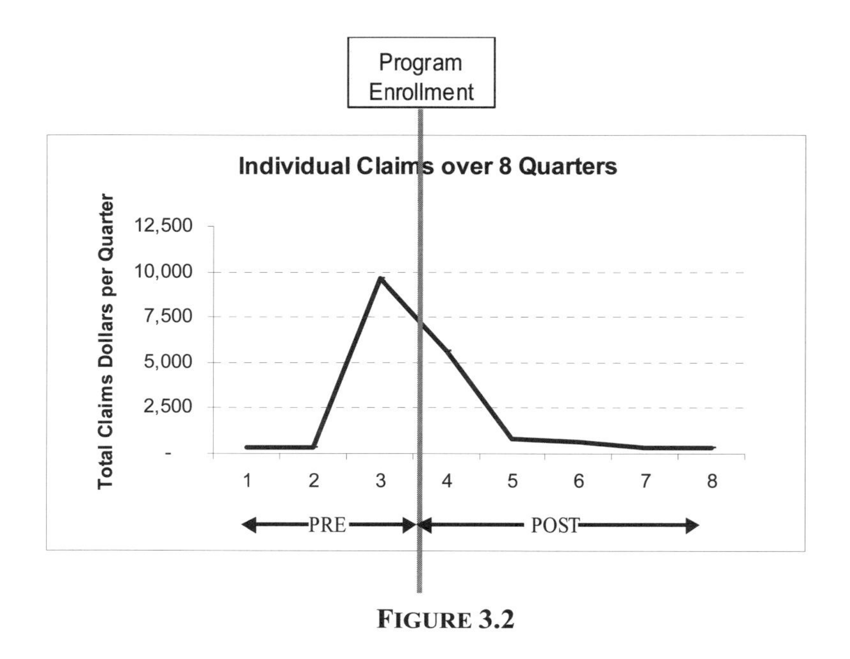

FIGURE 3.2

In addition to its effect at the individual level in the "patient as their own control" type studies, regression to the mean has implications for population studies. It is often assumed that, because individual member level regression (as illustrated above) is present, the entire population experience will exhibit the same phenomenon. This is not necessarily the case. A group of individuals identified through a sentinel event (such as a hospitalization) will exhibit regression to the mean; an entire population, consisting of members identified at different times, may or may not exhibit regression.

Table 3.1 demonstrates the more general impact that regression to the mean (claims increasing as well as decreasing) may have on an analysis. Note that Table 3.1 differs from Figure 3.1 and Figure 3.2, which show an individual's claim cost pattern over time, because Table 3.1 shows the claims experience of an entire population over two years. Only members who were eligible and had claims in Year 1 are included in this analysis, so new members or members who had no claims in Year 1 are excluded.

In Table 3.1, in which data are for the continuously enrolled members of a managed care plan for the two years 1997 and 1998, members are allocated into categories based on their cost-category in Year 1 ("Historic Period"). The members of this population are drawn from a health plan with limited managed care interventions: pre-authorization, some concurrent review and in-hospital case management, but no outpatient case management or disease management.

TABLE 3.1

$'000	Distribution of Members and Claims				
	Projection Period				
Historic Period Group	Historic Period Cost	$0 - $2	$2 - $25	$25+	Projection Period Cost
Low					
$0 - $2 87%	$324	$327	$5,368	$46,836	$831
		90%	10%	0%	
		90%	64%	40%	
Moderate $2 - $25 12%	$5,658	$668	$6,599	$47,811	$5,398
		55%	40%	5%	
		10%	34%	40%	
High $25+ 1%	$49,032	$ 847	$9,609	$58,489	$21,017
		26%	46%	28%	
		0%	2%	20%	
Total	$1,230	$ 355	$5,851	$49,377	$1,581

Source: Solucia Inc. data; 200,000 continuously enrolled members of an HMO; Baseline year; 1998; Projection period is 1999.

One percent of members have historical costs in excess of $25,000, with an average paid claim cost of $49,032. The outcome of each category is shown in Year 2 ("Projection Period"). Ninety percent of Year 1 low-cost members remain in the same category in Year 2, with approximately the same average cost. The second line under the projection period distribution of members and costs indicates the source of that period's membership in the prior year. For example, 64 percent of the intermediate group of members in Year 2 come from the prior year's low-cost members. Regression to the mean is illustrated by the outcome of the one percent of members who were high-cost in Year 1: 26 percent of these members are low-cost in Year 2, and 46 percent of these members are in the intermediate group. Only 28 percent of the members continue to experience high costs in Year 2, while nearly three-quarters of members have costs less than $25,000. The average cost of the high-cost members declines from $49,032 to $21,017 from Year 1 to Year 2.

The "Moderate" cost group in Table 3.1 consists largely of chronic patients. Note that in this example, if the population tracked is the Year 1 "Moderate" cohort, the average cost is observed to fall 4.6 percent from $5,658 in the baseline year to $5,398 in the intervention year, in the absence of any interventions. If the population tracked is the Year 1 moderate population compared with a similarly defined Year 2 moderate population, costs increase 3.4 percent, from $5,658 to $5,851.

Identifying Patients

The above discussion of regression to the mean argues against use of "patient as their own control" as a comparison group. A frequently used alternative is the "Population" approach, in which all members who meet the identification criteria in a baseline period are considered the comparison group, and all members who meet the same set of identifying criteria (irrespective of whether they were included in the baseline population, are enrolled in the program, etc.) are considered to be the intervention population. Very precise criteria should be established to identify chronic patients, and determine when they are included in the study. This method of identifying a comparison population relies on uniformity of the distribution of members with respect to the cost of their disease. Some members will be experiencing declining costs, as in the example above, while other members will be experiencing increasing costs as they experience a health-related event. Provided the distribution of member risk-status is similar in each year, this population approach will result in equivalent populations.

Establishing Uniform Risk Measure for Comparability

Different patients present widely differing combinations of co-morbidities, conditions, and other risk factors, in addition to different risk profiles at different times. Evaluation of outcomes requires a method for ensuring equivalence between populations. Specifying and identifying patient co-morbidities and risk factors continues to be a challenge of clinical epidemiology. Many of the risk factors that need to be considered in ensuring consistent risk-profiles are the same risk factors that actuaries use for pricing and underwriting health care coverage.

Claims data are subject to certain problems that can make them less reliable than medical record review or patient interviews for identifying chronically ill members and assigning a risk status to them. Patient interviews and chart reviews are impractical and subjective. Objective, transparent, and consistent definitions should be established that identify the population from which the target management candidates will be drawn, and whose experience will be tracked for financial outcomes measurement purposes. Identification criteria can influence the financial outcome of a program. At the same time, it should be remembered that clinician identification is not perfect either: conditions are not simple "binary" events (disease/non-disease). Rather, there are degrees of clinical disease and at times "fuzzy margins" at which it is as yet impossible to establish objectively whether an individual "has" the disease. In addition, in the absence of a unified Electronic Medical Record, not all of a patient's interactions with the medical system will be available in partial records, making identification less certain.

Patient Selection Bias

If randomized trials are not performed, there is always a potential problem of selection bias. Authors are divided about whether it is possible to adjust for bias. For example, Fitzner et al., [58] review different methods used by authors to avoid bias and confounding. All of these methods have in common two elements: the existence of bias is known and its extent is quantifiable. In the circumstance in which bias is suspected, but its extent is unknown, it appears to us that adjustment is difficult, if not impossible.

One of the most common sources of bias in evaluation is a study design that limits evaluations to those members who enroll in a voluntary program. By definition, in a voluntary program, those members who elect to enroll are a different risk-profile to those members who do not. Figure 3.3, taken from our unpublished data, tracks outcomes over time of different sub-populations from a chronic disease population subject to a disease management intervention. Unlike most DM programs, the chronic patients included in this study were randomized first, prior to enrollment. Thus the outcomes of the intervention and control groups (absent random fluctuations) represent a robust comparison for evaluation. Members were initially randomly assigned (prior to the start of the program) to intervention (75 percent) and control (25 percent). The point in time at which identification and assignment to the intervention is performed (start of the intervention program) is indicated by the vertical line. Participants were recruited from the intervention group, and the control group was untouched. The unit of outcomes measurement reported below in Figure 3.3 is bed-days per 1,000 per year.

Readers who are familiar with health plan bed-days per 1000 per year statistics will find these levels high. Remember, however, that these statistics are for a sub-set of the population, the chronic members only.

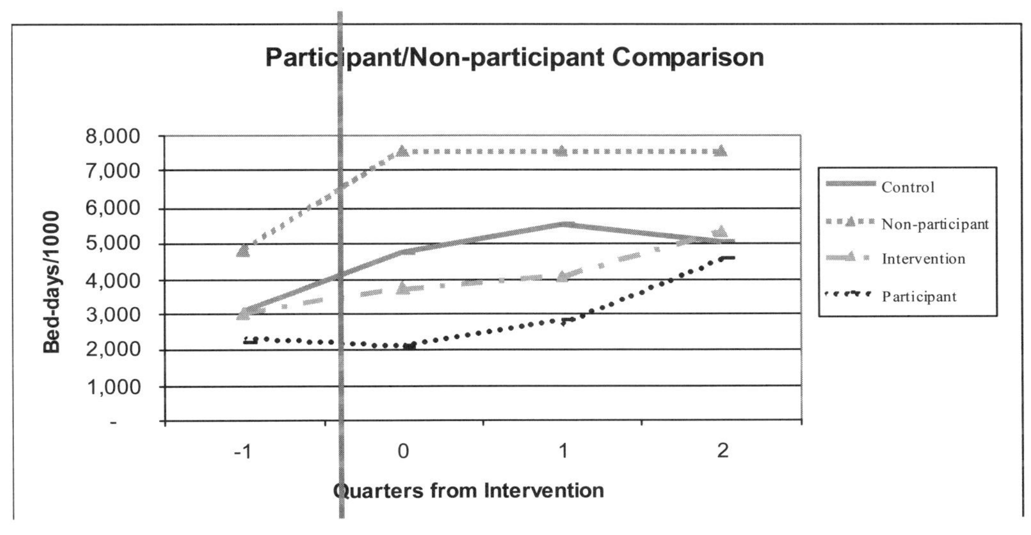

FIGURE 3.3

Two different member-outcome states are reported in Figure 3.3: members who enrolled in the program (Participants) and members who declined to enroll (Non-Participants). Members whom the nurse interventionists were unable to reach (No contact) are included in the Non-Participant group. Outcomes are compared with those of the control group. The effect of the intervention is shown by the difference between the Control and Intervention groups, and represents the reduction in total bed-days seen over the three quarters.

Comparison between the Intervention and Control groups is appropriate, because the members are assigned to these two populations based on objective criteria. Comparison between the participating (self-selected) population and the Control group is not appropriate because of the selection bias inherent in the participation process. Enrollment bias will be present in a program for a number of reasons:

- The sickest patients may be more difficult to contact if they are hospitalized or undergoing some other form of treatment;
- Moderately sick Commercial patients may be *easier* to reach because they are not actively at work;
- Patients who are less severely ill may be more likely to already be in control of their care and therefore will welcome working with a nurse; and
- Patients who are more severely ill are more likely to suffer depression which, in turn, inhibits their ability to self-manage and likelihood to enroll in a program.

The Intervention group consists of two sub-groups: Participants and Non-Participants. Overall outcomes of the intervention group compared with the control group (the difference between the two middle lines) indicate reduction in bed-days. It is important to note that the beginning (pre-program) utilization of the Intervention and Control groups (two middle lines) is the same, consistent with the random (unbiased) allocation of members between the intervention and control groups. Utilization of the Participant and Non-participant sub-groups is significantly different (in particular, the Non-participant group has higher beginning utilization), indicating selection bias. The patients who enrolled in the program (resulting from the ability of the health plan to reach the member, and then the patient's willingness to enroll when reached) represent a different experience group than those who did not enroll. Specifically, the non-participants had higher utilization than both the participants and the control group, indicating the effect of the enrollment bias.

Patient Drop Outs

Members may drop out of a follow-up study for a number of reasons: voluntary exit, termination from the health plan, transfer to a different group or product, or death. These factors can affect the outcomes. Within the enrolled group, the follow-up with different members is also potentially anti-selective; some patients will stay in a telephonic intervention program for the prescribed duration, while others will drop out because they are feeling better, or for other reasons.

General versus Specific Population

Some interventions are used only on an extremely selected, and therefore small, subset of potential enrollees; thus sample size can be problematic unless very large populations are available. Large-case management interventions, for example, tend to be applied in a very small subset (often less than ½ percent) of the population. The co-morbidities, outcomes and cost of these members are highly variable, making it difficult to apply standard study designs. At the same time, the effect of the intervention, while significant at the individual level, may be too slight relative to overall claims to allow its effect to be measured in the entire population. A measurement methodology that is appropriate for a chronic population (where the prevalence of disease is often five percent or more in a commercial population) may not be appropriate in a large-case management population with a prevalence of ½ percent.

3.3.5 Claims Issues in Study Design

Most evaluations will be based on administrative claims. This section discusses five considerations relative to claims: fixed time periods, member eligibility, claims run-out, outliers, and special problems with claims data.

Fixed Time Periods

Epidemiologists sometimes consider one year's data inadequate for outcomes evaluation because with continuous identification and program enrollment, all patients do not have equal "exposure." In addition, because of the time taken for claims to mature (see below), the amount of time needed to perform a rigorous evaluation of a program will be long, even if the time period is restricted to one year's incurred claims. For chronic disease management programs, however, there are usually a sufficient number of members with the condition that a "spread" of risk conditions will be assured, allowing for stability in measurement over time. Actuaries calculate exposure, even when a member is eligible for less than one year, so this factor should not be a problem. Short exposure periods must, however, allow sufficient time for the "process" aspects of a program to be completed: data collection, chronic member identification, communication, enrollment, and patient education.

Enrollment Issues/Eligibility

Actuaries know that eligibility files of most managed care organizations are frequently incomplete, making it difficult to identify patients. The timeliness of new member enrollment, or terminating member disenrollment should be factored into any study, since annual disenrollment rates exceed 20 percent in many plans. The drop-out effect of member disenrollment is further complicated by members who terminate in one plan or product, but who reappear in the health plan under a different member identifier (because they have joined a new group, are covered by a spouse, or changed products).

Claims Run-Out

Analysts must wait for physicians and other providers to submit claims; however, there is usually a lag of several months in claims submission. In addition, when claims are disputed as to eligibility, subrogation or primary payment, claims that are initially processed may be re-adjudicated or reversed, making it difficult to draw conclusions from immature claims data. While actuaries have techniques for handling immature data, these techniques generally depend on data that reflect a stable underlying operational state. By definition, the introduction of care management results in change to the operations of the health plan, potentially rendering projections based on the prior state invalid. Customers of medical management programs often want to see immediate results, and are not at all comfortable with the idea that they will be paying for a program when results will not be credible or stable for upwards of two years.

Outliers

Actuaries are familiar with the potentially distorting effect of outlier claims – atypical cases that may distort overall study results. In a DM program, outliers may be members with unusual conditions, individual large claims, or both.

Special Problems with Claims Data

The quality of claims data has improved substantially in the last 10 years. Hospital data is still vastly more complete and accurate than claims submitted by physicians. Pharmacy data, useful for identifying many conditions or identifying conditions on a more timely basis than hospital claims, may not be present in certain groups of patients. When chronic patients are identified through claims, it is important that the claims and coding on which the identification depends be consistent between groups and over time. Because there is no single agreed upon definition of administrative-claim-based chronic disease criteria, there is room for difference of opinion, and therefore "false positives" and "false negatives" occur in the identification of chronic members.

False positives are members identified as having a condition who do not, in fact, have the condition with which they are identified. False negatives are members who have the condition who are not identified through the identification algorithm. False positives in particular have an impact on financial outcomes measurement because, by definition, the false positive member does not have claims identifying the chronic disease in the intervention year (and is likely to be lower-cost than a member who does have the identifying claims). False negatives do not create this problem because they do not contribute claims costs.

3.4 RISK FACTORS

Now we will turn to the specific risk factors that must be considered in any measurement calculation and which should be reported in order to ensure comparability and reproducibility of results. In any study, various characteristics of the reference and intervention groups must be evaluated, so that the effect of the intervention on outcomes can be properly assessed. Statistical techniques may be used to adjust for differences, if needed. At a minimum, information should be given regarding the variable and its potential effect. The eight variables listed below are identified by economists and epidemiologists as "confounding variables." Actuaries know them as "risk factors," and are accustomed to allowing for them in pricing or underwriting health insurance coverage.

1. Demographic variables
2. Exclusionary conditions that exclude certain members
3. Exclusionary conditions that exclude certain claims
4. Persistency
5. Chronic prevalence and risk classification
6. Severity of illness
7. Contactability
8. Operational issues

At the very least, any study of outcomes needs to include reference to the values of these variables and the way in which they have been taken into consideration in the study design. When we consider that the issues implicit in a variable will be familiar to actuaries, we do not discuss the variable in detail. When a variable presents issues that are less familiar we provide additional information. We will include more discussion in Chapter 8.

3.4.1 Demographic Variables

Changes in the following variables (all of which are familiar to actuaries) can affect the result of any outcomes measurement exercise.

- Age
- Gender
- Medicare eligibility
- Other payer eligibility
- Other sources of services (either reimbursed or not reimbursed)
- Medical group election alternatives
- Product and benefits design/description

3.4.2 Exclusionary Conditions – Members

It is common in evaluations to exclude certain members from either the program or the evaluation, or both. "Exclusionary conditions" that eliminate a member from the care program include:

- Conditions with severe privacy restrictions on either data or contacts (e.g., HIV/AIDS, Mental Health).
- Management of conditions which the sponsoring organization has contracted-out to an outside vendor – either the claims associated with the condition (for example, capitated mental health) or the management of the condition (for example, cancer or maternity programs).
- Conditions that imply that the member is not a good clinical candidate for care management (e.g., institutionalization, members in case management, and members with End-Stage Renal Disease).
- Conditions that imply that a member is not a good financial candidate for care management (e.g., program sponsor is the secondary payer, implying that any financial gains accrue to the benefit of a party other than the program sponsor).

3.4.3 Exclusionary Conditions – Claims

It is common to exclude certain claims from an evaluation in order to reduce confounding and/or "noise" from conditions that are either not manageable or are subject to fluctuations.

Some categories of claims (maternity, mental health, cancer) are excluded from the measured outcomes experience because they involve conditions that DM does not aim to affect[4]. Some authors argue that non-medical (surgical) admissions should also be excluded because these categories are particularly subject to supply-induced demand, making it difficult to compare populations over time or geography when these categories are included in the measurement. There is substantial literature associated with the phenomena of supply-induced demand and practice variations, which is outside the scope of this book[5].

3.4.4 Persistency

It is important to understand the terms under which a member may enter/leave the underlying group. DM companies often work only with data on the chronic population (or even more narrowly, the sub-set of the chronic population enrolled in the DM program) and therefore do not have insight into overall enrollment trends in a health plan. Results may be affected by persistency of enrollment with the medical group, medical plan, product, employee tier, or employer. Re-enrollment frequency and identification of the member across products may be a contributor (either positively or negatively) to trend (used here in the actuarial sense, meaning the rate of increase in per member per month claims), as members enter or leave a group. Claims levels will also differ according to the availability of out-of-state and out-of-area coverage and the likelihood of services being provided in those settings. Finally, another important aspect is persistency in the care management program itself. Different DM companies have different rules about required length of enrollment in, and conditions for "graduation" from a program. Recording of this persistency (and availability of the data) is not consistent between companies and sometimes makes comparisons between programs and vendors difficult.

---

[4] The conditions cited here are examples of conditions that are excluded from "traditional" disease management programs. There are specialist programs, however, that address these conditions. It would obviously not be appropriate to exclude these conditions for one of these programs.

[5] The reader is referred to Lucas et al. [126], Wennberg et al. [211], [212] and [213]. for further information.

3.4.5 Chronic Prevalence and Risk

The basis of "risk" and savings opportunity in a DM program is **chronic prevalence**: after all, the more chronically ill people that are present in a population, the greater the opportunity to improve health and reduce costs. (See Chapter 6 for more detail about the economics of DM.)

Chronic prevalence is defined by Duncan [51] as:

$$\frac{\text{Number of individuals with the condition}}{\text{Total number of individuals in the population}}$$

This statistic is measured at a single point in time, and therefore the statistic value will vary when calculating chronic prevalence at different times. A more important consideration when comparing prevalence between populations is whether prevalence includes or excludes duplication (members who have more than one chronic condition are counted only once, or are counted each time they have a condition).

The target chronic diseases are typically Heart Failure, Diabetes, Ischemic Heart Disease, Asthma, and Chronic Obstructive Pulmonary Disease (COPD). The technical definition of any one of the target chronic diseases, which is a combination of occurrences of different claims codes, is crucial. Unfortunately, there is no uniform definition of chronic disease in use for either candidate identification or outcomes measurement purposes. Chronic condition definitions change over time, as new codes are added to code sets and new sources of data become available. Common examples of claims code sets include: ICD (International Classification of Diseases, 9th or 10th Edition Clinical Modification (ICD 9/10 CM); CPT-4 (Current Procedural Terminology, 4th Edition); HCPCS (Health Care Common Procedure Coding System); and NDC (National Drug Code). In any comparative study, objective criteria should be used that are easily applied, do not require manual intervention to perform, and can be readily implemented.

As an example of the issues involved in disease definitions, consider diabetes. The primary ICD-9 code for Diabetes mellitus is 250.0 (without mention of complications). A code in the 250.x series also indicates the presence of diabetes of a more serious nature.

250.1: Diabetes with ketoacidosis
250.2: Diabetes with hyperosmolarity
250.3: Diabetes with other coma
250.4: Diabetes with renal manifestations
250.5: Diabetes with ophthalmic manifestations
250.6: Diabetes with neurological manifestations
250.7: Diabetes with peripheral circulatory disorders
250.8: Diabetes with other specified manifestations
250.9: Diabetes with unspecified complications

A hospital claim with a primary code in the 250.0 series indicates that the admission was associated with a diagnosis of diabetes, and is therefore reasonably reliable. A hospital claim for another diagnosis but with an associated diabetes code may also be a reliable indicator of the diabetes diagnosis, but codes for other diagnoses are often less reliable than those for the primary diagnosis, because they may be inconsistently applied. Use of a 250.x code on an outpatient claim may less-reliably indicate the presence of diabetes. Provided the procedure and place of service indicates that the service was provided by a physician the diagnosis is probably reliable, but often more than one outpatient claim is required on different days in order to indicate the presence of diabetes with sufficient reliability. Diabetes may also be inferred from drug claims, particularly if the claim is for insulin. The increasing off-label use of some other medications means that the use of drug data for diagnostic purposes in some cases should be treated with caution. In the case of diabetes drugs, the oral generic drug (Metformin) may sometimes be used for conditions other than diabetes. Thus identification of diabetes by Metformin prescription alone is unlikely to be sufficiently accurate and will require validation by other claims (for example, office visits or diabetic supplies). These issues are often addressed through rules such as: claims for at least two face-to-face physician office encounters separated by at least 14 days, or four or more separate prescription re-fills for the identifying drug.

Examples of disease identification algorithms are:

- HEDIS (Health Plan Employer Data and Information Set) definitions
- Proprietary disease definitions, for example, those inherent in algorithms, such as D_xCG, ACG, etc. These may be more appropriate for a particular situation, but make comparability difficult.
- Some definitions depend on drug claims data or laboratory values, which are not uniformly available, making consistency and comparability difficult.
- Some disease definitions require clinical intervention (chart review). Others depend on self-reported data that are usually subjective, difficult and expensive to collect.

Duncan [51] contains a robust set of claims diagnosis-based definitions for further reference.

A patient's primary diagnosis (the condition, problem or other reason for the encounter that is chiefly responsible for the services provided) is usually more rigorously coded on claims than secondary diagnoses (other conditions or problems that affected a patient's treatment). However, in order to identify the chronic member and the member's co-morbidities, all diagnoses should be used. The accuracy of and rules for assigning ICD codes on medical claims by medical records technicians or billing personnel contributes to some of the "false-positive" issues.

The clinical view of a chronic disease is that once diagnosed, the disease continues for life. This view, however, is not always confirmed by the data. Some health plan members who meet a set of objective criteria for identification as a chronic condition member in Period 1, may not meet the same criteria in Period 2. This definition of "statistical false positive" is not the same as that used by clinicians or epidemiologists.

Given that identification of chronic condition is usually performed based on claims, we believe that our preference for re-qualification on an annual basis has merit in the DM outcome measurement context (although we do not lose sight of the fact that both clinical and statistical false positives[6] and false negatives may be present in any measurement). Ideally, a set of

[6] We use the term "statistical false positives (or negatives) to distinguish these types of members from true false positives and to highlight the fact that we are identifying conditions from claims data, not medical charts. Of course, a medical professional may falsely identify a condition as well (false positive). When using claims data to identify conditions, the failure of the member to meet the identifying conditions for chronic disease in a subsequent period suggests that the member was incorrectly identified in the prior period. We term this observation "statistical false positive."

identification definitions would be sufficiently sensitive to identify all members with the condition (limited false negatives). At the same time, the definitions should limit the number of false positives. Discussion of sensitivity and specificity is beyond the scope of this chapter and the reader is referred to Duncan [51] for definitions of sensitivity and specificity. There is an inverse relationship between sensitivity and specificity. It is likely that a wide net will catch “false positives,” or members who are identified as meeting the disease definition, but who do not actually have the disease.

Some obvious adjustments to the identification methodology can be made to ensure that members who appear to have a claim for a particular condition, but who, for example, may have had a test to “rule-out” the condition, are appropriately excluded. An example of a more difficult set of issues is with those members who are identified through drug claims in one period, but not in a second period: was the member a “false-positive” or did the member’s employer (or the member) switch drug coverage?

The minimum period of data required for consistent identification is related to the issue of disease definition: what minimum duration of data is required to accurately identify a member’s disease state? Frequently, members are assigned to chronic categories based on the prior 12 months’ claims experience. But is 12 months likely to result in a more accurate identification than six or 24 months of claims history?

In addition to chronic prevalence, risk and opportunity are affected by disease stratification and severity (e.g., Type 1 or 2 diabetes; Class III or Class IV Heart Failure[7]; or high-, moderate-, low-risk chronic members).

3.4.6 Disease Severity

Disease severity clearly affects a patient’s claims cost, and therefore the potential for savings. Disease severity is more difficult to capture from claims data. The available data sources are those discussed previously in the “Data Issues” section of this chapter, plus (once a patient is contacted and enrolled) self-reported data.

Many practitioners want to use risk-adjustment methods to assign a risk or severity “score” to a patient based on claims and diagnosis information. This method has some promise, where the risk-adjustment algorithms are “open” and can be replicated. The objective of DM, however, is to influence the patient’s disease state, achieving its aims through improvements in measures such as medication compliance and test scores (see Chapter 6). These are the same variables that affect the patient’s score, and there is potential for confounding. Issues related to confounding are further discussed in Chapter 7.

A consistent definition in terms of patient severity is critical for patient classification. Sever-

[7]Type 1 diabetes was previously called insulin-dependent diabetes mellitus or juvenile-onset diabetes. Type 1 diabetes may account for five percent to 10 percent of all diagnosed cases of diabetes. Type 2 diabetes was previously called non-insulin-dependent diabetes mellitus or adult-onset diabetes. Type 2 diabetes may account for about 90 percent to 95 percent of all diagnosed cases of diabetes. Class III Heart Failure results in marked limitation of physical activity. Patients are comfortable at rest. Less than ordinary activity causes fatigue, palpitation, dyspnea or anginal pain. Class IV patients have cardiac disease resulting in inability to carry on any physical activity without discomfort. DM companies differ in their number of member risk levels, and how members are assigned to those levels. While useful clinically, the assignment of Heart Failure classes requires clinical assessment and cannot be performed from administrative claims, making this type of stratification of limited usefulness for claims-based outcomes assessment.

ity can have two meanings, however, that do not necessarily produce the same member stratification: financial severity (those members at high risk of adverse financial outcomes) and clinical risk. There is little consistency in terms of patient risk classification in DM programs; vendors use different approaches that include some or all of financial or clinical risk, and gaps in care; some vendors classify into high, medium, and low-risk classes, and others classify into high and low only. Some vendors classify the high group as the top 10 percent of patients (ordered in terms of risk), while others use different percentages. Clearly, comparison between programs that define risk and determine the strata differently is difficult and subject to potential misinterpretation. In Chapter 9 we will discuss an approach to risk classification that addresses these issues.

A related issue is the need for a consistent definition in terms of the member's likelihood to benefit from DM. Unlike chronic disease, which (when assessed from claims history) is reasonably objective, likelihood to benefit is a subjective concept. Despite this, many programs assess candidates and select them based on likelihood to benefit from the program. If outcomes are assessed for the selected population only, the selection process clearly introduces a non-random bias. If outcomes are measured for an entire, objectively identified population, this bias may be avoided.

3.4.7 "Contactability"

It is not sufficient to identify a chronic population; chronic care management aims to involve the member in taking responsibility for the member's own healthcare. Disease Management programs depend on the ability of the manager to reach and engage the member. If the health plan does not have good contact data, or if the members choose to ignore contacts by the health plan or its representatives, the program will not succeed. Populations will vary with regard to this risk factor (HMO and other gatekeeper type plans, which require "positive" enrollment generally have better contact data than indemnity-type plans, for example), and the "contactability" of a specific population, or of a population at a period in time, should be disclosed in order to ensure transparency and comparability of results.

3.4.8 Operational Issues

Because all DM programs are not the same, it is important for comparative purposes that operational statistics be part of any study. The following are examples of measures that should be reported for any program that is being evaluated:

- Number of eligible (health plan enrolled) members;
- Number of chronic patients identified, and timing of the identification;
- A statement indicating how sensitivity (number of patients identified) vs. specificity (presence of false-positives) has been handled;
- Number of chronic patients "available" (valid contact information; not on a "do not call" list);
- Number of chronic patients contacted;
- Number of chronic enrollees in DM program;
- Length of time the member is involved in the intervention;

- A definition of "graduation" (intervention program completion by the member) and member graduation rates, and;
- Specification of the methodology applied to compare the reference population to the intervention population. Even within a particular methodology, different results may be obtained by the use of different assumptions with regard to variables, making full disclosure critically important.

3.5 CONCLUSIONS

In this Chapter, we have discussed a number of the definitional, measurement and data issues of which an actuary should be aware when performing a program evaluation. Many of these issues will be familiar to actuaries in other contexts (for example anti-selection or underwriting risk factors). Actuarial familiarity with the issues will increase the potential value of actuaries to an organization interested in objectively evaluating a program.

In Chapter 7 we will review commonly used measurement methodologies, and then in Chapter 8 lay out an actuarial-adjustment methodology for evaluating program management outcomes, including specifics of measures to address confounding and other issues mentioned here.

First, however, in Chapter 4, we review the literature on clinical outcomes and cost savings reported in studies of different types of programs.

APPENDIX 3.1: CAUSALITY

Any discussion of outcomes measurement needs to consider the role of causality, and the standard of proof required in *actuarial,* financial analysis or savings calculations.

Papers cited in the Bibliography approach outcomes measurement from the perspective of multiple users, both scientific and business. The scientific emphasis tends to promote a higher degree of proof than is likely to be encountered in a business setting. This higher standard in the scientific community results in a focus on the need for proof that the DM intervention "caused" the specific outcome, or "causality". Business users, while demanding considerable rigor in other aspects of an evaluation, (such as validation and reconciliation of source data) may be satisfied with a "demonstration" standard, where "association" between cause and effect may be sufficient, rather than the stricter test of "causation". Demonstration may be satisfied with an analysis that shows association between the intervention program and a favorable outcome, together with adequate demonstration that the results are not biased or confounded by factors that could impact the result.

Proof of causation requires that the mechanism whereby the outcome is achieved be unambiguously demonstrated. If the result to be proven is savings, for example, then a study that proves causation would have to establish "missing" components in the target population (such as compliance with best-practice medical care), then show how the intervention improved compliance with care in the population, and finally, led to the resulting financial outcomes.

The DMAA committee that drafted the *Principles for Assessing Disease Management Outcomes* recommends that "absent independently funded research trials using a randomized control design, …the preferred evaluation method for assessing causality of DM in achieving outcomes is comparison to an equivalent control group. This assessment should include a baseline measure in the intervention and control populations with a re-measure of the outcomes of interest following the intervention in the DM population versus the control group" (Fitzner [63]).

Wilson and MacDowell [219] refer to a causal pathway that can be used where "proof" is required, in a pure scientific sense. They describe a pathway as follows in Figure 3.4,[8] in which we provide an example of different types of metrics:

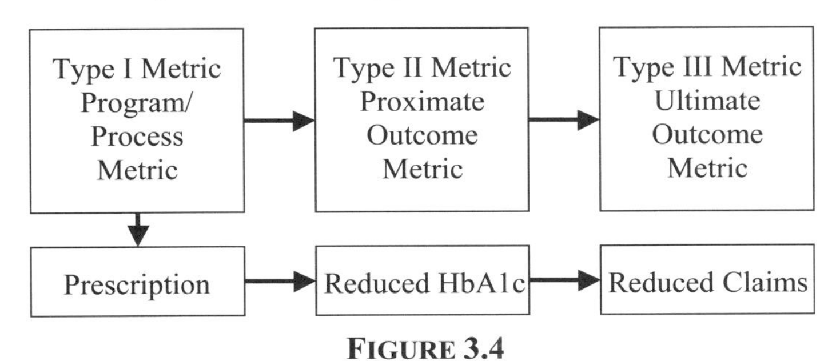

FIGURE 3.4

A "Type I" metric is the most basic measure. Such metrics determine the components of a process, such as units of input, rather than the results of a process, such as units of output. For example, a Type I metric in a DM program could be:

- A volume measure such as the overall number of members of a health plan;

[8] From Wilson and MacDowell [219]. Reproduced by permission

- The number of chronic members;
- The number of enrolled chronic members;
- The number of nurses assigned to manage patients;
- The number of calls attempted to chronic members over a period of time; or
- The number of prescriptions for a particular medication consumed by the population.

A "Type II" metric is an intermediate measure, and represents the process outcome of the input determined in the Type I metric. As such, it may measure the result of an input that contributes to the final output measure of interest. So if our ultimate desired outcome is reduced claims, an intermediate measure could be the rate at which patients re-fill their prescriptions, or the proportion of a diabetic population whose hemoglobin A1c score is less than 7.0 (the maximum level set by the American Diabetes Association as indicating blood sugar "control" in a diabetic).

Finally, a "Type III" metric is the outcome that the program has been designed to target, such as per member per month incurred claims in the chronic population.

Clearly, establishment of causality implies that it should be possible to trace the ultimate result back to its source (the inputs and improved outcomes that contribute to an improved financial measure). Conversely (and importantly in Disease Management financial outcomes measurement) it should be possible to demonstrate the process and clinical causal factors that lead to the clinical improvements that lead to the measured financial outcomes.

The Ultimate Outcome Metric of interest to actuaries and other financial buyers is the financial savings to the payer. Assuming that actual savings results are available, the steps to understand causality include:

- The mechanism that produced the savings results, i.e., the "causal pathway." First-level proximate metrics, for example, would include enrollment of chronic members. Higher-level (Type II) metrics would include an increase in testing and further stratification of high-risk members, increased medication adherence, increased compliance with physician-ordered treatments, or improved test-scores on clinical tests. Finally, the ultimate metric will be that metric of interest to the program sponsor – for example, reduced hospital admissions.

- The influence of treatment variations. Is there evidence, for example, that varying outreach efforts results in different enrollment experience (implying that enrollment is in fact controllable by the program, rather than a constant)?

- Consistency of the Proximate Outcome Metrics with the Ultimate Outcome Metrics (e.g., do we observe higher compliance or testing rates at the proximate level, and is this experience sufficient to lead to the observed Ultimate Outcome metric)? An observation of improved financial results, accompanied by deterioration in proximate measures such as test scores would tend to suggest that the improved financial results are aberrant. Conversely, as we note in Chapter 6 ("Understanding the Economics of Disease Management") there remains an unanswered question about how we reconcile improved clinical measures (proximate measures) with financial measures that do not show the same degree of improvement.

Although "demonstration" is a weaker standard than a scientific test of causality, if it is performed rigorously, it should still be sufficient for most financial buyers. A demonstration standard simply measures the comparative values in the Intervention and Reference populations, and assigns causality to the Intervention.

4 ESTIMATING SAVINGS, UTILIZATION RATE CHANGES AND RETURN ON INVESTMENT

A Selective Review of the Literature on Program Evaluation

4.1 INTRODUCTION

A large and rapidly expanding literature exists regarding care management programs. In keeping with the financial theme of this book, our interest in reviewing the literature is selective, limited to specific types of outcomes – either financial or utilization-related outcomes which are indicative of financial improvement or from which financial conclusions may be drawn. Published studies that address our objectives are a limited sub-set of the larger body of peer-reviewed literature.

"Savings" is one of many terms that is commonly used and is often not clearly defined. The Disease Management Association of America's (DMAA 2004) *Dictionary of Disease Management Terminology* [51] defines savings as follows:

> "Savings (medical cost savings) result from decreased health care resource utilization, in turn resulting from the beneficial effects of a DM program or intervention. Savings are usually calculated (rather than being observed directly) in the reconciliation process, and in turn may form part of a Return on Investment (ROI) calculation. Because we are attempting to measure something that has *not* occurred (as a result of the intervention), savings usually cannot be measured directly and, instead, are inferred or estimated from other observations. A robust study design is crucial to the derivation of the observations that are used in the savings calculation."

The DMAA definition goes on to point out that "savings" may be estimated directly (as the change in per member per month cost, for example) or indirectly (for example, as the change in hospital or Emergency Room utilization, converted to dollars using a unit cost).

Several other factors complicate evaluation and comparison of the financial savings literature:

1. Different Research Designs. Designs range from randomized controlled trials, before-and-after designs, and cohort studies without any reference population other than the population being evaluated (patient as their own control). (See Chapter 7 for discussion of different study designs.)

2. Basis of Savings Calculations. Some studies report savings for the specific (diseased) population only, and others report results for a larger population (from which the target population is drawn). When the reported statistic is a percentage, or a rate of return on investment, it is difficult to relate the results to a basis that enables comparison between studies. Many studies do not provide information about the cost

of the intervention program. We believe that the lack of comparability between studies is one of the greatest shortcomings that the industry must overcome.

3. Timing. As every reader knows, health care costs increase with time, often rapidly (trend), and a patient whose services cost $100 in 1990 might well have cost a health plan $250 for the same bundle of services in 2000.

4. Difference in Sample Size and Study Duration. The size of the study population, and duration of the study vary enormously. Academic studies tend to be smaller and briefer in duration. The competitive nature of managed care and financial pressures on publicly traded firms limit the type of study, and increases the potential for confounding as firms constantly implement new initiatives and business processes.

5. Clinical Focus of Published Studies. Some of the most comprehensive articles are research reviews and **meta-analyses**. A meta-analysis is a survey article that has synthesized and re-analyzed data from other comparable studies that have used the same or similar methods and procedures, to enable the generation of sufficient amounts of data for statistical analysis and more tests of significance than can be achieved by a single study. A meta-analysis often contains a "weighted" summary of results from the surveyed literature. The typical focus of a considerable amount of the literature is clinical, rather than financial outcomes. However, meta-analyses are challenging in care management because the variables, risk factors, and interventions underlying studies are so different, making comparisons particularly difficult. Preferably, information would be required on sub-sets of data (age, sex, risk, geography, etc.) to enable appropriate adjustments to be made for comparison purposes.

We limited our review of published outcomes to the peer-reviewed literature. There are many results from different programs, particularly of DM financial outcomes, that have appeared in "trade" publications. These results may be valid, but we have ignored them because they have not been subjected to the scrutiny of the peer review process. Even in the peer-reviewed literature, however, there are examples of studies that use questionable methodologies, and some of which we note in the detailed discussion below. Nevertheless, the fact that a study has been reviewed by industry experts gives some comfort that its conclusions are credible.

Before we discuss actual results of the literature search, we will briefly describe the tools available to actuaries and others interested in further researching the literature.

4.2 SEARCHING THE HEALTH CARE LITERATURE

A powerful, comprehensive and widely-used journal literature search system is PubMed® which is available at no charge, at least for accessing article abstracts.[1] This system was developed by the National Library of Medicine (NLM), located at the National Institutes of Health (NIH). The system contains bibliographic citations and author abstracts from more than 4,600 biomedical journals published in the United States and 70 other countries. PubMed includes over 14 million citations for biomedical articles back to the 1950s. These cita-

[1] Certain services may involve charges, such as gaining access to full-text articles of some journals.

tions are from MEDLINE and additional life science journals. PubMed includes links to many sites providing full text articles and other related resources. New competitors are also entering the market. One example that is likely to grow is a service offered by the popular search engine, Google, which may be accessed at www.scholar.google.com.

Access to PubMed is easily obtained by visiting the Web site www.ncbi.nlm.nih.gov/PubMed. The "PubMed Tutorial," a Web-based learning program, instructs users how to perform literature searches.

In Chapter 2, we discussed seven care management strategies. The earlier forms of care management (preauthorization, utilization review, concurrent review, and case management) were the subject of analyses in the 1980s, and their results are more accepted by the industry. More recently, less research attention has been directed towards the earlier forms of care management and thus fewer recent analyses have been published. The prevalence of these types of programs makes it virtually impossible to find a "virgin" population not subject to some form of utilization management against which to compare the results of a particular program. The three more recently developed forms of care management (disease management, specialty care management, and population management) have been the subject of most recent research attention. These forms of care management tend to be larger in their application and corresponding cost of implementation because the at-risk populations are often much larger than those who were subject to the older forms of interventions. Therefore, purchasers demand more careful scrutiny of the results, and more studies are beginning to be published.

One consequence of the increased focus on DM is the expanding membership in the DMAA. The DMAA has demonstrated its commitment to the evaluation of care management interventions by compiling a database of disease management-related research projects selected from more than 5,000 journal articles, available through a DMAA product called "LitFinder." This database is available to members of DMAA; researchers may access it for a fee. The information may be accessed through the DMAA's website, www.dmaa.org.

4.2.1 Methodology

Our search criteria and methodology for selecting articles for this literature review are described in Appendix 4.1. We used a four-stage method to identify articles in the medical literature that address financial outcomes of care management interventions. First, we adopted broad search criteria that located a very large number of articles dealing with care interventions. Next, we reviewed each article's abstract and eliminated articles in which there was no discussion or analysis of financial and/or utilization outcomes. In Stage 3, we obtained the full-text version of review articles or meta-analyses that led to other "candidate articles." Finally, we reviewed the remaining candidate articles to compile a list of those in which financial outcomes was an important (although not necessarily the principal) component. This process was subsequently supplemented by the addition of articles that were included in the CBO report (CB) [4] that were not identified by our search process, primarily because the CBO report includes articles about clinical as well as financial outcomes.

Without a detailed analysis of each article's methodology and corresponding implications any results should be treated with caution since methodological differences can produce varying financial results. We list more detailed information for each of the articles included in the Summary in Appendix 4.2, providing information to help the reader locate each article, assess the study and its results and compare with other studies. The information provided includes:

- Intervention Type
- Disease or condition targeted;
- Length of the intervention or study (or when conducted);
- Sample size (both Intervention and Reference population);
- Research (study) design; and
- Results (financial results: savings; utilization reduction, ROI, etc.).

For those results that are obtained from randomized control trials, readers may have more confidence in the published results than those that are obtained from pre-post or cohort studies. Given these caveats, the key articles and predominant research findings that estimate cost savings, reduced hospital utilization or ROI are summarized in Appendix 4.2.

Estimates of return on investment in the literature are generally rare, because ROI involves a calculation based on the one-time/startup costs of the intervention, estimated savings and the annual operating costs of the program. The reporting of ROI is more prevalent in disease management and to a lesser extent population management than in other interventions. A major impediment to estimating savings or ROI is the lack of reported information on costs of interventions. Where no ROI was published but sufficient data was provided to allow us to estimate an ROI, we have done so (and noted that the ROI is estimated).

4.2.2 Gross and Net Return on Investment

We report ROI using the convention encountered in the clinical and utilization management literature, that is, on what we term a "gross of cost" basis. On this basis, 2.0 ROI means that the program returns the cost of the program plus a 100 percent margin over cost. On a "net of cost" basis, the equivalent ROI is 100 percent. The "net of cost" basis is the more typical reporting method in business and other commercial applications. For some reason, the intervention literature generally reports on a "gross of cost" basis. It is important to understand this difference when reviewing results, but otherwise this convention should not present difficulties.

4.2.3 Publication Bias

Many of the articles reviewed and summarized in Appendix 4.2 demonstrate positive outcomes. Readers should be cautious about extrapolating results of these studies too broadly, because of "publication bias." Publication bias is the phenomenon that occurs because negative or zero results from an intervention tend not to be published, whereas studies with favorable or positive results are published. We found some articles that report either negative or no effect of the intervention, but their frequency in the literature is rare. A different but related issue is that of "self-interest bias," a phenomenon that occurs because entities with an interest in the results of a study are able to finance studies in which they have an interest. We have, of course, no way of estimating the frequency of "unsuccessful" studies that do not find their way to publication, or results that are not of interest to a sponsor.

4.3 SUMMARY OF RESULTS

TABLE 4.1

In all, 86 articles were analyzed in detail. Because some articles can be classified under more than one intervention type, we record results for 107 studies.

Intervention	Total No. of Studies	Major Findings
Preauthorization/ Utilization Review (UR)	9	Early studies show admission and bed-day reductions from UR in the range of 10% to 15%. Recent international studies of data not subject to managed care show considerable opportunity for utilization reduction. Early gains were not maintained as medical management models changed; there is also evidence of increased outpatient utilization due to inpatient UR. More recently these reductions are in the range of 2% to 3%; savings are estimated at between $25 and $74 per member per year; we estimate ROI of 4.60 based on reported intervention cost of $16/member for this study.
Concurrent Review	5	Early gains due to Concurrent Review were not maintained as medical practice patterns changed. Current evidence that Concurrent Review can reduce bed-days by 2% to 3%. One study in a hospital setting showed ROI of 0.9 (savings < cost of review).
Case Management (sometimes called Intensive Case Management) (CM or ICM)	22	Reported results are variable (depending on target condition and program). Evidence exists of clinical improvement and reduction in utilization due to CM, particularly for heart disease. A survey of CM financial outcomes for Diabetes found no valid studies. ROIs in the range of 2 to 6 times reported.
Demand Management	6	Evidence exists that Demand Management reduces unnecessary physician and ER visits. Financial results indicate a return of between 1.37 to 1.0 and 3.86 to 1.0.
Disease Management	52	For one population (multi-disease) program that reported PMPM savings, gross savings are estimated at approximately $1.45 PMPM. For programs that report ROI, the range is 1.2 to 6.4. Highest savings are reported for heart diseases. Moderate savings are reported in diabetes and mixed results (in some cases no savings) for Asthma. A recent study using a randomized control showed no discernible savings.
Specialty Case Management	5	Relatively few studies. Prevalence of members with target conditions makes them a poor candidate for randomized control trials. Evidence shows support for financial outcomes in mental health and some high-cost diseases, such as Renal Diseases.
Population Management	8	Evidence reported of dollar savings within population-wide programs. One study reported an ROI of 5.0 to 1.0. Studies of programs to intervene within entire chronic condition sub-populations report measurable PMPM savings.
TOTAL	107	

4.4 DISCUSSION OF RESULTS BY INTERVENTION TYPE

4.4.1 Preauthorization/Utilization Review

The opportunity for reducing utilization by conducting utilization review (UR) is well-demonstrated by a study by DeCoster et al. [39] of Canadian and international data (in which medical management is less prevalent) who found that 51 percent of admissions surveyed were inappropriate, while 67 percent of admissions had inappropriate or unnecessary days of stay. U.S. studies conducted in the 1980s and early 1990s show reductions in admissions and bed-days of between 4 percent and 12 percent due to preauthorization review.

Greater reductions are seen in some studies when UR is combined with other interventions. Wickizer & Lessler [217] surveyed the literature on UR, including preauthorization review. Preauthorization was found to reduce admissions significantly (approximately 10 percent). In combination with concurrent review, preauthorization reduced inpatient hospital days by 12 percent. There was an offsetting increase in outpatient utilization, resulting in a net reduction of approximately 5 percent in net per capita medical costs. Other studies by Wickizer found little evidence of actual hospitalization denial (<2 percent) in insured populations.

Whether reduction in length-of-stay has an impact on quality of care outcomes is researched by many authors: Lessler & Wickizer [115] found that patients who had their length of stay reduced by two or more days were 2.6 times as likely to be readmitted within 60 days of discharge. In specialty areas (e.g., substance abuse), utilization review had a significant impact on length of stay (up to 50 percent reduction in bed-days). Obstetric admissions are heavily reviewed in the preauthorization process (40 percent of all admissions are reviewed), but generate few bed-day reductions, as these admissions are routinely approved. Another study by Wickizer & Lessler [217] showed some relation between reductions in requested length of stay and higher re-admission rates. A study of a randomized controlled population by Rosenberg, et al. [175] showed that patients subject to preauthorization in a population previously not subject to utilization review had fewer procedures per 1000 than a group with automatic approval when procedures were subject to mandatory second opinion. Authorization requirements for admissions and length-of-stay did not appear to have substantial effect, although the authors concluded that there is a secondary (sentinel) effect as doctors learn what procedures are likely to be turned down.

Scheffler Sullivan & Ko [180] analyzed the effect of preauthorization and other interventions on Blue Cross Blue Shield plans over the period 1980 – 1988. This study found that, over the period, the combination of preadmission and concurrent review resulted in reduced admissions of 5.3 percent, a 4.8 percent reduction in days/1000 and a 4.2 percent reduction in inpatient payments. Preadmission certification and concurrent review programs saved $26.59 per enrollee in 1988.

Khandker et al. [107] conducted a large study in the early 1990s, which found that net, after costs, utilization review accounted for reductions of 4.5 percent in costs, or $57.60 per member per year, for a 3.50 return on investment. Finally, a recent study by Flynn et al. [64] showed how medical management and medical practice has changed and adapted over time. While early results of utilization review showed impressive reductions of 10 percent to 15 percent in admissions, later studies showed that only 2 percent to 3 percent of admissions were denied.

4.4.2 Concurrent Review

We found relatively few studies of concurrent review on its own. The majority of references for this intervention are review articles. Murray & Henriques [142] studied concurrent reviews conducted by hospital staff in a hospital setting, and found 313 days denied (94 patients) for an average savings of $478 per day saved. The estimated cost per review was $12.64 (13,126 reviews conducted). "The most startling result of this study is the high cost of conducting the review process". Although not addressed directly by the study, the concurrent review process observed in this study does not pay for itself (we estimate a return on investment of 0.90).

The study by Scheffler, Sullivan & Ko [180] estimates the effect of preauthorization and concurrent review interventions together at between 4 percent and 5 percent, depending on whether costs, bed-days or admissions are measured. Flynn et al. [64] found that extended stays are requested in one-third of admissions, and that 5 percent to 10 percent of these were reduced by concurrent review. Wickizer et al. [217]) found similar results to the Flynn study: between 2 percent and 3 percent of all days are reduced by concurrent review.

The conclusion on this intervention is similar to that on UR (preauthorization). After significant early success, the effect of the intervention has been internalized by the system, resulting in only a small but positive beneficial effect on utilization. The Murray & Henriques finding, that the economics of concurrent review are unfavorable, is a conclusion that deserves further analysis. We address the economics of intervention programs ourselves in Chapter 6 of this book.

4.4.3 Case Management

Flynn, Smith and Davis [64] in their survey of the utilization management literature report state that "Case management results appear to be highly variable, depending on the specifics of the populations and programs. Some programs even increase utilization." The study by Capomolla et al. [22] is an example of a study that shows increased utilization, in this case, of prescription drugs – a 50 percent higher rate of utilization by the intervention group compared with the control group. This study does not, however, follow the population long enough to determine whether the increased prescription drug utilization ultimately led to reduced consumption of other services. Calhoun and Casey [20] published one of the few studies that report savings on a PMPM basis, in this case $1.90 PMPM in a large managed care plan case management program for different conditions. Many of the studies reviewed report clinical, not financial, outcomes.

Many of the favorable financial outcomes appear in populations with heart failure. Cline et al. [29] show a 36 percent reduction in annual cost of a heart failure intervention group, compared with a control group. U.S. studies by Laramee [112] (cost reductions of between 14 percent and 26 percent in costs in heart failure patients); Heidenreich et al. [94], (over 100 percent difference in costs between intervention and control populations followed between two and six months of an event); and Naylor [145], (50 percent cost reduction in the intervention population) showed favorable outcomes in small, randomized studies of heart failure populations. An indication of the suspect quality of many of the published studies is evident in the extensive analysis of results of case and disease management in diabetes populations by Norris et al. [149] who found that out of a total of 602 articles considered, no studies of case management met the authors' requirements for study validity, and that only two studies met the quality criteria for evaluation of outcomes from disease management.

Studies that report costs and ROI are rare, although several exist on heart failure management programs. Phillips et al. [164] report the components of an ROI calculation. For U.S. programs, this study reports an intervention cost of $80.76 PMPM and average savings of $536 PMPM, from which we estimate an implied ROI of 6.60. Riegel et al. [174] report an ROI of 2.26 and a study by Rich [171] reports results of $460 (savings) and $216 (cost of intervention) for an ROI of 2.13, but this result may be understated because the study period is less than one year. The Phillips article discusses discharge planning, an important component of case management, which was found to have little effect on surgical patients but reduced readmissions for medical patients (who have more opportunity for self-care).

4.4.4 Specialty Case Management

The study by Wickizer & Lessler [217] found significant positive impact of specialty care management programs. Behavioral health programs are particularly able to demonstrate favorable results of utilization management. For example, a preauthorization program reduced length of stay (up to 50 percent reduction in bed-days) in a mental health/substance abuse setting. On the other hand, obstetric admissions are heavily reviewed in the preauthorization process (40 percent of all cases are reviewed), but generate few bed-day reductions, as these admissions are routinely approved. In another study, Liu, Sturm & Cuffel [123] examined the effect of preauthorization on outpatient behavioral health utilization and found that the length of treatment authorized drove total treatment duration.

Cancer DM is an example of a specialty case management program that has grown in the last few years. A recent paper by Costich & Lee [32] demonstrated 14 percent reduction in services, 11.1 percent reduction in average case cost, 30 percent reduction in injectable drug costs for support care and 47 percent increase in home/hospice care. As cases were more likely to be referred to a hospice setting, the average length of hospice stay increased from 11.2 days to 33.7 days.

Bruce [16] reported an estimated reduction of medical costs of 8 to 10 percent among patients with chronic renal failure. As care management becomes more specialized, the specialized management (and "carving out") of rare and costly diseases, such as End-stage renal disease, is likely to grow, with increasing methodological problems for those who are interested in validating outcomes.

4.4.5 Demand Management

An early study of Demand Management was conducted by Vickery et al. [202]. This study is included in our bibliography because of its importance, although it falls technically outside our date parameters for articles. The Vickery study, which used a randomized design, found reduced ambulatory care (17 percent reduction) and reduced minor illness utilization (35 percent reduction) as a result of a program of education and telephonic access to clinical resources. However, there was no significant difference in hospital inpatient utilization between intervention and control groups. Vickery estimates returns of $2.50 to $3.50 for each dollar spent on education interventions, largely through reduced physician and Emergency Room utilization.

Delichatsios et al. [40] in a survey study reported a 33 percent reduction in emergency department visits, as a result of telephone medical care provided by physicians. A study by Viner et al. [205] (reported later under Population Management) has data about self-referral to the Emergency Room, and awareness of Emergency Room authorization requirements in a health plan setting. This study indicates a significant opportunity to educate members about both authorization procedures and responsibility for their own care.

Lattimer et al. [113] investigated the use of telephone nurse consultations using decision support software. This UK study analyzed the value of a nurse support line making available after hours information and triage to patients. This study found that nurses were able to manage 50 percent of all calls without referral to a physician, and without adverse quality impact. The study also estimated the financial aspects of the program. The authors report savings of £94,422 (U.S. $172,580) arising from reduced emergency admissions and an additional £16,928 (U.S. $30,939) savings from reduced physician office costs, for a total of £111,350 (U.S. $203,519). The cost of the telephone consultation program was £81,237 per year (U.S. $148,480), implying a return on investment of 1.37. O'Connell, et al. [150] conducted a pre-post study of medical claims data in a health plan setting. Access to nurse triage services resulted in significant reduction in emergency room visits (3 to 4 percent reduction) and physician office utilization (4 to 5 percent reduction). Claims costs were reduced $1.12 PMPM for all plan members. The estimated program costs were $0.55. A range of estimated Return on Investment is calculated, varying between 1.37 and 2.03.

A survey article by Sabin [178] reports on two studies. The first study involves Blue Cross Blue Shield of Oregon, in which savings of $184 per member per year were reported due to the introduction of a triage line (no costs are reported). A second study by Ernst & Young for the George Washington University Health Plan (Sabin op. cit.) found returns of between 2.69 and 3.86 for each dollar invested in a triage line from reduced ER and physician visits, over a one-year period.

4.4.6 Disease Management

The literature on disease management burgeoned in the mid-1990s. The early focus was on individual diseases, particularly asthma, congestive heart failure (CHF), and diabetes. In Appendix 4.2 we list a number of studies that analyze the effect of DM on individual disease states. It is not always possible to classify a study uniquely into a particular category of intervention (for example when a case management program is targeted at members who have a chronic, rather than an acute condition). In these cases we have classified the results of the study under both disease management and case management.

The disease management literature is more extensive than other interventions. Studies that are reviewed here range from single, disease-specific, case management-type interventions with the highest-risk patients, to chronic-population interventions and even multi-disease population studies. While certain care management interventions such as preauthorization and demand management are older, standardized and reasonably mature, disease management programs are newer with relatively little standardization around the techniques used, the individuals targeted, intervention types (ranging from educational interventions through more-intensive case management models) or the outcomes reported. For this reason we report findings by disease and intervention type, when available. Studies of DM are more likely, however, to report financial results; nearly one-third of our surveyed articles reported useable ROI data. Reported ROI for disease management programs ranged from 1.2 – 6.4 annually per dollar invested with one or two outliers above this level. The broad disparity is due to differing diseases, enrollment, cost structures of DM programs, measurement methodologies and costs included in analysis. A recent, highly-valid study of a telephonic program for CHF patients (Galbreath [67a]) indicates no observable savings in the intervention group. This study is important because it uses a randomized control approach, covers a credible population of patients and follows them for a total of 18 months.

Below, we examine the literature on individual disease DM as well as multiple disease states.

1. Asthma
   Evidence of financial improvement from asthma DM is mixed. While there is one randomized control study that reports savings (Ghosh et al. [70]), other randomized trials do not appear to indicate significant differences between intervention and control groups. Where significant savings are reported (e.g. by Gomaa et al. [85], and Lucas et al. [125]), the studies use pre-post designs, or claims exclude outpatient pharmacy, and results must therefore be viewed with caution. A Dutch study by Schermer et al. [181] showed increased costs in the intervention group when compared with the control group. A review of the literature on financial outcomes by Bodenheimer et al. [12] finds three asthma studies with either no significant savings or higher costs in the intervention group.

2. Diabetes
   There is a wide variety of literature on diabetes management, both clinical and behavioral. The CBO study [4], in particular, cites a number of clinical and operational studies (including several in the United Kingdom). Examples of the clinical literature include a Center for Disease Control (CDC) study that examined two interventions, one for hypertension control and the other for glycemic control. Cost of the hypertension control intervention was more than offset by reduced complications, while the reverse is true of the glycemic control intervention. A summary of the studies that include a claims cost element is provided in Table 4.2 below, although (unlike for studies of heart disease) the data are fewer and in no case was ROI directly reported. In only one article was sufficient information provided to derive an ROI. Savings per diabetic member per month ranged from $11 to $145.

TABLE 4.2

Summary of Diabetes Studies That Include a Claims Cost Element			
Author(s)	**Savings (PMPM)**	**Cost (PMPM)**	**ROI**
Gomaa, Muntendam & Morrow [85]	$145	Not reported	N/A
Klonoff & Schwartz [110]	Not reported	Not reported	1.44 to over 8.0
Leatherman et al. [114]	Not reported	Not reported	1.2
Lynne [129]	27%; estimated by author at $40 PMPM	Not reported	Not reported
Rubin, Dietrich & Hawk [177]	$50	Not reported	N/A
Sidorov, et al. [185]	$108	$83	1.2
Snyder, et al.[186]	$98	$56	1.8
Testa & Simonson [193]	$11	Not reported	N/A
Villagra & Ahmed [203]	$26	Not reported	N/A

The study by Klonoff & Schwartz specifically looked at the economics of diabetes management programs and found that the effect of improved glycemic control differs between Type 1 and Type 2 diabetics,[2] with glycemic control producing savings for Type 2 diabetes, but not Type 1. These authors report studies indicating that diabetes self-management programs produce ROI ranging from 1.44 to over 8.00. The authors conclude, however, that: "the economic value of case management for diabetes is unclear," as is the evidence of specific programs aimed at lipid control, weight reduction or smoking cessation for diabetics."

A study of a program at the New York PPO, GHI Incorporated by Lynne, reported significant savings in a diabetic population (27 percent lower cost in the intervention period, compared with the baseline period). We estimated PMPM savings by applying the non-participant trend ($584/$440) to the participant baseline cost ($320). The difference between projected baseline cost ($426) and actual cost ($386) is the estimated savings. However, this study is typical of many in the literature that track a cohort of participants both pre- and post-intervention, making the results highly susceptible to regression to the mean.

The Snyder study reports an ROI for the program. The program costs are $56 per diabetic member per month (no information is provided regarding costs that are included in this amount). The reported ROI is 3.37. However, the authors achieve this level of ROI by "grossing up" their earlier reported savings of $98.49 per diabetic member per month by a trend factor (24.7 percent) derived from the non-chronic population. Without the trend adjustment, ROI would be 1.76. This study follows the same cohort, both pre- and post-program, and in addition reports the continuously-enrolled members over this period only. The choice of a continuously enrolled cohort potentially excludes those members who die during the program (and who are known to incur high expenses in the last few weeks of life) so that this methodology is likely

[2] A discussion of differences between Type I and Type II diabetes may be found in Chapter 3.

to over-state the intervention program savings. We report these results to illustrate the importance of methodological issues and the difficulty in drawing meaningful conclusions, even from the peer-reviewed literature.

Even more problematic, with respect to diabetes, are two aspects of the clinical literature. First, there are numerous valid studies that show clinical improvement in diabetic populations as a result of DM interventions. For example, the studies of Aubert et al. [7], Domurat [46], Litzelman et al. [122], O'Connor et al. [151] and Sadur et al. [179], many of which are cited in the CBO study, all show improved clinical measures as a result of the intervention. However, as noted elsewhere in this book, a causal link between clinical and financial improvement has not been proven. There are occasional references in some of the literature to the fact that any financial improvement may take a considerable time to emerge. For example, the studies of Bodenheimer et al. [12] and Leatherman et al. [114] both note that the time for savings emergence may be as long as 10 years. A UK study (Jolly et al. [101] of heart patients, but relevant here because of the link between diabetes and heart disease), notes the difficulty of maintaining improvement in a population, once the intervention is over.

Second, a number of the studies in the bibliography are of UK programs. The health risk environment is, of course, different in the U.S., so direct comparisons are not possible. However, many of the UK programs focus on changing behavior at the physician practice level, rather than at the patient level, and results are decidedly mixed. In some, but by no means all cases, clinical improvements are achieved. In no case is financial information provided, so that it is not possible to determine whether the improvements were financially positive or negative. These results need to be considered carefully by those bodies (for example CMS) that believe that the future improvement of chronic care and the cost of chronic care lie with physician practices.

3. <u>Heart Failure</u>
The largest literature on the effectiveness of disease specific interventions exists for heart failure (which also has the largest per patient and per event costs). Reported results, both clinical and financial, are uniformly favorable. A number of studies had generally comparable results for both savings and cost of interventions, as summarized in Table 4.3, below:

TABLE 4.3

Summary of Heart Failure Studies That Include a Claims Cost Element			
Author(s)	**Savings (PMPM)**	**Cost (PMPM)**	**ROI**
Wheeler [215]	$150	$31	4.8
Cline, Israelsson, Willenheimer, Broms & Erhardt [29]	$108	$17	6.4
Rich, Beckham. Wittenberg et al. [171]	$38	$28	1.4
Riegel, Carlson, Kopp, LePetri, Glaser & Unger [174]	$83	$37	2.2
Gomaa, Muntendam & Morrow [85]	$145	Not reported	N/A
Fonarow, Stevenson, Walden et al. [65]	$817	$25	32,7
Hoffman (Commercial) [98]	$685	Not reported	N/A
Hoffman (Medicare) [98]	$386	Not reported	N/A
Vaccaro, Cherry, Harper & O'Connell [200]	$439	$219	2.0
Whellan, Gaulden, Gattis et al. [216]	$714	Not reported	N/A
Galbreath, Krasuski, Smith et al. [67a]	Not material	Not reported	N/A

The results of the Rich et al. [172] paper are not included in this table since they are the same as Rich et al. [171].

In the case of the Vaccaro study (2001), the population represented among the sickest of the heart failure population, and the intervention delivered was intense. The populations analyzed by Fonarow et al. and Hoffman were similarly high-risk heart failure populations, which may account for the high ROI result in terms of ROI for the Fonarow study (which appears inconsistent with other studies). The interventions and target population with lower reported cost savings in the Wheeler and Gomaa et al. studies represent less-risky populations and less-intensive interventions. In the case of both Rich and Riegel, the populations and interventions are similar to those of Whellan and Vaccaro, although both the Rich and Riegel studies follow patients for less than one year. The Galbreath study is the most-recently published, covers a credible population, and uses a randomized control methodology. This study indicates no discernable savings, and therefore implies negative return on investment (although ROI and costs are not reported).

4. <u>Multiple diseases</u>

There are few studies of multiple diseases published in the peer-reviewed literature. The study by Cousins et al. [33] is an early example, and reports savings of $1.45 PMPM and cost of $0.51 PMPM for an ROI of 2.84. Unlike the other studies reported above for which PMPM cost numbers are calculated for the chronic population only, the Cousins data are for the entire population (both chronic and non-chronic). Chronic prevalence in a commercial population is generally in the range of 5 percent to 6 percent, which implies the use of a multiplier in the range of 15.0 to 20.0. Applying such a multiplier to the Cousins reported savings would produce comparable per chronic member savings data to that reported above.

4.4.7 Population Management

A study by Viner [205] demonstrates the opportunity for population management. One of the enduring issues of health utilization is the number of patients presenting at the Emergency Room for treatment, rather than seeking treatment through a primary care physician. It is generally believed that considerable savings could be achieved in the healthcare system by encouraging use of primary providers and discouraging use of emergency facilities. Viner's study found that 83 percent of members with Emergency Room visits were self-referred. Eleven percent of members with an ER visit are re-admitted to the ER later. A high percentage of these patients were unaware that payment for their visits could be denied.

Lynch et al. [128] evaluated a population-based approach to care management. The population-based approach contrasts with DM in that it is disease-neutral, whereas DM focuses on patients with target conditions. The population-based approach incorporates data analysis, predictive modeling and selective management of those members predicted to be at the greatest risk. The Lynch study reports a reduction of 5.3 percent in total commercial admissions, and 3.0 percent reduction in total Medicare population admissions. The study also reports a reduction of 35.7 percent in claims for the high-risk sub-set of the combined Medicare and commercial populations. This study illustrates a common problem with sub-population management: an external vendor seldom has access to the full population's claims data to conduct a population-wide paid claims analysis. Because no other information is provided, it is not possible to relate these savings to overall population costs.

Ketner [105] reported program savings in the initial year in the range of $.03 PMPM for asthma, $0.13 PMPM for CHF, and $0.27 for diabetes in their population health management program. Morgan et al. [140] reported a randomized controlled study of a Canadian program aimed at patients with cardiovascular disease who were provided with information about treatment choices. They report a significant reduction (21 percent) in the number of patients seeking revascularization (an invasive technique) versus alternative treatments, with no reduction in health status or satisfaction. Gomaa, Muntendam & Morrow [85] report on the results of a telephonic program that uses automated interventions to deliver educational materials to members with certain chronic diseases. These authors report savings of between $400 and $1,000 per member per year, depending on condition. Program costs are not reported, but likely result in ROI between 2.00 and 4.00. (This program is difficult to classify because it contains elements of both DM and Population Management, and thus we have reported it in both the Disease Management and Population Management analyses)

4.5 CONCLUSION

The Congressional Budget Office (CBO) study [4] found that "there is insufficient evidence to conclude that DM programs can generally reduce the overall cost of health care." The CBO analysis concluded (among other things) that there are many studies of DM that show positive clinical outcomes, while the studies that do demonstrate favorable financial outcomes are often small-scale, randomly-controlled (therefore valid), academic studies of high-risk populations.

We have a broader mission with this book, to survey the financial outcomes of seven different types of care management intervention programs. For many of these interventions, (UR, case management) value was successfully demonstrated in the 1980s and 1990s and this value is no longer questioned. Disease management, the focus of the CBO report and of many purchasers in the health insurance industry, is newer and more subject to question. We have found few published, peer-reviewed studies of large-scale programs that met the CBO's criterion of "generally reducing the overall cost of healthcare." However, there are many studies that show sufficient promise to suggest that DM is worth pursuing, but with care. We should also note here that in no cases were any of the reviewed DM programs specifically implemented to achieve the CBO's objective of "reducing the overall cost of health care." In Chapter 6, we return to this topic in more detail, arguing that a program designed to achieve financial savings will be different than one designed to improve member satisfaction, or to improve quality, or interact with providers. Our selective review of the program evaluation literature suggests that, as we broaden programs from the small-scale interventions to the larger populations, we should keep in mind certain principles of program design and management:

1. The population that is to be subject to the intervention should be chosen with care. In part, this is because not all diseases are equally promising financially. But the capability of the patient to take responsibility for his/her own care is also a factor;

2. Due concern needs to be given to the economics of the intervention program, particularly bearing in mind that the personnel who perform the interventions are relatively costly;

3. The objectives of a program should be clearly defined, and the program should be designed and managed to achieve those goals. If the objective is financial savings, the program will be different than one whose goal is increased member satisfaction;

4. Interventions require the active, engaged participation of both providers and patients. Programs that aim at one or the other seem to be less successful; and

5. Financial savings may take a long time to emerge. During this period, active follow-up and continued engagement may be required to maintain the gains from the program.

Our review of approximately 2,000 abstracts resulted in the identification of 85 articles that reported useable utilization or financial outcomes, or both. In most cases, the literature supports the hypothesis that interventions result in both clinical and financial improvement (there are some exceptions, such as asthma disease management, and some case management interventions). The effect of publication bias must, however, be noted here.

The early literature on preauthorization and utilization management supported the hypothesis that these interventions significantly reduced cost, although this effect has lessened over the years. There is an extensive literature on case management, some of which supports the hypothesis of savings, although the methods used to produce these estimates are often less robust than some of the population-based evaluation methods for other interventions. Some of the newer intervention types, such as demand management and population management, appear to show promise of both savings (from much larger populations than the more traditional interventions), lower administrative cost per plan member and the potential for earlier intervention.

Many of the articles reviewed, and much of the more recent literature in this area, involve disease management programs. The number of disease management articles reporting useable financial outcomes data is encouraging. The literature supports the hypothesis that DM programs produce measurable financial savings, at least in most cases. The reporting of cost data is weaker than the reporting of clinical or savings data, however, making it difficult to assess a return on investment in many cases. In addition, many of the reported studies took place in either academic settings, or were followed for relatively short time periods. The value of similar interventions within large commercial applications and implementations, over periods of longer than one year, remains to be conclusively demonstrated. Also remaining to be satisfactorily demonstrated is the causal link from input to (savings) outcome. Many studies show improvement in utilization as a result of a Disease Management Program. These studies are rarely accompanied by similar financial improvement, an anomaly that has yet to be explained. Similarly, the few valid studies that show financial savings have not demonstrated the changes (behavior change, improved compliance, etc.) that imply the causality.

APPENDIX 4.1 METHODS USED TO FIND ARTICLES

We used a four-stage method to identify articles in the medical literature that address financial outcomes of care management interventions. First, we adopted broad search criteria that identified a very large number of articles dealing with care interventions. Next, we reviewed each article's abstract and eliminated articles in which there was no discussion or analysis of financial and/or utilization outcomes. In Stage 3, we obtained the full-text version of review articles or meta-analyses that led to other "candidate articles." Finally, we reviewed the remaining candidate articles to compile a list of articles in which financial outcomes was an important (although not necessarily the principal) component. This process was subsequently supplemented by the addition of articles that were included in the CBO report [4] that were not identified by our search process, primarily because the CBO report includes articles about clinical as well as financial outcomes.

The source of articles was PubMed and the DMAA database (LitFinder). We used the following PubMed MeSH[3] terms, subheadings or descriptors: care management, disease management, utilization review, economic evaluation, utilization management, case management, predictive modeling, cost control. We decided to use these MeSH descriptors after trying various other terms, as well as noticing the MeSH terms in some of the most widely quoted or seminal articles.

The number of articles in LitFinder is much smaller and organized by disease. We reviewed the abstract of each article in LitFinder; most of them were not relevant to our needs because of their emphasis on clinical outcomes.

We found it convenient to conduct eight separate searches using PubMedd – one run using each of the eight MeSH terms. We limited our initial search to articles published in 1990 or later, and in peer-reviewed journals. The date cut-off was relaxed in three instances. The Vickery [202] article was included because it is a seminal contribution to demand management analysis (a topic that has not seen many articles published in the last 10 years). Second, we included articles from the CBO study with financial outcomes published prior to 1990. Finally, a small number of articles published prior to 1990 were identified in Stage 3 of our search strategy as described below. The result was eight sets of articles. It was possible, of course, for an article to appear in more than one set. Each of the articles in each file (a total of approximately 2,500 articles) was reviewed, based on the information available in PubMed. Any article with no clearly identified author was eliminated from further consideration. Articles without an abstract were removed unless the article's title suggested an emphasis on financial outcomes.

In Stage 3, the full-text versions of three types of articles were obtained:

- articles which focused on the *evaluation* of an intervention;
- "review" articles, which summarized previous research on a particular intervention; and
- meta-analyses.

[3] MeSH is the National Library of Medicine's controlled vocabulary thesaurus. It consists of sets of terms naming descriptors that permit searching at various levels of specificity. The MeSH terms are assigned by skilled subject analysts at the National Library of Medicine who examine journal articles.

The references in these Stage 3 articles were used to identify other candidate articles, some of which were published prior to 1990.

The Stage 1, Stage 2 and Stage 3 articles are far too lengthy to list here. Detailed descriptions of the 86 articles that met our criteria, which we term "Stage 4 articles," appear in Appendix 4.2. Each of these filtered articles directly or indirectly reported the effect of various managed care interventions on medical costs, utilization, and return on investment. Each article was then categorized by type of intervention: Preauthorization/Utilization Review, Concurrent Review, Case Management, Demand Management, Disease Management, Specialty Care Management and Population Management. In some articles, more than one intervention was used. In these cases, the same article may appear twice (occasionally, three times). Allowing for those articles that appear more than once, 107 articles are analyzed, of which 21 are meta-analyses or review articles and 83 are primary research articles. A summary of articles by intervention type is given in Table 4.4 below:

TABLE 4.4

Intervention	Total Number of Studies	Number of Review Articles
Pre-authorization/Utilization Review	9	3
Concurrent Review	5	5
Case Management	22	3
Specialty Case Management	5	0
Demand Management	6	1
Population Management	8	3
Disease Management	52	6
TOTAL	107	21

Next, data was extracted from the article and summarized by disease, length of study, sample size, medical cost changes, utilization changes, program costs and ROI. Results may be seen in Appendix 4.2.

Approximately one-half of the articles concern Disease Management. This "newer" intervention tends to be implemented in larger and more costly programs, resulting in more interest in cost-benefit. DM has gained acceptance by managed care organizations, patients, and physicians, and become a growth industry in which many new firms have been established and prospered within the last 10 years. Specialty case management has attracted much less interest and hence has been the focus of fewer research projects. Utilization review and case management are older managed care interventions, and research on these interventions tends to be less recent.

Our experience using PubMed convinced us that no literature search in this field can possibly be comprehensive. PubMed results are sensitive to the MeSH terms that are chosen. The MeSH terms that are assigned in PubMed by NLM indexers determine whether an article met (or did not meet) the criteria used in the four stages of our review process. If we had chosen different MeSH terms, we would have extracted a different list of final articles.

APPENDIX 4.2 SUMMARY OF MAJOR ARTICLES BY INTERVENTION TYPE

Preauthorization

1. Bailit, H.L., and C. Sennett. 1991."Utilization Management as a Cost-Containment Strategy." *Health Care Finance Review Annual Supplement* 87-93.
   Intervention: Utilization Management
   Disease/Condition: Varied
   Length of Time of Intervention/Study: Varied
   Sample Size: Varied, but all Medicare patients
   Research Design: Survey Article
   Key Results: Only 2 percent to 3 percent of admissions are denied. Khandker study: IP expenses lowered by 8 percent and total health care costs by 4.5 percent. Gotowka study: psychiatric and substance abuse reduction of 16.6 percent of net inpatient costs. Inpatient and outpatient procedures were reduced by 11 percent.

2. DeCoster, C., N.P. Roos, K.C. Carriere, and S. Peterson. 1997. "Inappropriate Hospital Use by Patients Receiving Care for Medical Conditions: Targeting Utilization Review." *Canadian Medical Association Journal* 157 (7): 889-96.
   Intervention: Utilization review (Pre-authorization)
   Disease/Condition: Varied
   Length of Time of Intervention/Study: 1993-1994
   Sample Size: 3,904 patients receiving care at 26 hospitals
   Research Design: Retrospective chart review
   Key Results: Canadian and International studies show that between 7 percent to 43 percent of admissions for adults are inappropriate. Corresponding statistics for inappropriate days are 20 percent to 48 percent. In this study, inappropriate admissions amount to 51 percent and inappropriate bed-days amount to 67 percent.

3. Flynn, K.E., M.A. Smith, and M.K. Davis. 2002. "From Physician to Consumer: The Effectiveness of Strategies to Manage Health Care Utilization." *Medical Care Research and Review* 59 (4): 455-81.
   Intervention: Utilization Review (pre-authorization, case management, concurrent review)
   Disease/Condition: Varied
   Length of Time of Intervention/Study: N/A
   Sample Size: N/A
   Research Design: Survey Article
   Key Results: Early studies of Utilization Review suggest that Preauthorization for hospitalization reduced admissions by 10 percent to 15 percent. Later studies show that denials have fallen to 2 percent to 3 percent. Inpatient hospitalization has been offset by outpatient services. Concurrent Review: approximately one-third of admissions request extended stays. Studies show that concurrent review reduces these stays by 5 percent to 10 percent. Case Management results appear to be highly variable, depending on the specifics of the populations and programs. Some programs even increase utilization. Population Management: provision of patient information to providers appears to improve the process of care but not financial outcomes.

4. Khandker, R.K., and W.G. Manning. 1992. "The Impact of Utilization Review on Costs and Utilization." *Developments in Health Economics and Public Policy* 1: 47-62.
   Intervention: Utilization Review (pre-authorization).
   Disease/Condition: Varied
   Length of Time of Intervention/Study: Study occurred between 1987 and 1990 based on Aetna claims data.
   Sample Size: 176,000 patients in 828 accounts with UR compared with 468,000 patients in 4,381 accounts without UR.
   Research Design: Historical cohort
   Key Results: UR reduces inpatient costs by approximately 8 percent through reduced length-of-stay. Reduced hospital days was 12 percent. No discernible substitution of outpatient for reduced inpatient services. Overall savings of 4.5 percent.

5. Khandker, R.K., W.G. Manning, and T. Ahmed. 1992. "Utilization Review Savings at the Micro Level." *Medical Care Research and Review* 30(11): 1043-52.
   Intervention: Utilization Review (pre-authorization), case management, physician gatekeeping
   Disease/Condition: Varied
   Length of Time of Intervention/Study: Study occurred between 1997 and 2000 based on Aetna claims data.
   Sample Size: 580,000 patients based on 5,300 employer accounts
   Research Design: Historical cohort
   Key Results: Average reduction in bed-days amounts to about 8 percent. Reduction in admissions was 5.6 percent or $74 per employee per year (1988 dollars). Once administrative costs are subtracted, there is a net savings of 4.5 percent or $57.60. Program cost is $16/member for an implied ROI of 3.50.

6. Lessler, D.S., and T.M. Wickizer. 2000. "The Impact of Utilization Management on Readmissions Among Patients with Cardiovascular Disease." *Health Services Review* 34 (6): 1315-29.
   Intervention: Utilization Review (Pre-authorization)
   Disease/Condition: Cardiovascular disease
   Length of Time of Intervention/Study: Data based on utilization management decisions made between 1989-1993.
   Sample Size: 4,326 inpatient reviews conducted on patients with cardiovascular disease
   Research Design: Historical cohort
   Key Results: Intervention resulted in few denials for admission. Length-of-stay was reduced by 17 percent for medical and 19 percent for surgical admissions. Patients who had their l-o-s reduced by two days or more were 2.6 times more likely to be re-admitted within 60 days.

7. Rosenberg, S.N., D.R. Allen, J.S. Handte, T.C. Jackson, L. Leto, B.M. Rodstein, S.D. Stratton, G. Westfall, and R. Yasser. 1995. "Effect of Utilization Review in a Fee-for-Service Health Insurance Plan." *New England Journal of Medicine* 333 (20).
   Intervention: Utilization Review
   Disease/Condition: Varied.
   Length of Time of Intervention/Study: 8 months mean duration
   Sample Size: 3,702 members subject to review and 3,743 control group
   Research Design: Randomized controlled trial
   Key Results: Intervention group experienced 2.6 percent fewer instances of 20 target sur-

gical procedures requiring review, and 3.3 percent fewer physician and outpatient procedures. In the following year, the intervention group had a slightly higher rate of procedures than the control group, though the difference was not statistically significant.

8. Scheffler, R.M., S.D. Sullivan, T.H. Ko. 1991. "The Impact of Blue Cross and Blue Shield Plan Utilization Management Programs." 1980-1988. *Inquiry* 28 (3): 263-75.
   Intervention: Utilization management (Pre-authorization; concurrent review; second surgical opinion)
   Disease/Condition: Varied
   Length of Time of Intervention/Study: 9 years (1990-1998)
   Sample Size: 7 Blue Cross and Blue Shield plans
   Research Design: Historical study based on claims data from Blues plans
   Key Results: Preadmission and concurrent review combined experienced a 5.3 percent reduction in admissions, 4.8 percent reduction in days/1000 and 4.2 percent reduction in inpatient payments. Preadmission certification and concurrent review programs saved $26.59 per enrollee in 1988.

9. Wickizer, T.M., and D. Lessler. 2002. "Utilization Management: Issues, Effects and Future Prospects." *Annual Review of Public Health* (23): 233-35.
   Intervention: Utilization Review (pre-authorization; concurrent review; Case Management
   Disease/Condition: General conditions
   Length of Time of Intervention/Study: Varies
   Sample Size: Varies
   Research Design: Meta-Analysis
   Key Results: Pre-authorization reduces admissions significantly (± 10 percent); concurrent review modestly (2 percent to 3 percent); Combined effect on hospital days = – 12 percent. (offset by increased outpatient utilization). Net change ± 5 percent. Other studies by Wickizer and Lessler found little evidence of actual hospitalization denial (<2 percent) in insured populations. In specialty areas (e.g. substance abuse) utilization had a significant impact on length of stay (up to 50 percent reduction in bed-days). Obstetric admissions are heavily reviewed (40 percent of all reviews), but generate few bed-day reductions as they are routinely approved. Another study by Wickizer and Leffler showed some relation between reductions in requested length of stay is associated with higher readmission rates. Case Management Results: discharge planning had little effect on surgical patients but reduced re-admissions for medical patients (who have more opportunity for self-care) in a randomized study (Naylor et al.).

Concurrent Review

1. Flynn, K.E., M.A. Smith, and M.K. Davis. 2002. "From Physician to Consumer: the Effectiveness of Strategies to Manage Health Care Utilization." *Medical Care Research and Review* 59 (4): 455-81.
   Intervention: Utilization Review (pre-authorization, case management, concurrent review)
   Disease/Condition: Varied
   Length of Time of Intervention/Study: N/A
   Sample Size: N/A

Research Design: Survey Article
Key Results: Early studies of Utilization Review suggest that Preauthorization for hospitalization reduced admissions by 10 percent to 15 percent. Later studies show that denials have fallen to 2 percent to 3 percent. Inpatient hospitalization has been offset by outpatient services. Concurrent review: approximately one-third of admissions request extended stays. Studies show that concurrent review reduces these stays by 5 percent to 10 percent. Case Management results appear to be highly variable, depending on the specifics of the populations and programs. Some programs even increase utilization. Population Management: provision of patient information to providers appears to improve the process of care but not financial outcomes.

2. Murray, M.E., and J.B. Henriques. 2003. "An Exploratory Cost Analysis of Performing Hospital-Based Concurrent Utilization Review." *American Journal of Managed Care* 9 (7): 512-18.
   Intervention: Concurrent utilization review
   Disease/Condition: Varied – Inpatient services
   Length of Time of Intervention/Study: 12 months
   Sample Size: 13,126 reviews of preauthorization decisions
   Research Design: Random clinical sample
   Key Results: 313 days denied (94 patients) for an average savings of $478 per day saved. The estimated cost per review was $12.64. ROI was not calculated by the study but equals 0.9 (i.e. Intervention does not pay for itself).

3. Phillips, C.O., S.M. Wright, D.E. Kern, R.M. Singa, S. Shepperd, and H.R. Rubin. 2004. "Comprehensive Discharge Planning With Postdischarge Support for Older Patients With Congestive Heart Failure, A Meta-Analysis." *Journal of the American Medical Association* 291:1358-67.
   Intervention: Concurrent Review (Discharge Planning), Case Management
   Disease/Condition: Heart Failure
   Length of Time of Intervention/Study: 3 to 12 months; 8 months on average
   Sample Size: Meta-Analysis; 18 studies; 3,304 patients;
   Research Design: Meta-Analysis
   Key Results: Re-admission rate in the intervention population was lower by 19 percent; different types of intervention did not produce different outcomes, implying that home visits with or without telephonic interventions are equally efficacious. Increased clinic visits, however, did not result in improvement. ROI estimate of 3.74 based on one home visit and one discharge planning session.

4. Scheffler, R.M., S.D. Sullivan, and T.H. Ko. 1991. "The Impact of Blue Cross and Blue Shield Plan Utilization Management Programs." *Inquiry* 1980-1988; 28 (3): 263-75.
   Intervention: Utilization Management (Pre-authorization; Concurrent Review; second surgical opinion)
   Disease/Condition: Varied
   Length of Time of Intervention/Study: 9 years (1990-1998)
   Sample Size: 7 Blue Cross and Blue Shield plans
   Research Design: Comparative analysis
   Key Results: Historical study based on claims data from Blues plans.

5. Wickizer, T.M., and D. Lessler. 2002. "Utilization Management: Issues, Effects and Future Prospects." *Annual Review of Public Health* (23): 233-54
   Intervention: Utilization management (Pre-authorization; Concurrent Review; Case Management)
   Disease/Condition: General conditions
   Length of Time of Intervention/Study: Varies
   Sample Size: Varies
   Research Design: Meta-Analysis
   Key Results: Pre-authorization reduces admissions significantly (± 10 percent); Concurrent Review modestly (2 percent - to 3 percent); Combined effect on hospital days = – 12 percent. (offset by increased outpatient utilization). NET change ± 5 percent. Other studies by Wickizer and Lessler found little evidence of actual hospitalization denial (<2 percent) in insured populations. In specialty areas (e.g. substance abuse) utilization had a significant impact on length of stay (up to 50 percent reduction in bed-days). Obstetric admissions are heavily reviewed (40 percent of all reviews), but generate few bed-day reductions as they are routinely approved. Another study by Wickizer and Leffler showed some relation between reductions in requested length of stay is associated with higher re-admission rates. Study by Rosenberg (randomized controlled) showed that patients subject to pre-authorization had fewer procedures per 1000 than a group with automatic approval. Case Management Results: discharge planning had little effect on surgical patients but reduced re-admissions for medical patients (who have more opportunity for self-care) in a randomized study (Naylor et al.).

Case Management

1. Allen, J.K., R.S. Blumenthal, S. Margolis, D.R. Young, E. R. Miller III, and K. Kelly. 2002. "Nurse Case Management of Hypercholesterolemia in Patients with Coronary Heart Disease: Results of a Randomized Clinical Trial." *American Heart Journal* 144 (4): 678-86.
   Intervention: Case Management Disease Management
   Disease/Condition: Nurse case management of hypercholesterolemia in CHD patients post-Revascularization
   Length of Time of Intervention/Study: 1 year
   Sample Size: 228
   Research Design: Randomized Controlled Test
   Key Results: Results in the intervention group were: lower total and LDL cholesterol levels; a significantly higher percentage of the intervention group reached target LDL level; favorable changes in diet and exercise patterns; no significant changes in Body Mass Index in either intervention or control group. No financial outcomes or cost data were provided in the study.

2. Aubert, R.E., et al. 1998. "Nurse Case Management to Improve Glycemic Control in Diabetic Patients in a Health Maintenance Organization." *Annals of Internal Medicine* 129 (8): 605-12.
   Intervention: Case Management Disease Management
   Disease/Condition: Nurse case management of hyperglycemia in Diabetes patients.
   Length of Time of Intervention/Study: 1 year

Sample Size: 138
Research Design: Randomized Controlled Test
Key Results: 72 percent of patients completed follow-up. Primary outcome measure was Hemoglobin A1c score (HbA1c). HbA1c score was reduced in the intervention group from 9.0 to 7.3 versus 8.9 to 8.3 in the control group. (Well-controlled HbA1c is considered to be 7.0 or below.) Patients in the intervention group were twice as likely to report improved health status. No financial outcomes or cost data were provided in the study.

3. Calhoun, J., and P. Casey. 2002. "Case Management Redesign in a Managed Care System: One Company's Experience." *Managed Care Quarterly* 10 (4): 8-12.
Intervention: Case Management
Disease/Condition: Five types of Case Management: high-risk medical, catastrophic, maternal and child, and disease management (asthma and diabetes)
Length of Time of Intervention/Study: 1986-2001
Sample Size: 280,000 enrollees
Research Design: N/A
Key Results: Case Management is credited with saving $1.90 PMPM for the entire enrolled population; program costs are not reported.

4. Capomolla, S. 2002. "Cost/Utility Ratio in Chronic Heart Failure: Comparison Between Heart Failure Management Program Delivered by Day Hospital and Usual Care." *Journal of the American College of Cardiology* 40 (7): 1289-66.
Intervention: Case Management/Disease Management
Disease/Condition: Heart Failure
Length of Time of Intervention/Study: 9-15 months
Sample Size: 234 prospective patients (122 in usual community care and 112 in day hospital)
Research Design: Randomized Controlled trial--comparing effectiveness and cost/utility between heart failure management program delivered through usual care and a day hospital.
Key Results: Patients enrolled in the intervention incurred 2.7 percent cardiac events, compared with 10.6 percent in the control group. The intervention group used more prescription drugs ($741 vs. $490). Cost savings are reported in terms of QALYs only and cannot be converted to conventional terms. Savings of $1,068 for each quality adjusted life year gained are reported.

5. Cline, C.M., B.Y. Israelsson, R.B. Willenheimer, K. Broms, and L.R. Erhardt. "1998 Cost Effective Management Program for Heart Failure Reduces Hospitalization." *Heart* 80 (5): 442-46.
Intervention: Case Management; Disease Management
Disease/Condition: Heart Failure
Length of Time of Intervention/Study: 1 Year
Sample Size: 190 patients in Sweden (aged 65-84) hospitalized for Heart Failure
Research Design: Prospective control trial
Key Results: Care managed patients experienced a longer mean time to re-admission, and fewer hospital days. Mean annual cost in the intervention group was $2,294 vs. $3,594 for the control group (a reduction of 36.2 percent).

6. Costantini, O., K. Huck, M.D. Carlson, K. Boyd, C.M. Buchter, P. Raiz, and C.M. Buchter. 2001. "Impact of a Guideline-Based Disease Management Team on Outcomes of Hospitalized Patients with Congestive Heart Failure." *Archives of Internal Medicine* 161:177-82.
   Intervention: Case Management/Disease Management
   Disease/Condition: Heart Failure
   Length of Time of Intervention/Study: one year
   Sample Size: 283 care managed patients and 126 concurrent non-care managed patients
   Research Design: Two groups: pre- program and concurrent control group study
   Key Results: Care managed patients experienced higher rates of ACE inhibitor use and adherence to care guidelines, when compared with both the pre-program and concurrent control groups. The intervention group experienced lower costs than both the pre- and concurrent control groups: 9 percent lower than pre-group, and 39 percent lower than the concurrent group. Cost of interventions is not reported.

7. DeBusk, R.F., et al. 1994. "A Case-Management System for Coronary Risk Factor Modification after Acute Myocardial Infarction." *Annals of Internal Medicine.* 120 (9): 721-29.
   Intervention: Home-based Case Management (telephone/mail).
   Disease/Condition: Heart (Post-MI)
   Length of Time of Intervention/Study: two months
   Sample Size: 293 patients under 70 years old.
   Research Design: Randomized control trial
   Key Results: 70 percent of intervention group ceased smoking versus 53 percent in control group. Cholesterol levels were lower and functional status was higher. No financial data were published.

8. Fitzgerald, J.F., D.M. Smith, D.K. Martin, J.A. Freedman, and B.P. Katz. 1994. "A Case Manager Intervention to Reduce Readmissions." *Archive of Internal Medicine* 154 (15): 1721-29.
   Intervention: Case Management
   Disease/Condition: Varied
   Length of Time of Intervention/Study: 12 months
   Sample Size: 688 patients > 45 years old. Identified through the VA system.
   Research Design: Randomized control trial
   Key Results: Intervention group patients had more frequent visits per patient per month to the general medicine clinic. No significant differences were detected in readmissions or readmission bed-days between intervention and control groups.

9. Flynn, K.E., M.A. Smith, and M.K. Davis. 2002. "From Physician to Consumer: the Effectiveness of Strategies to Manage Health Care Utilization." *Medical Care Research and Review.* 59 (4): 455-81.
   Intervention: Utilization Review (Pre-authorization, Case Management, Concurrent Review)
   Disease/Condition: Varied
   Length of Time of Intervention/Study: N/A
   Sample Size: N/A
   Research Design: Survey Article
   Key Results: Early studies of Utilization Review suggest that Preauthorization for hospitalization reduced admissions by 10 percent to 15 percent. Later studies show that denials have fallen to 2 percent to 3 percent. Inpatient hospitalization has been offset by outpa-

tient services. Concurrent Review: approximately one-third of admissions request extended stays. Studies show that concurrent review reduces these stays by 5 percent to 10 percent. Case Management results appear to be highly variable, depending on the specifics of the populations and programs. Some programs even increase utilization. Population Management: provision of patient information to providers appears to improve the process of care but not financial outcomes.

10. Gordon, N.F., C.D. English, A.S. Contractor, R.D. Salmon, R.F. Leighton, B.A. Franklin, and W.L. Haskell. 2002. "Effectiveness of Three Models for Comprehensive Cardiovascular Disease Risk Reduction." *American Journal of Cardiology* 89 (11): 1263-68.
    Intervention: Case Management/Disease Management
    Disease/Condition: two less costly approaches compared to contemporary phase II cardiac rehab program; one alternative involved nurse case-managers and the second involved a community-based program.
    Length of Time of Intervention/Study: 12 weeks
    Sample Size: 155; 52 in the contemporary rehab program, 54 in a nurse-case managed, CV risk reduction program, and 49 in a community-based program.
    Research Design: Randomized control trial
    Key Results: Programs had similar clinical outcomes. Relative to cost, the community based program had the greatest potential to save costs.

11. Gorski, L.A., and K.A. Johnson. 2003. "Disease Management Program for Heart Failure." *Lippincott's Case Management* 8 (6): 265-73.
    Intervention: Case Management/ Disease Management
    Disease/Condition: Heart Failure
    Length of Time of Intervention/Study: two - six months
    Sample Size: 74 patients
    Research Design: Cohort follow up study.
    Key Results: 35 percent decrease in hospitalizations; $2,200 reduction in claims per patient.

12. Heidenreich, P.A, C.M. Ruggiero, and B.M. Massie. 1999. "Effect of a Home Monitoring System on Hospitalization and Resource Use for Patients with Heart Failure." *American Heart Journal* 138 (4).
    Intervention: Case Management
    Disease/Condition: Heart Failure
    Length of Time of Intervention/Study: two to six months
    Sample Size: 68 patients
    Research Design: Matched control group (86 patients)
    Key Results: 13 percent reduction in intervention group claims (from $8,500 to $7,400); control group claims increased by 104 percent (from $9,200 to $18,800).

13. Laramee, A.S., S.K. Levinsky, J. Sargent, R. Ross, and P. Callas. 2003. "Case Management in a Heterogeneous Congestive Heart Failure Population: A Randomized Controlled Trial." *Archive of Internal Medicine* 163 (7): 809-17.
    Intervention: Case Management/Discharge Planning
    Disease/Condition: Congestive Heart Failure
    Length of Time of Intervention/Study: 90 days
    Sample Size: 287
    Research Design: Randomized controlled clinical trial
    Key Results: Inpatient and outpatient median costs and readmission median cost were reduced 14 percent and 26 percent for intervention group. Intervention group showed im-

proved adherence to treatment. Intervention and Control groups showed equal 90-day re-admission rates.

14. Lynch, J.P., S.A. Forman, S. Graff, and M.C. Gunby. 2000. "High Risk Population Health Management – Achieving Improved Patient Outcomes and Near-Term Financial Results." *American Journal of Managed Care* 6 (7): 781-91.
    Intervention: Population Management/Case Management
    Disease/Condition: Varied. 1.1 percent of highest risk patients in this population
    Length of Time of Intervention/Study: two years (first baseline)
    Sample Size: 60,000 commercial; 15,000 Medicare Risk
    Research Design: Pre-Post study (Baseline/Intervention year). Baseline not adjusted.
    Key Results: Commercial admissions reduced by 5.3 percent; Medicare admissions reduced by 3.0 percent; 35.7 percent reduction in cost.

15. Naylor, M.D., D. Brooten, R. Campbell, B.S. Jacobsen, M. Mezey, M.V. Pauley, and J.S. Schwartz. 1999. "Comprehensive Discharge Planning and Home Follow-Up of Hospitalized Elders." *Journal of the American Medical Association* 281 (7): 613-620.
    Intervention: Case Management (Discharge Planning)
    Disease/Condition: Heart Disease.
    Length of Time of Intervention/Study: Up to 24 weeks
    Sample Size: 186 control group; 177 intervention group. Mean age 75.
    Research Design: Randomized control
    Key Results: Intervention group patients less likely to be re-admitted at 24 weeks (20 percent versus 37 percent); Total cost of the intervention group was about 50 percent of that of the control group.

16. Naylor, M.D. D. Brooten, R. Jones, R. Lavizzo-Mourey, M. Mezey, and M.V. Pauley. 1994. "Comprehensive Discharge Planning for the Hospitalized Elderly." *Annals of Internal Medicine* 120 (12): 999-1006.
    Intervention: Case Management (Discharge Planning)
    Disease/Condition: Heart Disease.
    Length of Time of Intervention/Study: Up to 24 weeks
    Sample Size: 276 patients over age 70.
    Research Design: Randomized control
    Key Results: reduced readmissions, hospital days and costs.

17. Norris, S.L. et al. 2002. "The Effectiveness of Disease and Case Management for People with Diabetes." *American Journal of Preventive Medicine* 15-38.
    Intervention: Case Management
    Disease/Condition: Diabetes.
    Length of Time of Intervention/Study: N/a
    Sample Size: N/a
    Research Design: Literature Review
    Key Results: No studies were found of Case Management Financial Outcomes that met the study's requirements for study validity.

18. Phillips, C.O., S.M. Wright, D.E. Kern, R.M. Singa, S. Shepperd, and H.R. Rubin. 2004. "Comprehensive Discharge Planning with Postdischarge Support for Older Patients with Congestive Heart Failure, A Meta-Analysis." *Journal of the American Medical Association.* 291:1358-67.
    Intervention: Utilization Review (Discharge Planning), Case Management
    Disease/Condition: Heart Failure
    Length of Time of Intervention/Study: three to 12 months; eight months on average
    Sample Size: Meta-Analysis; 18 studies; 3,304 patients;
    Research Design: Meta-Analysis
    Key Results: Re-admission rate in the intervention population was lower by 19 percent; different types of intervention did not produce different outcomes, implying that home visits with or without telephonic interventions are equally efficacious. Increased clinic visits, however, did not result in improvement. ROI estimate of 3.74 based on one home visit and one discharge planning session.

19. Rich, M.W., V. Beckham, B. Gray, C. Wittenberg, C.L. Leven, and P. Luther. 1996. "Effect of a Multidisciplinary Intervention on Medication Compliance in Elderly Patients with Congestive Heart Failure." *American Journal of Medicine* 101 (3): 270-6.
    Intervention: Case Management/Disease Management
    Disease/Condition: Heart failure
    Length of Time of Intervention/Study: 30 $\pm$ two days
    Sample Size: 156 patients over age 70
    Research Design: Randomized controlled trial
    Key Results: A multi-disciplinary follow up intervention is associated with improved medication compliance in the intervention population (88 percent versus 81 percent in the control group). The intervention group experienced 33 percent fewer re-admissions and 31 percent fewer hospital days than the control group, although the difference is not statistically significant.

20. Rich, M.W., V. Beckham, C. Wittenberg, C.L. Leven, K.E. Freddland, and R.M. Carney. 1995. "A Multidisciplinary Intervention to Prevent the Re-admission of Elderly Patients with Congestive Heart Failure." *New England Journal of Medicine* 333 (18): 1190-95.
    Intervention: Case Management/ Disease Management
    Disease/Condition: Heart failure
    Length of Time of Intervention/Study: 90 day follow up
    Sample Size: 282 patients over age 70; intervention 142, control 140.
    Research Design: Randomized controlled trial
    Key Results: 90-day re-admission rate for the intervention group was 36 percent; 90-day readmission rate for control group was 46 percent. Multiple readmissions were reduced from 16.4 percent in the control group to 6.3 percent in the intervention group. Intervention cost averaged $336; overall cost of care was less in the intervention group by $460, suggesting an ROI of 1.37 (Note that study period was $<$ one year).

21. Riegel, B., B. Carlson, Z. Kopp, B. LePetri, D. Glaser, and A. Unger. 2002. "Effect of a Standardized Nurse Case-Management Telephone Intervention on Resource Use in Patients with Chronic Heart Failure." *Archive of Internal Medicine* 162 (6): 705-12.
    Intervention: Case Management/Disease Management
    Disease/Condition: Heart failure
    Length of Time of Intervention/Study: three- and six-month measurements

Sample Size: 281 physicians/358 patients
Research Design: Randomized controlled clinical trial (physicians randomized)
Key Results: Heart failure (HF) re-hospitalization 45.7 percent lower in intervention group at three months; 47.8 percent lower at six months; HF hospital days and multiple re-admissions were significantly lower in intervention group at six months. Inpatient HF costs were 45.5 percent lower at six months; no evidence of cost shifting to outpatient setting; patient satisfaction with care was higher in intervention group. Savings per patient was estimated at $1,000, and intervention cost was $443, for an ROI of 2.26.

22. Wickizer, T.M. and D. Lessler. 2002. "Utilization Management: Issues, Effects and Future Prospects." *Annual Review of Public Health* 23: 233-54.
Intervention: Utilization Review (Pre-authorization; Concurrent Review)/Case Management
Disease/Condition: General conditions
Length of Time of Intervention/Study: Varies
Sample Size: Varies
Research Design: Meta-Analysis
Key Results: Pre-authorization reduces admissions significantly (± 10 percent); Concurrent Review modestly (2 percent to 3 percent); Combined effect on hospital days = – 12 percent. (offset by increased outpatient utilization). NET change ± 5 percent. Other studies by Wickizer and Lessler found little evidence of actual hospitalization denial (< 2 percent) in insured populations. In specialty areas (e.g., substance abuse) utilization had a significant impact on length of stay (up to 50 percent reduction in bed-days). Obstetric admissions are heavily reviewed (40 percent of all reviews), but generate few bed-day reductions as they are routinely approved. Another study by Wickizer and Leffler showed some relation between reductions in requested length of stay is associated with higher re-admission rates. Study by Rosenberg (randomized controlled) showed that patients subject to pre-authorization had fewer procedures per 1000 than a group with automatic approval. Case Management Results: discharge planning had little effect on surgical patients, but reduced re-admissions for medical patients (who have more opportunity for self-care) in a randomized study (Naylor et al.).

Specialty Case Management

1. Bruce, D., and J. Dickmeyer. 2001. "Don't Overlook Disease Management Programs for Low-Incidence, High-Cost Diseases to Improve Your Bottom Line." *Journal of Health Care Finance* 28 (2): 45-9.
Intervention: Disease Management/Specialty Case Management
Disease/Condition: Chronic renal failure
Length of Time of Intervention/Study: N/A
Sample Size: 650 Patients
Research Design: N/A
Key Results: 66 percent reduction in bed-days; 35 percent reduction in admissions; 83 percent reduction in ER visits; cost reduction of 8 percent – to 10 percent.

2. Costich, T./ D., and F.C. Lee. 2003. "Improving Cancer Care in a Kentucky Managed Care Plan: A Case Study of Cancer Disease Management." *Disease Management* 6 (1): 9-20.
   Intervention: Disease Management/Specialty Case Management
   Disease/Condition: Cancer
   Length of Time of Intervention/Study: One year; 1999-2000
   Sample Size: 1,146 enrolled patients
   Research Design: Trend adjusted cohort study
   Key Results: 14 percent reduction in services; 11.1 percent reduction in average case cost; 30 percent reduction in injectable drug costs for support care; 47 percent increase in home/hospice care; average length of hospice stay increased from 11.2 days to 33.7 days.

3. Gattis, W.A., V. Hasselblad, D. J. Whellan, and C. M. O'Connor. 1999. "Reduction in Heart Failure Events by the Addition of a Clinical Pharmacist to the Heart Failure Management Team." *Archives of Internal Medicine* 159: 1939-45.
   Intervention: Specialty Case Management (Pharma)
   Disease/Condition: Heart Failure
   Length of Time of Intervention/Study: six months
   Sample Size: 180 enrolled patients; randomly assigned to intervention and control.
   Research Design: Randomized control study
   Key Results: higher use of ACE inhibitors in the intervention population.

4. Leatherman, S., D. Berwick, D. Iles, L.S. Lewin, F. Davidoff, T. Nolan, and M. Bisognano. 2003. "The Business Case for Quality: Case Studies and an Analysis." *Health Affairs* 22 (2): 17-30.
   Intervention: Specialty Case Management (pharma)
   Disease/Condition: Varied
   Length of Time of Intervention/Study: N/A
   Sample Size: Various (Survey article)
   Research Design: Various (Survey article)
   Key Results: One study of Specialty Case Management (Pharma) produced savings of $750 per patient, but program was discontinued because of difficulties with penetrating eligible population (participation was 5.8 percent). Lipid management program produced estimated ROI of 2:1 (cost was $145 per patient).

5. Liu, X., R. Sturm, and B.J. Cuffel. 2000. "The Impact of Prior Authorization on Outpatient Utilization in Managed Behavioral Health Plans." *Medical Care Research and Review* 57 (2): 182-95.
   Intervention: Specialty Care Management (mental health) Pre-authorization.
   Disease/Condition: Managed Mental Health
   Length of Time of Intervention/Study: All plans operated between January 1, 1996 and December 31 1997, and all members were eligible during the two years.
   Sample Size: 7,611 episodes (5,607 patients) in the five-visit group, and 2,703 (or 1,884 patients) in the 10-visit group.
   Research Design: Quasi-experimental. Used conditional logistic regression to model the probability of terminating treatment at visit *n* conditional on having at least *n* visits.
   Key Results: Patients whose treatment is authorized in increments of five sessions are nearly three times more likely to terminate treatment at exactly the 5th visit than if their treatment is authorized in increments of 10 sessions conditional on being in treatment until the 5th visit. The likelihood of termination peaks in both the five- and 10-session authorization at the 10th visit, but the difference is not statistically significant. The authorization effect differs by provider type and is weaker among psychiatrists than among non-physician providers.

Demand Management

1. Delichatsios, H., M. Callahan, and M. Charlson. 1998. "Outcomes of Telephone Medical Care." *Journal of General Internal Medicine* 13 (9): 579-85.

   Intervention: Telephone medical care.
   Disease/Condition: Varied
   Length of Time of Intervention/Study: July 29-Aug. 18, 1996.
   Research Design: Cross-sectional study. A scripted telephone survey was administered to each subject within one week of the first call. Survey addressed patient outcomes, symptom relief, patient satisfaction, and alternatives to telephone medical care.
   Key Results: 33 percent of patients reported that their telephone consultation had avoided an Emergency Room visit.

2. Lattimer, V., F. Sassi, S. George, et al. 2000. "Cost Analysis of Nurse Telephone Consultation in Out of Hours Primary Care: Evidence from a Randomized Controlled Trial." *British Medical Journal* 320: 1053-57.
   Intervention: Telephone medical care (UK).
   Disease/Condition: Varied
   Length of Time of Intervention/Study: one year
   Sample Size: 14,000 calls in a cooperative consisting of 55 practitioners servicing 97,000 registered patients.
   Research Design: Randomized controlled clinical trial.
   Key Results: Savings of £94,422 arising from reduced emergency admissions to hospital. Additional £16,928 savings for general practice arose from reduced travel to visit patients at home and fewer surgery appointments within three days of a call. Also showed a reduction in short stays in hospital (one to three days). Total savings were £111,350 and ROI was 1.37.

3. Morgan, M.W., R.B. Deber, H. A. Llewellyn-Thomas, P. Gladstone, R.J. Cusimano, K. O'Rourke, G. Tomlinson, and A.S. Detsky. 2000. "Randomized, Controlled Trial of an Interactive Videodisc Decision Aid for Patients with Ischemic Heart Disease." *Journal of General Internal Medicine* 15 (10): 685-93.
   Intervention: Demand Management (Shared Decision Making)
   Disease/Condition: Coronary Artery Disease
   Length of Time of Intervention/Study: 1995-1996
   Sample Size: 240 ambulatory patients
   Research Design: Randomized controlled trial
   Key Results: Intervention group chose to pursue revascularization less frequently than the control group (58 percent versus 75 percent). At six months, 52 percent of the intervention group and 66 percent of the controls had undergone revascularization (21 percent reduction). Health and patient satisfaction scores were not significantly different in the two groups.

4. O'Connell, J.M., D.A. Johnson, J. Stallmeyer, and D. A. Cokington, 2001. "Satisfaction and Return-on-Investment Study of a Nurse Triage Service." *American Journal of Managed Care* 7 (2): 159-69.
   Intervention: Demand Management
   Disease/Condition: Varied
   Length of Time of Intervention/Study: Varied
   Sample Size: 60,000 members of a health plan
   Research Design: pre-post study design
   Key Results: Access to nurse triage services resulted in significant reduction in emergency room visits (3 to 4 percent) and physician office utilization (4 to 5 percent). Claims costs were reduced $1.12 PMPM for all plan members. The estimated program costs were $0.55. A range of estimated return on investment is calculated, varying between 1.37 and 2.03.

5. Sabin, M. 1998. "Telephone Triage Improves Demand Management Effectiveness." *Healthcare Financial Management* 52(8): 49-52.
   Intervention: Demand Management
   Disease/Condition: Varied
   Length of Time of Intervention/Study: N/A
   Sample Size: N/A
   Research Design: Survey analysis
   Key Results: Reports a Blue Cross Blue Shield of OR study of 14,000 members who showed savings of $184 per member per year. A George Washington University Health Plan study of telephone triage showed returns of 2.69 to 3.86 for investment in the program from reduced emergency room and physician visits over a 12-month period.

6. Vickery, D.M., et al. 1983. "Effect of a Self-Case Education Program on Medical Visits." *Journal of the American Medical Association* 250: 2952-56.
   Intervention: Demand Management
   Disease/Condition: Varied
   Length of Time of Intervention/Study: 1979-1981
   Sample Size: 1,625 households
   Research Design: prospective randomized controlled trial
   Key Results: Reduced ambulatory care (17 percent reduction) and reduced "minor-illness" utilization (35 percent reduction) as a result of a program of education and telephonic access to clinical resources. However, there was no significant difference in hospital inpatient utilization between intervention and control groups. Estimated returns of $2.50 to $3.50 for each dollar spent on education interventions.

Population Management

1. Fries, J.F., D.A. Bloch, H. Harrington, N. Richardson, and R. Beck. 1993. "Two-Year Results of a Randomized Controlled Trial of Health Promotion Program in a Retiree Population: The Bank of America Study." *American Journal of Medicine* 94: 57-64.
   Intervention: Population Management (Educational interventions)
   Disease/Condition: Varied
   Length of Time of Intervention Study: two years
   Sample Size: 4,712
   Research Design: Randomized control trial.

Key Results: Incremental claims reduction averaged $149 in the intervention group; Overall health scores increased 12 percent compared with control group. Program cost $30 per eligible member per year, for an ROI of 5.0 to 1.0.

2. Gomaa, W., P. Muntendam, and T. Morrow. 2001. "Technology-Based Disease Management, a Low-Cost, High-Value Solution for the Management of Chronic Disease." *Disease Management Health Outcomes* 9 (10).
Intervention: Population Management/Disease Management
Disease/Condition: Asthma/Diabetes/Heart Disease
Length of Time of Intervention Study: nine-month follow up
Sample Size: 93,414 total participants
Research Design: Adjusted cohort study comparing participant and non-participant outcomes
Key Results: Asthma savings amounted to $456 per year; Heart Disease: $1,737 and $464 for diabetes. Program cost was not disclosed.

3. Ketner, L. 1999. "Population Management Takes Disease Management to the Next Level." *Health Financial Management.*53 (8): 36-9.
Intervention: Population Management
Disease/Condition: Varied
Length of Time of Intervention Study: Varied by study
Sample Size: Multiple
Research Design: Meta-Analysis
Key Results: Diabetes Program Savings: $0.27 PMPM in year one, $0.25 PMPM in year two and eventually $1.37 PMPM in the fifth year. Asthma Program Savings: $0.03 PMPM. CHF Program Savings: $0.13 PMPM

4. Leatherman, S., D. Berwick, D. Iles, L.S. Lewin, F. Davidoff, T. Nolan, and M. Bisognano. 2003. "The Business Case for Quality: Case Studies and an Analysis." *Health Affairs* 22 (2): 17-30.
Intervention: Population Management
Disease/Condition: Varied
Length of Time of Intervention Study: N/A
Sample Size: Various (Survey Article)
Research Design: Various (Survey article)
Key Results: Population Management (smoking cessation and wellness) showed "weak returns" with the health plan unable to report a predictable, measurable ROI. Reported savings from a wellness program at General Motors amounted to $53 per employee per year, but no data on costs or ROI are reported.

5. Lynch, J.P., S.A. Forman, S. Graff, and M.C. Gunby. 2000. "High Risk Population Health Management – Achieving Improved Patient Outcomes and Near-Term Financial Results." *American Journal of Managed Care* 6 (7): 781-91.
Intervention: Population Management (Case Management)
Disease/Condition: Varied. 1.1 percent of highest risk patients in this population
Length of Time of Intervention Study: two years (first baseline)

Sample Size: 60,000 commercial; 15,000 Medicare Risk
Research Design: Pre-Post study (Baseline/Intervention year). Baseline not adjusted.
Key Results: Overall Commercial Admissions reduced by 5.3 percent; Overall Medicare admissions reduced by 3.0 percent; 35.7 percent reduction in cost (in the high-risk population only).

6. Morgan, M.W., R.B. Deber, H.A. Llewellyn-Thomas, P. Gladstone, R.J. Cusimano, K. O'Rourke, G. Tomlinson, and A.S. Detsky. 2000. "Randomized, Controlled Trial of an Interactive Videodisc Decision Aid for Patients with Ischemic Heart Disease." *Journal of General Internal Medicine* 15 (10): 685-93.
   Intervention: Population Management (Educational Intervention)
   Disease/Condition: Heart Disease
   Length of Time of Intervention Study: six-month follow-up.
   Sample Size: 240 patients with heart disease; candidates for elective revascularization.
   Research Design: Randomized control.
   Key Results: Initial decision: 23 percent lower intent to pursue revascularization. At six-month follow-up, 21 percent lower revascularization rate in the intervention group versus the control group. General health and satisfaction scores were similar for each group.

7. Viner, K.M., M. Bellino, T.D. Kirsch, P. Kivela, and J.C. Silva. 2000. "Managed Care Organization Authorization Denials: Lack of Patient Knowledge and Timely Alternative Ambulatory Care." *Annual of Emergency Medicine* 35 (3): 272-76.
   Intervention: Population Management
   Disease/Condition: Study followed patients denied authorization for Emergency Room visits; assessing patient awareness of health plan preauthorization procedures/requirements.
   Length of Time of Intervention Study: seven months
   Sample Size: 151 did not receive ER authorization; 138 interviewed and 104 responses
   Research Design: Interview
   Key Results: 83 percent of ER visits occurred because of patient-diagnosed emergency; 4 percent instructed to go to ER are denied; (86 percent unaware that health plan could deny payment); 37 percent reported awareness of requirement for pre-authorization; 11 percent returned to Emergency Room with subsequent 4 percent admitted.

8. Vinicor, F., et al. 1987. "Diabeds: A Randomized Trial of the Effects of Physician and/or Patient Education on Diabetes Patient Outcomes." *Journal of Chronic Disease* 40 (4): 345-56.
   Intervention: Population Management (Educational Intervention)/ Disease Management
   Disease/Condition: Diabetes
   Length of Time of Intervention Study: seven months
   Sample Size: 532 patients randomly assigned to different interventions, including routine care.
   Research Design: Randomized control.
   Key Results: Clinical outcomes only were measured. The combination of patient and physician education produced significant improvements in key clinical markers. Some clinical problems persisted (obesity; hyperglycemia) leading the authors to conclude that a more focused program may be more effective. No financial results were reported.

Disease Management

1. Allen, J.K., R.S. Blumenthal, S. Margolis, D.R. Young, E.R. Miller III, and K. Kelly. 2002. "Nurse Case Management of Hypercholesterolemia in Patients with Coronary Heart Disease: Results of a Randomized Clinical Trial." *American Heart Journal* 144 (4): 678-86.
   Intervention: Case Management/Disease Management
   Disease/Condition: Nurse case management of hypercholesterolemia in CHD patients post-revascularization.
   Length of Time of Intervention/Study: one year
   Sample Size: 228
   Research Design: Randomized Controlled Test
   Key Results: Results in the intervention group were: lower total and LDL cholesterol levels; a significantly higher percentage of the intervention group reached target LDL level; favorable changes in diet and exercise patterns; no significant changes in Body Mass Index in either intervention or control group. No financial outcomes or cost data were provided in the study.

2. Aubert R.E., et al., 1998. "Nurse Case Management to Improve Glycemic Control in Diabetic Patients in a Health Maintenance Organization." *Annals of Internal Medicine* 129 (8): 605-12.
   Intervention: Case Management/Disease Management
   Disease/Condition: Nurse case management of hyperglycemia in diabetes patients.
   Length of Time of Intervention/Study: one year
   Sample Size: 138
   Research Design: Randomized Controlled Test
   Key Results: 72 percent of patients completed follow-up. Primary outcome measure was Hemoglobin A1c score (HbA1c). HbA1c score was reduced in the intervention group from 9.0 to 7.3 versus 8.9 to 8.3 in the control group. (Well-controlled HbA1c is considered to be 7.0 or below.) Patients in the intervention group were twice as likely to report improved health status. No financial outcomes or cost data were provided in the study.

3. Bailey, W.C., C.L. Kohler, J.M. Richards Jr., R.A. Windsor, C.M. Brooks, L.B. Gerald, B. Martin, D.M. Higgins, and T. Liu. 1999. "Asthma Self-Management: Do Patient Education Programs Always Have an Impact?" *Archives of Internal Medicine* 159 (20): 2422-88.
   Intervention: Disease Management
   Disease/Condition: Asthma
   Length of Time of Intervention/Study: two years
   Sample Size: 221
   Research Design: RCT. Measured three self-management treatments: (1) replication if the self-management program developed at the University of Alabama at Birmingham that was previously shown to be efficacious. (2) modified version of this program including only the core elements. (3) usual care program.
   Key Results: Patients in educational group did no better in terms of use of health care services than usual care group.

4. Bodenheimer, T., E.H. Wagner, and K. Grumbach. 2002. "Improving Primary Care for Patients with Chronic Illness." *Journal of the American Medical Association* 288 (15): 1909-14.
   Intervention: Disease Management
   Disease/Condition: Multi
   Length of Time of Intervention/Study: n/a
   Sample Size: n/a
   Research Design: Literature review.
   Key Results: Review of 39 studies of ambulatory diabetes and other chronic care programs. Thirty-two studies showed improvement in at least one process or outcome measure. The authors went on to inquire whether there was evidence of cost savings as well. A total of 27 articles were reviewed reporting financial outcomes (many of which are part of this analysis). Results were mixed: some articles show immediate cost-savings; others show no evidence of savings, while three asthma studies show no savings or higher costs in the intervention group than in the control group. The authors, who are diabetes experts, conclude that the time for cost-savings to emerge in diabetes is likely to be longer than in heart disease or asthma. Several studies are cited that show savings in a diabetes population; however, the authors also draw attention to evidence from several studies of "recidivism" or a tendency for the initially favorable results to be reversed over time.

5. Bratton, D.L., M. Price, L. Gavin, K. Glenn, M. Brenner, E.W. Gelfand, and M.D. Klinnert. 2001. "Impact of a Multidisciplinary Day Program on Disease and Health Care Costs in Children and Adolescents with Severe Asthma: a Two-Year Follow-Up Study." *Pediatric Pulmonology* 31(3): 177-89.
   Intervention: Disease Management
   Disease/Condition: Asthma
   Length of Time of Intervention/Study: two years
   Sample Size: 98 pediatric patients under age 18
   Research Design: Cohort study; patients enrolled in the study were compared to patients that had been enrolled in the NJDP 10 years earlier
   Key Results: Total utilization was calculated at $16,250 at time 0, $1,902 at year one, and $690 at year two. (Results should be viewed with caution because of Cohort study design.)

6. Bruce, D., and J. Dickmeyer. 2001. "Don't Overlook Disease Management Programs for Low-Incidence, High-Cost Diseases to Improve Your Bottom Line." *Journal of Health Care Finance* 28 (2): 45-9.
   Intervention: Disease Management/Specialty Case Management
   Disease/Condition: Chronic renal failure
   Length of Time of Intervention/Study: N/A
   Sample Size: 650 Patients
   Research Design: N/A
   Key Results: 66 percent reduction in bed-days; 35 percent reduction in admissions; 83 percent reduction in ER visits; cost reduction of 8 percent – to 10 percent.

7. Centers for Disease Control (CDC). 2002. "Cost-Effectiveness of Intensive Glycemic Control, Intensified Hypertension Control, and Serum Cholesterol Level Reduction for Type 2 Diabetes." *Journal of the American Medical Association* 287 (19): 2542-51.
   Intervention: Disease Management
   Disease/Condition: Diabetes
   Length of Time of Intervention/Study: N/A

Sample Size: N/A
Research Design: QALY analysis using the UK prospective diabetes study
Key Results: Intensified hypertension control in diabetics reduces costs relative to moderate hypertension control. Intensive glycemic control increases costs. Intensive glycemic control leads to a 0.3 increase in life expectancy (0.19 QALY). Cost of intervention was $12,213, offset in part by reduced complications. Result is a cost of $41,384 per QALY. Intensive hypertension control results in 0.47 year increase in life expectancy and 0.40 increase in QALY. Cost of intervention was $3,708 and was completely offset by reduced complications.

8. Cline, C.M., B.Y. Israelsson, R.B. Willenheimer, K. Broms, and L.R. Erhardt. 1998. "Cost Effective Management Program for Heart Failure Reduces Hospitalization." *Heart* 80(5): 442-46.
Intervention: Case Management/Disease Management
Disease/Condition: Heart Failure
Length of Time of Intervention/Study: one Year
Sample Size: 190 patients in Sweden (aged 65-84) hospitalized for Heart Failure
Research Design: Prospective control trial
Key Results: Care managed patients experienced a longer mean time to re-admission, and fewer hospital days. Mean annual cost in the Intervention group was $2,294 versus $3,594 for the control group (a reduction of 36.2 percent).

9. Costantini, O., K. Huck, M.D. Carlson, K. Boyd, C.M. Buchter, P. Raiz, and C.M. Buchter. 2001. "Impact of a Guideline-Based Disease Management Team on Outcomes of Hospitalized Patients with Congestive Heart Failure." *Archives of Internal Medicine* 161: 177-82
Intervention: Case Management/Disease Management
Disease/Condition: Heart Failure
Length of Time of Intervention/Study: one year
Sample Size: 283 care managed patients and 126 concurrent non-care managed patients
Research Design: Two groups: pre-program and concurrent control group study
Key Results: Care managed patients experienced higher rates of ACE inhibitor use and adherence to care guidelines, when compared with both the pre-program and concurrent control groups. The intervention group experienced lower costs than both the pre- and concurrent control groups: nine percent lower than pre-group, and 39 percent lower than the concurrent group. Cost of interventions is not reported.

10. Costich, T.D., and F.C. Lee. 2003. "Improving Cancer Care in a Kentucky Managed Care Plan: A Case Study of Cancer." *Disease Management* 6 (1): 9-20.
Intervention: Disease Management/Specialty Case Management
Disease/Condition: Cancer
Length of Time of Intervention/Study: 1 year; 1999-2000
Sample Size: 1,146 enrolled patients
Research Design: Trend adjusted cohort study
Key Results: 14 percent reduction in services; 11.1 percent reduction in average case cost; 30 percent reduction in injectable drug costs for support care; 47 percent increase in home/hospice care; average length of hospice stay increased from 11.2 days to 33.7 days.

11. Cousins, M., and Y. Liu. 2003. "Cost Savings for a PPO Population with Multi-Condition Disease Management: Evaluating Program Impact Using Predictive Modeling with a Control Group." *Disease Management* 6 (4): 207-17.
    Intervention: Disease Management
    Disease/Condition: Asthma, diabetes, coronary artery disease.
    Length of Time of Intervention/Study Sample Size: two years
    Research Design: Members of PPO plans: 1,009 in study group and 2,491 in control group Matched control group constructed from ASO population; costs predicted with predictive model
    Key Results: ROI of 2.84:1.00 and $1.45 gross savings per member per month.

12. Domurat, E.S. 1999. "Diabetes Managed Care and Clinical Outcomes: The Harbor City, California Kaiser Permanente Diabetes Care System." *American Journal of Managed Care* 5 (10): 1299-1307.
    Intervention: Disease Management
    Disease/Condition: Diabetes
    Length of Time of Intervention/Study Sample Size: 1995-1997; 2,617 enrolled; 5,993 usual care.
    Research Design: Enrolled versus non-enrolled populations (this research design is suspect).
    Key Results: An automated system, supporting nurse interventions decreases utilization rates and increases testing in the diabetic population. No financial results are reported.

13. Fonarow, G.C., L.W. Stevenson, J.A. Walden, N.A. Livingston, A.E. Steimle, M.A. Hamilton, J. Moriguchi, J.H. Tillisch, and M.A. Woo. 1997. "Impact of a Comprehensive Heart Failure Management Program in Hospital Re-admission and Functional Status of Patients with Advanced Heart Failure." *Journal of American College of Cardiology* 3 (30): 725-32.
    Intervention: Disease Management
    Disease/Condition: Advanced heart failure; functional status III or IV
    Length of Time of Intervention/Study: three years
    Sample Size: 214 accepted for heart transplantation and discharged after evaluation
    Research Design: cohort study
    Key Results: Intervention group experienced 85 percent reduction in hospital re-admissions. Estimated cost-reduction due to the intervention (net of hospital intervention costs estimated at $300 per patient) was $9,800.

14. Galbreath, A.D., R.A. Krasuski, B. Smith, K.C. Stajduhar, M. Kwan, R. Ellis, and G.L. Freeman. 2004. "Long-Term Health Care and Cost Outcomes of Disease Management in a Large, Randomized, Community-Based Population with Heart Failure." *Circulation* 110; 1-9.
    Intervention: Telephonic Disease Management
    Disease/Condition: Congestive Heart Failure.
    Length of Time of Intervention/Study: 18 months.
    Sample Size: 1,069 patients.
    Research Design: Randomized Control.
    Key Results: Participants in DM enjoyed increased survival probability. Improvement was more marked in sicker patients (NYHA class III and IV). Health care utilization was not reduced by DM and there were no financial savings observed.

15. Ghosh, C.S., P. Ravindran, M. Joshi, and S.C. Stearns. 1998. "Reductions in Hospital use from Self Management Training for Chronic Asthmatics." *Social Science and Medicine* 46 (8): 1087-93
Intervention: Disease Management
Disease/Condition: Asthma
Length of Time of Intervention/Study: one year
Sample Size: 276 patients in tertiary care in India.
Research Design: Randomized control trial
Key Results: 53.2 percent reduction in days hospitalized for intervention group, likelihood of hospitalization decreased by 26 percent, average days hospitalized during year fell 38 days for control group and 22 days for intervention. Intervention experienced 46.7 percent reduction in ER visits, and 14 percent reduction in likelihood of having ER visit. Average number of patients with ER visits fell from 43.6 to 27.2. Indirect costs for intervention group were 48 percent less, direct costs down by 16 percent. Average total cost was 22 percent less for intervention than control.

16. Gomaa, W., P. Muntendam, and T. Morrow. 2001. "Technology-Based Disease Management, a Low-Cost, High-Value Solution for the Management of Chronic Disease." *Disease Management Health Outcomes* 9 (10).
Intervention: Population Management; Disease Management
Disease/Condition: Asthma/Diabetes/Heart Disease
Length of Time of Intervention Study: nine month follow up
Sample Size: 93,414 total participants
Research Design: Adjusted cohort study comparing participant and non-participant outcomes
Key Results: Asthma savings amounted to $456 per year; Heart Disease: $1,737 and $464 for diabetes. Program cost was not disclosed.

17. Gordon, N.F., C.D. English, A.S. Contractor, R.D. Salmon, R.F. Leighton, B.A. Franklin, and W.L. Haskell. 2002. "Effectiveness of Three Models for Comprehensive Cardiovascular Disease Risk Reduction." *American Journal of Cardiology* 89 (11): 1263-68.
Intervention: Case Management/Disease Management
Disease/Condition: two less costly approaches compared to contemporary phase II cardiac rehab program; one alternative involved nurse case-managers and the second involved a community-based program.
Length of Time of Intervention/Study: 12 Weeks
Sample Size: 155; 52=contemporary rehab program, 54=nurse-case managed CV risk reduction program, 49=community based
Research Design: Randomized control trial
Key Results: Programs had similar clinical outcomes. Relative to cost, the community-based program had the greatest potential to save costs.

18. Gorski, L.A., and K. Johnson. 2003. "A Disease Management Program for Heart Failure." *Lippincott's Case Management* 8 (6): 265-73.
Intervention: Case Management/Disease Management
Disease/Condition: Heart Failure
Length of Time of Intervention/Study: two to six months

Sample Size: 74 patients
Research Design: Key Results: 35 percent decrease in hospitalizations. $2,200 reduction in claims per patient.

19. Hoffman, J. 2001. "Broad Disease Management Interventions: Reducing Health Care Costs for Plan Members with Congestive Heart Failure." *Disease Management Health Outcomes* 9 (10): 527-29.
Intervention: Disease Management
Disease/Condition: Heart Failure
Length of Time of Intervention/Study: 12 months baseline (1997-8); 12 months intervention (1998-9).
Sample Size: 16,000 Commercial member months; 47,000 Medicare member months.
Research Design: Historical Control (Baseline versus Intervention). No adjustment applied because the underlying trend in costs could not be estimated. Therefore, there is still potentially some confounding from this factor.
Key Results: Savings of $8,220 per chronic member per year (commercial) and $4,632 per chronic member per year (Medicare) were reported (29 percent and 20 percent reductions respectively).

20. Jolly, K., F. Bradley, S. Sharp, H. Smith, S. Thompson, A.L. Kinmonth, and D. Mant. 1999. "Randomized Controlled Trial of Follow-Up Care in General Practice of Patient with Myocardial Infarction and Angina." *British Medical Journal* 318: 706-11.
Intervention: Disease Management; nurse-led program to coordinate post-discharge care of at-risk patients in the community. Intervention is both with patient and provider.
Disease/Condition: Heart Failure
Length of Time of Intervention/Study: 12 months
Sample Size: 597 patients
Research Design: Randomized control. Randomized on medical practice group, not patient.
Key Results: No difference in smoking cessation rates between intervention and control groups. No significant differences in key clinical measures (lipids, blood pressure) between intervention and control groups. Improved processes in the practice, but not health outcomes of patients.

21. Jolly, K., F. Bradley, S. Sharp, H. Smith, and D. Mant. 1998. "Follow-Up Care in General Practice of Patient with Myocardial Infarction and Angina." *Family Practice* 15 (6): 548-55.
Intervention: Disease Management; nurse-led program to coordinate post-discharge care of at-risk patients in the community. Intervention is both with patient and provider.
Disease/Condition: Heart Failure
Length of Time of Intervention/Study: 12 months
Sample Size: 597 patients; 67 practices.
Research Design: Randomized control. Randomized on medical practice group, not patient.
Key Results: Some evidence of increased follow-up by physicians with patients; however, the authors conclude that, to achieve changes in patient behavior, intervention at the practice level is insufficient and a different model is required to see behavior change in patients.

22. Kauppinen, R., V. Vilkka, H. Sintonen, T. Klaukka, and H. Tukiainen. 2001. "Long-Term Economic Evaluation of Intensive Patient Education During the First Treatment Year in Newly Diagnosed Adult Asthma." *Respiratory Medicine* 95 (1): 56-63.
Intervention: Disease Management
Disease/Condition: Asthma
Length of Time of Intervention/Study: five years
Sample Size: 162 newly diagnosed adult asthmatics.
Research Design: Randomized Control Test; intervention was intensive patient education, control was conventional patient education.
Key Results: Differences in costs for the intervention and control groups in the first year but not cumulatively at five years. First year ROI was 1.5. Intervention group had fewer sick-days than Control Group. Short-term financial advantage to the intervention group was not maintained; no difference in outcome costs or total costs after five years.

23. Kinmonth, A.L., A. Woodcock, S. Griffin, N. Spiegal, and M.J. Campbell. 1998. "Randomized Controlled Trial of Patient-Centered Care of Diabetes in General Practice." *British Medical Journal* 317: 1202-08.
Intervention: Disease Management
Disease/Condition: Diabetes
Length of Time of Intervention/Study Sample Size: 250 intervention versus 360 control. Twelve-month follow-up.
Research Design: Randomized control group.
Key Results: This study aimed to test the effect of training of providers in the management of chronic disease. While some improvement in patient satisfaction was observed, other measures did not show improvement (Body mass index and other markers were higher for the intervention group, and glycemic control was no better for the intervention group).

24. Klonoff, D.C., and D.M. Schwartz. 2000. "An Economic Analysis of Interventions for Diabetes." *Diabetes Care* 23 (3): 390-404.
Intervention: Disease Management
Disease/Condition: Diabetes
Length of Time of Intervention/Study: Varied
Sample Size: Varied
Research Design: Literature review of 17 interventions for diabetes; limited economic analysis.
Key Results: Diabetic Retinopathy screening and treatment was shown to be cost-saving or at least break-even; Pre-conception care: one California study shows savings of $5.19 for each dollar invested; in another health plan study, savings amount to over $3,000 per mother for an ROI of $1.86. Diabetic Nephropathy: savings of over $5,000 per patient were reported. Improved glycemic control: not found to be net cost-saving for Type I diabetes but may be for Type II. Diabetes self-management programs (similar to a DM program) were found to produce ROI from 1.44 to over 8.0. Case Management: evidence of the "economic value of case management for diabetes is unclear." Unclear evidence of Medical Nutrition therapy or Self-monitoring of blood glucose. No evidence of the financial effects of lipid control, blood pressure or weight control, or foot-care has been published.

25. Leatherman, S., D. Berwick, D. Iles, L.S. Lewin, F. Davidoff, T. Nolan, and M. Bisognano. 2003. "The Business Case for Quality: Case Studies and An Analysis." *Health Affairs* 22 (2): 17-30.
Intervention: Disease Management
Disease/Condition: Diabetes
Length of Time of Intervention/Study: N/A
Sample Size: Various (Survey article)
Research Design: Various (Survey article)
Key Results: Diabetes Disease Management produced more benefits, although studies at HealthPartners (ROI: 1.23) and Independent Health indicated a long pay-back period (10 years).

26. Litzelman, D.K., C.W. Slemenda, C.D. Langefeld, L.M. Hays, M.A. Welch, D.E. Bild, E. S. Ford, and F. Vinicor. 1993. "Reduction of Lower Extremity Clinical Abnormalities in Patients with Non-Insulin-Dependent Diabetes Mellitus." *Annals of Internal Medicine* 119 (1): 36-41.
Intervention: Disease Management
Disease/Condition: Diabetes
Length of Time of Intervention/Study Sample Size: 395 diabetic patients
Research Design: Randomized control study
Key Results: This intervention focused on a specific outcome for diabetics. Foot-care: Intervention consisted of initial training plus regular follow-ups from professional. Control group patients were approximately 2.4 times more likely to have skin lesions than the intervention population. The intervention population were also more likely to have foot examinations during office visits and to have physician education sessions.

27. Lucas, D.O., L.O. Zimmer, J.E. Paul, D. Jones, G. Slatko, W. Liao, and J. Lashley. 2001. "Two-Year Results from the Asthma Self-Management Program: Long-Term Impact on Health Care Services, Costs, Functional Status and Productivity." *Journal of Asthma* 38(4): 321-33.
Intervention: Disease Management
Disease/Condition: Asthma
Length of Time of Intervention/Study: two years
Sample Size: 137 asthmatics in MCOs or employer groups
Research Design: two-year follow-up Pre-Post design
Key Results: No decrease in work or school missed due to asthma at the end of Year one; 50 percent reduction in lost days reported in Year two. Reduction in smoking at Year one (3.7 percent reduced to 1.3 percent; further reduced to 0.9 percent in Year two). Significant reductions in admissions, ER visits and hospital days, resulting in $175,317 claims savings, MCOs and employer plans saved a net $125,817. ROI of 2.54. (Medication was not included in this analysis.)

28. Lukacs, S.L., E.K. France, A.E. Baron, and L.A. Crane. 2002. "Effectiveness of an Asthma Management Program for Pediatric Members of a Large HMO." *Archives of Pediatric and Adolescent Medicine* 156 (9): 872-76.
Intervention: Disease Management
Disease/Condition: Asthma
Length of Time of Intervention/Study: 18 months
Sample Size: 298 patients under age 18 at Kaiser Permanente having moderate to severe asthma

Research Design: Case/control study: intervention group participated in an outpatient-based program that provides comprehensive evaluation, education, and follow-up. They were compared to a control that did not participate in the program.
Key Results: Increase in inhaled cortico-steroid medications. There was no significant difference in the proportion of patients who were hospitalized or visited the Emergency Room.

29. Lynne, D. 2004. "Diabetes Disease Management in Managed Care Organizations." *Disease Management* 7 (1).
Intervention: Disease Management
Disease/Condition: Diabetes
Length of Time of Intervention/Study: three years (pre and post-enrollment).
Sample Size: GHI (New York) 8,000 eligible; 1,368 followed.
Research Design: Pre- post study (two baseline and one post-program year).
Key Results: Financial results published show 20 percent increase in the PMPM cost for the participant group and 33 percent increase in costs of the non-participant group. Baseline cost of the participant group is significantly lower than that of the non-participant group (27 percent lower) making the results highly susceptible to selection bias.

30. McAlister, F.A., F. Lawson, K K. Teo, and P W. Armstrong. 2001. "Randomized Trials of Secondary Prevention Programmes in Coronary Heart Disease: Systematic Review." *British Medical Journal* 323: 957-62.
Intervention: Disease Management
Disease/Condition: Heart Failure
Length of Time of Intervention/Study Sample Size: 11 trials/2,067 patients. Two weeks-12 months.
Research Design: Review Article
Key Results: Eight studies reported claims data; all but one reported savings. Models that employed nurse follow-up were more successful at savings costs than models using telephonic interventions. No cost data were reported so calculation of ROI and cost-effectiveness of more-intensive nurse-based interventions is not feasible.

31. McAlister, F.A., et al. 2001. "A Systematic Review of Randomized Trials of Disease Management Programs in Heart Failure." *American Journal of Medicine* 110: 378-84.
Intervention: Disease Management
Disease/Condition: Heart failure
Length of Time of Intervention/Study: three months to 12 months
Sample Size: 97 to 1,396
Research Design: Meta-Analysis
Key Results: Authors reviewed 416 citations; only nine met criteria for randomization and reported results for multi-disciplinary teams and hospitalization rates. All studies reported reductions in hospitalizations versus the control; average reduction in hospitalizations was 24 percent. In addition, two studies focusing on providers were reported that these interventions resulted in no significant difference in hospitalizations of the intervention group, compared with the control group.

32. Naji, S. 1994. "Integrated Care for Diabetes: Clinical, Psychosocial, and Economic Evaluation." *British Medical Journal* 308: 1208-12.
Intervention: Disease Management
Disease/Condition: Diabetes
Length of Time of Intervention/Study Sample Size: 274 diabetic patients.
Research Design: Randomized control.
Key Results: Many outcomes measured showed no difference between the integrated care model and usual care, including measures of metabolic control, unscheduled admissions, etc. The integrated care group had more (and longer) office visits. Patient cost was lower for these patients.

33. Norris, S.L., et al. 2002. "The Effectiveness of Disease and Case Management for People with Diabetes." *American Journal of Preventive Medicine* 15-38.
Intervention: Case Management
Disease/Condition: Diabetes.
Length of Time of Intervention/Study: N/A
Sample Size: N/A
Research Design: Literature Review
Key Results: No studies were found of Case Management financial outcomes that met the requirements for study validity.

34. O'Connor, P., et al. 1996. "Continuous Quality Improvement Can Improve Glycemic Control for HMO Patients with Diabetes." *Archives of Family Medicine* 5: 502-06.
Intervention: Disease Management
Disease/Condition: Diabetes.
Length of Time of Intervention/Study: 12 months prior/18 months post-implementation.
Sample Size: 121 intervention/122 comparison population.
Research Design: Randomized (participating clinic versus non-participating clinic).
Key Results: HbA1c score fell 6 percent in the intervention group at 12 months and 11 percent at 18 months, compared with no significant change in the control group. Outpatient utilization and claims were not significantly different between intervention and control.

35. Piette, J.D., et al. 2000. "Do Automated Calls with Nurse Follow-Up Improve Self-Care and Glycemic Control among Vulnerable Patients with Diabetes?" *American Journal of Medicine* 108: 20-27.
Intervention: Disease Management
Disease/Condition: Diabetes.
Length of Time of Intervention/Study: N/A
Sample Size: 280 patients.
Research Design: Randomized control study
Key Results: More frequently reported self-care monitoring (foot-monitoring; weight; glycemic control; medication compliance). The intervention group reported a slightly lower HbA1c score. No difference in admission rates.

36. Rich, M.W., V. Beckham, B. Gray, C. Wittenberg, C.L. Leven, and P. Luther. 1996. "Effect of a Multidisciplinary Intervention on Medication Compliance in Elderly Patients with Congestive Heart Failure." *American Journal of Medicine* 101(3): 270-76.
Intervention: Disease Management /Case Management
Disease/Condition: Heart failure

Length of Time of Intervention/Study: 30 ± two days
Sample Size: 156 patients over age 70
Research Design: Randomized controlled trial
Key Results: A multidisciplinary follow up intervention is associated with improved medication compliance in the intervention population (88 percent versus 81 percent in the control group). The intervention group experienced 33 percent fewer re-admissions and 31 percent fewer hospital days than the control group, although the difference is not statistically significant.

37. Rich, M.W., V. Beckham, C. Wittenberg, C.L. Leven, K.E. Freddland, and R.M. Carney. 1995. "A Multidisciplinary Intervention to Prevent the Re-admission of Elderly Patients with Congestive Heart Failure." *New England Journal of Medicine* 333 (18): 1190-95.
Intervention: Disease Management/Case Management
Disease/Condition: Heart failure
Length of Time of Intervention/Study: 90-day follow-up
Sample Size: 282 patients over age 70; intervention 142, control 140.
Research Design: Randomized controlled trial
Key Results: 90-day readmission rate for the intervention group was 36 percent; 90-day readmission rate for control group was 46 percent. Multiple re-admissions were reduced from 16.4 percent in the control group to 6.3 percent in the intervention group. Intervention cost averaged $336; overall cost of care was less in the intervention group by $460, suggesting an ROI of 1.37 (Note that study period was < one year).

38. Riegel, B., B. Carlson, Z. Kopp, B. LePetri, D. Glaser, and A. Unger. 2002. "Effect of a Standardized Nurse Case-Management Telephone Intervention on Resource Use in Patients with Chronic Heart Failure." *Archive of Internal Medicine* 162 (6): 705-12.
Intervention: Disease Management/Case Management
Disease/Condition: Heart failure
Length of Time of Intervention/Study: three and six months
Sample Size: 281 physicians/358 patients
Research Design: Randomized controlled clinical trial (physicians randomized)
Key Results: Heart failure (HF) re-hospitalization 45.7 percent lower in intervention group at three months; 47.8 percent lower at six months; HF hospital days and multiple re-admissions were significantly lower in intervention group at six months. Inpatient HF costs were 45.5 percent lower at six months; no evidence of cost shifting to outpatient setting; patient satisfaction with care was higher in intervention group. Savings per patient was estimated at $1,000, and intervention cost was $443, for an ROI of 2.26.

39. Rubin, R.J., K.A. Dietrich, and A.D. Hawk. 1998. "Clinical and Economic Impact of Implementing a Comprehensive Diabetes Management Program in Managed Care." *Journal of Clinical Endocrinology Medicine* 83 (8): 2635-41.
Intervention: Disease Management
Disease/Condition: Diabetes
Length of Time of Intervention/Study: two years; 1/95-12/96.
Sample Size: approximately 7,000 diabetics in a managed care population of 360,000
Research Design: Retrospective Analysis

Key Results: Significant increases in clinical quality indicators are reported (HbA1c scores; cholesterol screening; eye tests; etc.). The specific diabetic care program "Diabetes NetCare" yielded savings of $50 PMPM (12.3 percent reduction). Program costs are not reported.

40. Sadur, C.N., N. Moline, M. Costa, D. Michalik, D. Mendlowitz, S. Roller, R. Watson, B. E. Swain, J.V. Selby, and W.C. Javorski. 1999. "Diabetes Management in a Health Maintenance Organization: Efficacy of Care Management Using Cluster Visits." *Diabetes Care* 22 (12): 2011-17.
    Intervention: Disease Management
    Disease/Condition: Diabetes
    Length of Time of Intervention/Study: six month intervention/18 month follow-up.
    Sample Size: 97 intervention and 88 control patients enrolled in a Kaiser, California HMO.
    Research Design: Randomized controlled trial.
    Key Results: The intervention improved glycemic control: 1.3 percent reduction in the intervention group versus 0.2 percent reduction in control. Lower admission rates in the intervention group than the control group. Seventeen percent increase in physician visits by the intervention group. No cost data were reported.

41. Schermer, T.R., B.P. Thoonen, G. van den Boom, R.P. Akkermans, R.P. Grol, H.T. Folgering, C. van Weel, and C.P. van Schayck. 2002. "Randomized Controlled Economic Evaluation of Asthma Self-Management in Primary Health Care." *American Journal of Respiratory Medicine* 6 (8): 1062-72.
    Intervention: Disease Management
    Disease/Condition: Asthma
    Length of Time of Intervention/Study: two years
    Sample Size: 98 self-management and 95 usual care Dutch patients
    Research Design: Randomized controlled trial.
    Key Results: The cost of the program amounted to Euros 189 per patient; the program resulted in slightly higher costs for the intervention group than the control group (primarily because of higher medication usage). Overall cost is therefore higher for the intervention group. The authors analyze productivity data to estimate the (indirect) value of lower lost-time, which slightly more than offsets the higher program costs.

42. Sidorov, J., R. Shull, J. Tomcavage, S. Girolami, N. Lawton, and R. Harris. 2002. "Does Diabetes Disease Management Save Money and Improve Outcomes? A Report of Simultaneous Short-Term Savings and Quality Improvement Associated with a Health Maintenance Organization-Sponsored Disease Management Program Among Patients Fulfilling Health Employer Data and Information Set Criteria." *Diabetes Care* 25 (4): 684-89.
    Intervention: Disease Management
    Disease/Condition: Diabetes
    Length of Time of Intervention/Study: two years
    Sample Size: 6,799 Health Plan diabetes patients from 295,000 members. Identified through HEDIS criteria
    Research Design: Retrospective claim review of the outcomes of an opt-in program
    Key Results: $394.63 PMPM if in DM program, $502.48 PMPM if not in DM program; Savings of $107.86 PMPM estimated. Program cost for year one is estimated at $83.33 per enrolled member per month, for an ROI of 1.29.

43. Snyder, J. W., J. Malaskovitz, J. Griego, J. Persson, and K. Flatt. 2003. "Quality Improvement and Cost Reduction Realized by a Purchaser through Diabetes." *Disease Management* (6): 233-41.
Intervention: Disease Management
Disease/Condition: Diabetes
Length of Time of Intervention/Study: three years
Sample Size: 663 (422 continuously participating) diabetics
Research Design: Pre-post cohort study (Baseline/Intervention year). Baseline not adjusted.
Key Results: From baseline to year three, medical costs fell 26.8 percent from baseline to intervention year. Per diabetic member per month savings over this period amounted to $98.49. Return on Investment (ROI) was 3.37. Claims did not include prescription drugs.

44. Sullivan, S.D., K.B. Weiss, H. Lynn, H. Mitchell, M. Kattan, P.J. Gergen, R. Evans, and National Cooperative Inner-City Asthma Study (NCICAS) Investigators. 2002. "The Cost-Effectiveness of an Inner-City Asthma Intervention for Children." *Journal of Allergy and Clinical Immunology* 110 (4): 576-81.
Intervention: Disease Management
Disease/Condition: Asthma (pediatric)
Length of Time of Intervention/Study: two years
Sample Size: 1033 children and their families in eight sites in seven urban inner-city areas completed the first year, and 961 completed the second year.
Research Design: Prospective cost-effectiveness analysis alongside a randomized trial. Intervention group received comprehensive social worker-based education program and environmental control. Part of the National Cooperative Inner-city Asthma Study.
Key Results: Cost of the intervention was $337 per child over two years. In Year one, direct medical costs rose by $244.75 in the intervention group, compared with the control group. The intervention improved results in terms of symptom free days but this did not translate into financial savings.

45. Testa, M.A., and D.C. Simonson. 1998. "Health Economic Benefits and Quality of Life During Improved Glycemic Control in Patients with Type 2 Diabetes Mellitus: a Randomized, Controlled, Double-Blind Trial." *Journal of the American Medical Association* 280 (17): 1490-96.
Intervention: Disease Management
Disease/Condition: Diabetes (type 2 diabetes)
Length of Time of Intervention/Study: three-week treatment monitored for 12 weeks.
Sample Size: 569 volunteers with type 2 diabetes
Research Design: Double-blind, randomized, placebo-controlled, parallel trial. Intervention group were given hyperglycemic.
Key Results: Hospitalizations were comparable for both groups. Patients reporting one or more ambulatory care visits decreased by 15 for intervention group, yielding an estimated savings of $11 per patient a month. Intervention group members showed significantly less absence from work.

46. Vaccaro, J., J. Cherry, A. Harper, and M. O'Connell. 2001. "Utilization Reduction, Cost Savings and Return on Investment for the PacifiCare Chronic Heart Failure Program." *Disease Management* 4 (3): 131-38.
Intervention: Disease Management
Disease/Condition: Heart failure
Length of Time of Intervention/Study: six months.
Sample Size: data collected on 52 patients. There were 700 patients enrolled in the program at the time of the study.
Research Design: Cohort study of the PacifiCare "Taking Charge of Your Heart Health Program."
Key Results: $4,882 saved for all-cause hospitalization, $389 for all-cause ER visit, and $5,271 for total cost saved per member per year. ROI estimated at approximately 2.00.

47. Villagra, V., and T. Ahmed. 2004. "Effectiveness of a Disease Management Program for Patients with Diabetes." *Health Affairs* (23) 4: 255-66.
Intervention: Disease Management
Disease/Condition: Diabetes
Length of Time of Intervention/Study: 1998-2000
Sample Size: 55,439 health plan members with Diabetes
Research Design: Two designs: Pre-post and geographic controls
Key Results: Different results were seen in the two different study designs: geographic controls showed $120 PMPM reduction in cost in the intervention group and $26 reduction between intervention and control in the pre- post study. Program cost is not reported although the authors state that savings exceeded costs irrespective of outcomes measurement methodology.

48. Wagner, E., and N. Sandhu. 2001. "Effect of Improved Glycemic Control on Health Care Costs and Utilization." *Journal of the American Medical Association* 285 (2): 182-89.
Intervention: Disease Management
Disease/Condition: Diabetes
Length of Time of Intervention/Study: 1992-1997
Sample Size: 4,749 patients (average age of 60) enrolled in a staff model HMO in Washington state.
Research Design: Historical cohort
Key Results: Mean total health care costs were $685 to $950 less each year in the improved (case) cohort but these differences were only statistically significant after year one. Authors conclude that complicated cases do not lead to cost reductions in initial years.

49. Weingarten, S.R., M.S. Riedinger, L. Conner, T.H. Lee, I. Hoffman, B. Johnson, and A. G. Ellrodt. 1994. "Practice Guidelines and Reminders to Reduce Duration of Hospital Stay for Patients with Chest Pain: An Interventional Trial." *Annals of Internal Medicine* 120 (4): 257-63.
Intervention: Disease Management (Physician intervention)
Disease/Condition: Patients admitted to coronary care/intermediate care units with chest pain at low risk for complications
Length of Time of Intervention/Study: Sept. 1, 1991 – Aug. 31, 1992; one year
Sample Size: 375
Research Design: Prospective controlled clinical trial with alternate method
Key Results: Increase in compliance from 50 percent to 69 percent; decrease of 26 percent

in length of stay; total (direct and indirect) cost reduction $1,397/patient; no difference in complications between intervention and control. When reminders were withdrawn, practice patterns reverted to pre-intervention levels, and even after a year of the program, a significant percentage of physicians failed to practice according to the guidelines.

50. Weingarten, S., J.M. Henning, E. Badamgarav, K. Knight, V. Hasselblad, A. Gano, and J. Ofman. 2002. "Interventions Used in Disease Management Programmes for Patients with Chronic Illness—Which Ones Work? Meta-Analysis of Published Reports." *British Medical Journal* Vol. 325.
Intervention: Disease Management
Disease/Condition: 102 articles evaluating 118 programs; many different diseases. Different types of intervention, both patient- and provider-focused.
Length of study: Varied by study
Sample Size: Multiple
Research Design: Meta-Analysis
Key Results: Provider-focused interventions: modest but significant improvement in disease control; diabetes and depression showed the most significant benefits. Forty-four percent of patient-focused intervention programs produced significant improvement in disease control; greatest improvement was found in depression, asthma and hypertension. Patient education produced a small but significant improvement in control. Patient reminders produced similar results.

51. Wheeler, J. 2003. "Can a Disease Self-Management Program Reduce Health Care Costs? The Case of Older Women with Heart Disease." *Medical Care Volume* 41 (6): 706-15.
Intervention: Disease Management
Disease/Condition: Heart Disease
Length of Time of Intervention/Study: 36 months – three points in time in which data was collected
Sample Size: 227 intervention and 216 control; female only, 60 years and older
Research Design: Randomized controlled trial
Key Results: Program participants experienced 46 percent fewer inpatient days and 49 percent lower inpatient costs. Cost savings were estimated at $150 PMPM, while the program cost was $374 per participant, or $31 PMPM. Hospital cost savings exceeded program costs by a ratio of approximately 5 to 1.

52. Whellan, D.J., L. Gaulden, W.A. Gattis, B. Granger, S.D. Russell, M.A. Blazing, M.S. Cuffe, and C.M. O'Connor. 2001. "The Benefit of Implementing a Heart Failure Disease Management Program." *Archives of Internal Medicine* 161 (18): 2223-28.
Intervention: Disease Management
Disease/Condition: Heart Failure
Length of Time of Intervention/Study: one year. 1998-9
Sample Size: 117 patients enrolled in the Duke Heart Failure Program
Research Design: Pre-enrollment/Post-enrollment study of enrolled patient experience
Key Results: Outpatient costs of participants increased significantly ($55 PMPM) but inpatient costs declined by $580 PMPM. Total cost per PMPM fell by $714 PMPM.

5 THE USE OF THE VALUE CHAIN IN DISEASE MANAGEMENT PROGRAM PLANNING

5.1 INTRODUCTION

Value Chain analysis, Porter [166][1], developed by Professor Michael Porter of Harvard University, is a useful tool in the planning and management of Disease Management programs. As applied in manufacturing, the value chain concept is that value is added to a product as it passes through different stages in the chain of activities. At each stage, the value added is greater than the cost of the production activity involved. Breaking the disease management process into its strategic components is a useful exercise for several reasons:

1. Disease Management (DM) is a collection of different activities that call on expertise from different industries or backgrounds (for example, information systems, analytics, consumer marketing, health education, behavioral psychology, clinical medicine, pharmaceutical therapy, etc.). Disease management providers combine these activities in different ways and different quantities. Program assessments are focused on total program outcomes, not on the effectiveness of, or the contribution to the outcomes of the component parts. A value chain analysis provides a framework for analyzing the effectiveness or value of the different components, and how well they work as an integrated product.
2. The different combinations of components make disease management a good candidate for "dose-response[2]" analysis. For example: what components, in what quantities, applied to which patients (members), add the most value to the final outcome? In order to do so, however, an analytical structure is necessary so that components of the "dose" and "response" may be identified. The DM industry has been slow to adopt consistent definitions of the components of DM that will allow different vendors and approaches to be compared.
3. The evolution of the disease management industry over the last 10 years has tended to run counter to the deconstructed or component-assembled model of service provision. Indeed, the history of the industry over this period has been one of outsourced disease management, with the provision of all DM services for a number of diseases generally provided by a single DM company. Whereas in the 1990s, the industry was dominated by in-house programs or those offered by pharmaceutical companies, growth in the past several years has come from outsourcing programs by commercial insurers, em-

[1] See also [59].

[2] The Dose-response relationship describes the change in effect on an organism caused by differing levels of exposure (or doses) to a stressor (usually a chemical, although this may also be an intervention such as DM). Studying dose response, and developing dose response models, is central to determining "safe" and "hazardous" levels and dosages for drugs, potential pollutants, and other substances to which humans are exposed.

ployers, state Medicaid plans, etc. So great has this growth been that the cost of disease management services in a typical health plan may now be the largest single outsourcing cost faced by the plan. Rarely does a large payer perform its own disease management in-house. Use of a single outsourced vendor by a payer, however, results in the payer purchasing the vendor's "bundle" of components, whether or not the vendor is providing these in the appropriate quantity or mix, and whether or not the vendor provides "best-of-breed" services for each component. Service providers do not report in a way that enables a purchaser to determine whether all components are equally efficient, and, if appropriate, to substitute a different service model or even a different provider for specific services. While this model has generally been successful for program sponsors, it has not contributed to greater transparency and understanding of the importance of individual components and elements of the DM Value Chain.

4. The bundling of outsourced DM components makes it difficult to compare performance between vendors, or to study the "dose-response" effect of using different configurations of components. Occasionally, a vendor will publish results in this area, such as Health Dialog's analysis of its "Deeper Dive" program, but these analyses are rare. Attempts to standardize, or at least define the components of a Disease Management program in order to be able to make comparisons between programs or vendors have met with little success in the industry, although as the industry matures, these attempts may be more frequent.

5.2 THE DM VALUE CHAIN - OVERVIEW

As we apply the Value Chain concept to DM, we deconstruct the DM process into six components, each of which triggers the next component. These components are illustrated in Figure 5.1. In addition, there are typically a number of support services without which an entity cannot operate (Information Systems, Human Resources, etc.). We focus in this discussion on the strategic components of disease management.

The DM Value Chain™

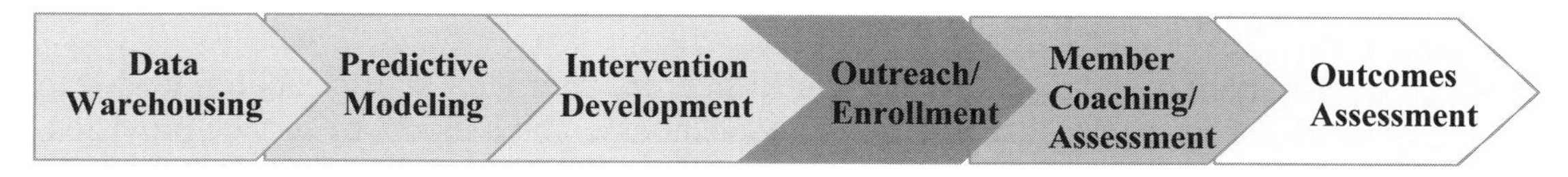

Support Services: Information Technology; Human Resources; etc.

FIGURE 5.1

The DM value chain consists of:

1. Data warehousing
2. Predictive modeling
3. Intervention development
4. Outreach and enrollment
5. Member assessment and coaching
6. Outcomes measurement

The key to understanding and applying the value chain concept to DM lies in understanding each of these six components, summarized in Figure 5.2. In the next section we will discuss each of these components in more detail.

Components of the DM Value Chain™

Data Warehousing	Predictive Modeling	Intervention Development	Outreach/ Enroll-ment	Member Coaching/ Assessment	Outcomes Assessment
• Create warehouse of administrative and eligibility data • Create and maintain electronic patient record. •Identify member conditions •Target populations for intervention	• Apply predictive models/target for intervention/risk rank. • Identify gaps in care • Identify provider patterns	• Development of programs and interventions • Development of campaigns to deliver interventions to target populations • Provider integration • Member referral/transfer between programs	• Deploy members to campaigns • Staff management/caseload assignment • Reach members • Enroll members • Follow-up/transition between programs	• Perform assessments • Maintain member enrollment • Coach members • Refer members • Graduate members/maintenance program	Measure outcomes • Clinical • Financial • Operational • Member/provider

FIGURE 5.2

5.3 COMPONENTS FOR ESTABLISHING PROGRAMS

In this section we provide a check-list of the components that should be considered in order to establish a successful program. The check-list may also be used by the sponsor of an outsourced program as it conducts a review of its vendor or seeks a "best-of-breed" provider. An important requirement of a program (insourced or outsourced) is availability of metrics/benchmarks to assess performance. It has generally been difficult to make comparisons within the industry, due to a lack of published data and a lack of common definitions. We should not minimize the amount of work required to identify best-of-breed vendors, and evaluate their potential cost and benefit as part of a program. However, for the program sponsor that is able to conduct this type of ongoing evaluation there is potential reward; both in holding the outsourced vendor accountable for performance, and/or changing a vendor for a particular service when the primary vendor is not performing adequately.

No.	Item	Definition
1.	Data provision and warehousing	a. Timeliness and accuracy. 1. Warehouse should integrate membership and medical and drug claims data. 2. Ability to integrate lab results, disability and workers compensation data, and self-reported data to create a rich member record. 3. Warehouse should be refreshed monthly. b. Condition identification. 1. Warehouse should append member condition identification to the member record using a standard algorithm (e.g. one of the risk grouper products) or a transparent algorithm agreed with client. 2. Condition identification is within guideline norms for the population, e.g. approximately 2.5% to 3.5% for a commercial diabetes population. c. Gaps in care identification. 1. Usually performed using a vendor's own algorithms, based on professional practice guidelines, applied to the claims data available in the warehouse. 2. Physician profiling: identification of physician practice patterns, physician quality and efficiency indicators. d. Warehouse should be able to accommodate self-reported, lab results (LOINC), biometric, and physician-derived data at least as a future capability.
2.	Predictive Modeling	a. Definition of risk: some vendors define risk in terms of prior cost, managing members who have exhibited high cost in the past. Others define risk in terms of clinical markers, managing those members whose clinical markers are suboptimal. As discussed elsewhere in this text, we favor an actuarial definition of risk in which a high risk member is one who has a high probability of experiencing a high-cost event in the short-term (six to 12 months). b. Accuracy of the predictive models. At a minimum, the predictive model used to identify candidates for management should estimate the likelihood of the event being managed occurring in the management period. If the member has a low likelihood of a risky event, the member is not a good candidate for nurse management (but may be a good candidate for another type of program using less expensive resources). c. Numbers. There is no absolute standard of specificity for a particular model because vendors treat the sensitivity/specificity trade-off in different ways. A coaching model that is able to process large numbers of members, including those with relatively low risk, may use a less sensitive model, leaving it to the initial assessment process to risk-rank identified members. A program that has fewer resources or that lacks a cost-effective method of outreach to coaching candidates should use a model with higher specificity. A good program will be able to demonstrate the specificity of its predictive models as well as their accuracy (the percentage of each percentile's predicted members that experience the predicted event). d. Timeliness. While predictive accuracy is important, it is equally important that any predictive model find the high-risk candidates *before* the event. In evaluating a predictive model, consider those members who have had the targeted event: were they identified by the predictive model? If not, why not? If they were identified was the issue one of timing or failure of the program to engage an identified member? e. Stratification. 1. How many strata does the initial (claims based) predictive model segment? 2. How are the strata determined – clinically, economically, resource availability or by another process? 3. Does the vendor employ a dynamic re-stratification process incorporating self-reported and assessment data to re-stratify the member list? 4. If the member list is re-stratified, how frequently is this done?

3.	Intervention Programs	a. What diseases are covered? b. How many programs are employed? c. What incidental programs (e.g., smoking cessation, weight loss) are offered? d. What is the objective of the intervention program? e. What is the evidence basis for the program and specific interventions or methods? f. What means does the intervention program use to reach its objectives with the patients? g. How many interventions are included in a program? h. What is the process for evaluating and assessing improvement under the program? i. How is "patient fatigue" avoided (balance between keeping the member in the program, the member's willingness to work at behavior change, and the resources required to keep the member motivated)? j. What process exists to graduate a member when improvement is indicated? k. What follow-up and support programs exist for members who have graduated from the program?
4.	Outreach	a. How are targets identified for the program? What numbers of targets are initially identified? What is the process for identifying and deploying targets that are identified later? b. How many members are identified for initial and subsequent outreach? How many attempts are made to reach members? What is the expected reach rate? What is the expected conversion (enrollment) rate from those reached? c. What is the expected contact rate (valid contact information is supplied)? What process is used to increase the contact rate? What other outreach and enrollment tools are employed (Mail, auto-dialing, etc.)? d. What is the outreach process employed? For example, is there a separate enrollment process using enrollers, or is enrollment performed by nurses? Deployment to the nursing and intervention process; timeliness, outbound reach and engagement rates.
5.	Program Statistics	a. Target rates. b. Reach rates. c. Enrollment (conversion) rates. d. Persistency in program rates/percentage of members who fail to complete the scheduled program duration. e. Rates of termination from program 1. graduation (completing). 2. voluntary termination rates. f. Member Assessment: Assessment and member re-stratification process. g. Assessment practiced at the time of enrollment. h. Frequency of re-stratification.
6.	Outcomes and Reporting	a. Administrative. 1. Numbers of members identified, stratified and targeted for intervention. 2. Numbers of members reached and enrolled. 3. Numbers of members graduating from the program. b. Clinical. c. Targets for clinical improvement (see Appendix 5.1). d. Financial. 1. Generally, programs set Return on Investment as a target. However, ROI depends on the cost of a program, and for that reason, we recommend making savings rather than ROI basis of evaluation and comparison.

5.4 THE ROLE OF VALUE CHAIN COMPONENTS IN PROGRAM DESIGN AND ASSESSMENT

By adding detail to the Value Chain we define the types of expertise required to establish a successful program, as well as segmenting the activities in categories in which we would want to identify measures and metrics to determine what constitutes "success." In the area of outreach, for example, a program component is "Reach Members." A successful program will reach a high percentage of targeted members. In order to assess program success we need to have available metrics on program targeting as well as reach rates. We will also want to know the factors that make reaching members difficult, such as the percentage of members who cannot be contacted. Each component will have its own process that may be deconstructed, mapped, and evaluated. In the previous section, we listed a number of variables – some qualitative but mostly quantitative – that are useful for program evaluation and comparison.

The original Porter concept of the Value Chain was that each component of the chain added more value than its cost. Grouping services together into bundles is a first step towards allowing them to be costed, and if necessary, priced. Costing and pricing services are straightforward, but assessing their value is not easy. For example, what value does Predictive Modeling contribute to outcomes? To be able to accurately identify member risk levels with respect to a future event – from highest (those who need an intervention) to lowest (those who may be left in a maintenance mode) allows resources to be allocated more efficiently to interventions, thus reducing overall input of costly clinical resources. Even more valuable would be a predictive model that not only ranked members by risk level but over-laid the member "intervenability[3]." Yet the efficiency and effectiveness of different Predictive Models is rarely assessed in evaluating DM programs, and we have never seen evidence of cost-benefit analysis applied to the problem.

Another example of a DM function that lends itself to Value Chain analysis is Outreach. DM companies approach the function of Identification, Outreach and Enrollment differently. One model targets 100% of all chronic members for an initial assessment, with enrollment for follow-up interventions then determined by the result of the initial screening. An alternative model uses Predictive Modeling and other statistical techniques to reduce the universe of chronic members to those at highest *statistical* risk of an event, aiming to enroll all of these members. Which of these two models is more productive? Which of these models offers the greatest contribution to the overall outcome? The first alternative appears to be more costly, based on vendor pricing. Does the additional investment of effort produce sufficient return to justify its use?

Another advantage of the deconstruction of the DM process that accompanies the Value Chain approach is a focus on interventions and their objectives. The central functions of the Value Chain are the creation of intervention programs and campaigns, the process of outreach to engage and enroll the target members, and the process of member assessment and coaching. The objective of disease management is to increase member compliance with best practice care, and to change the behavior of those members who are not compliant or who practice a life-style that is not conducive to good health. This focus is important because, to

[3] Intervenability is a combination of the member condition (is the member's condition conducive to self-management with external coaching support) and member's readiness to change behavior.

produce a beneficial health and financial outcome from a program, change has to be effected. Too often, insufficient attention is paid to the fundamentals: what is the program aiming to accomplish? Is the program purely educational or is it aiming to change behavior? What behavior is it looking to change? What type of training is most effective for the nurses who perform interventions – clinical training or motivational interviewing? Is it more beneficial for a patient to remain in a regularly-scheduled program of coaching and education than allowing the patient to determine when to interact with the coach? The first alternative is clearly more resource-intensive and may prove frustrating to some members, but capitalizes on the "repetition" concept that has been the basis of educational programs for centuries. It also capitalizes on a personal approach that allows the intervention to be tailored to the individual's learning style, health literacy, motivation and preferences.

Another key area in which more definition and assessment could prove valuable is the provider-involvement model. DM programs that are offered via nurse telephonic management generally inform the patient's provider of the patient's enrollment, and sometimes of a patient's status change (risk-level). Other models aim to provide more communication to the patient's provider regarding the patient status. Alternative models exist that aim to inform the provider of deviation from clinical best practices, intending to drive change in provider as well as patient behavior. A Value Chain analysis would identify the cost and benefits of different models and attempt to determine which model produces more favorable clinical and financial patient outcomes.

Focusing on the Value Chain components allows us to identify interim measures of progress. For example, if the intervention program aims to achieve its result by increasing compliance with best-practice standards of care, these need to be enumerated and compliance measured over time. Examples of some of the typical metrics that should be tracked are provided in Appendix 5.1.

5.5 MANAGING THE INTERVENTION PROGRAM USING THE VALUE CHAIN

As the Value Chain analysis suggests, there are many significant components that need to be coordinated in implementing a program. Indeed, one of the strongest reasons to outsource an entire program to a specialist vendor is the experience of such a vendor with the coordination of these components. Attempting to obtain, train, and coordinate resources within the ongoing operational environment of a health plan, for example, is challenging. Equally challenging is the idea of obtaining services from different vendors for each Value Chain component, and integrating and coordinating the services. Whether a program is managed internally or outsourced, however, the sponsor's interest is the same: is the program focusing on the correct things, delivering services efficiently and at minimal cost, and producing the expected outcomes? For the program sponsor that is willing to take this approach, the Value Chain offers an opportunity to identify and measure the components necessary to implement a successful program. For the program sponsor that chooses to outsource a program, it is still useful to focus on this functional approach and to require that a vendor provide pricing and target metrics for program components, particularly if industry benchmarks are available with which to compare a vendor's performance.

APPENDIX 5.1 – CLINICAL PERFORMANCE MEASURES TO BE TRACKED[4]

METRIC	HEART DISEASE - DEFINITION OF METRIC
Beta-blocker post-MI*	Percentage of IHD[5] members post-MI taking beta-blockers (e.g., in the prior 6 or 12 months; or with no prescription-fill gap exceeding 14 days.)
LDL target level	Percentage of members with IHD at target LDL <100 mg/dL. (use last measure to report) (ATP-III Guideline) (Sometimes also reported in result strata, e.g., percentage with LDL < 100; 100-129; and ≥ 130.)
BP at target	Percentage of IHD members with BP <130/90[6]. (Use last measure to report) (ACC/AHA Guideline)
Antiplatelet therapy	Percentage of all IHD members taking an aspirin* or antiplatelet drug.
Fasting lipid panel	Percentage of members with IHD diagnosis who had fasting lipid panel assessed within the measurement year per ATP-III.
LDL screening*	Percentage of IHD members with LDL screening performed on or between 60 and 365 days after discharge for an acute cardiovascular event (AMI, PTCA, CABG).
LDL level*	Percentage of IHD members with LDL level <100 mg/dL on or between 60 and 365 days after discharge for an acute cardiovascular event.
ACE inhibitors/ Angiotensin Receptor blocker (ARB)	Percentage of IHD members post-MI taking ACE inhibitors or angiotensin receptor blocker (ARB) for ACEI intolerance.
Lipid-lowering agent	Percentage taking a statin, fibrate, or cholesterol-binding agent.
Screening for diabetes	Percentage of non-diabetic members with IHD and additional risk factors specified in the current American Diabetes Association guideline, who had FPG assessed.
Smoking cessation counseling*	Percentage of IHD members who were either recent quitters (within last 12 months) or current smokers who were seen by a practitioner and had received advice to quit smoking.
Smoking quit rate	Percentage of IHD members who reported smoking at the beginning of the measurement period who at the time of measurement had quit smoking.
Flu vaccination	Percentage of all IHD members who received a flu vaccination within the last 12 months.
Pneumococcal (pneumonia) vaccination*	Percentage of all IHD members who have ever received a pneumococcal vaccine.
Admission for MI	Hospital admissions per thousand IHD members for MI within the measurement period
Depression screening	Percentage of all IHD members who had a depression screening in accordance with United States Preventive Services Task Force (USPSTF)

*HEDIS Standard.

NOTE: When medications are identified as the metric, it is assumed that no contraindication exists.

[4] Members who have a clinical contraindication for any of these medications should be excluded from the evaluation.

[5] Also called CAD (Coronary Artery Disease).

[6] JNC VII standard remains 140/90 but currently under review. Use lowest appropriate BP where other diseases are present in conjunction with heart disease: e.g., diabetes and chronic kidney disease 130/80 (American Heart Association/ American College of Cardiology Guideline).

METRIC	HEART FAILURE - DEFINITION OF METRIC
ACE inhibitors/ angiotensin receptor blocker (ARB) or hydralazine/isosorbide	Percentage of members with heart failure taking ACE inhibitors or in ACE-intolerant patients taking ARBs or hydralazine/isosorbide.■
Beta-blocker	Percentage of members with heart failure taking a beta-blocker.■
BP at target	Percentage of HF members with BP <130/90[7]. (ACC/AHA Guideline)
ASA, other antiplatelet or anticoagulant	Percentage of HF members with atrial fibrillation taking warfarin, aspirin, or other antiplatelet medication.
Ventricular function	Percentage of members with heart failure having left ventricular ejection function (LVEF) documented.
Spironolactone	Percentage of members with severe (class III / IV) heart failure who are taking spironolactone.■ or eplerenone for members with gynecomastia.
Smoking quit rate	Percentage of HF members who reported smoking at the beginning of the measurement period who at the time of measurement had quit smoking.
Flu vaccination	Percentage of all HF members who received a flu vaccination within the last 12 months.
Pneumococcal (pneumonia) vaccination*	Percentage of all HF members who have ever received a pneumococcal vaccine.
Health status	Percentage of HF members who reported improvement in health status. This should be assessed using a standard validated instrument such as SF-8, -12, or -36; Minnesota Living with Heart Failure Index, or New York Heart Association status.
Effectiveness of member education	Percentage of HF members who comply with daily weights. Percentage of HF members who comply with sodium restriction. Percentage of HF members who comply with medication regimen (definition of and method for determining compliance should be stated). Percentage of HF members who have a rescue plan in place.
30-day readmit	Percentage of HF members readmitted to the hospital with a primary diagnosis of heart failure within 30 days of hospital discharge for heart failure.
Emergency department visits	Rate (number per 1000 heart failure members) of ED visits with heart failure primary diagnosis or for pulmonary edema.
Hospital admits	Rate (number per 1000 heart failure members) of hospital admissions for HF.
Depression screening	Percentage of all HF members who had a depression screening in accordance with United States Preventive Services Task Force (USPSTF).

■ Confined to systolic dysfunction.

*HEDIS Standard

NOTE: When medications are identified as the metric, it is assumed that no contraindication exists.

[7] JNC VII standard remains 140/90 but currently under review. Use lowest appropriate BP where other diseases are present in conjunction with heart disease: e.g., diabetes and chronic kidney disease 130/80 (American Heart Association/ American College of Cardiology Guideline).

METRIC	DIABETES - DEFINITION OF METRIC
Foot examination	Percentage of members with diabetes who completed one foot examination using Semmes-Weinstein monofilament, palpation of pulses and visual examination in the measurement year.
ACE inhibitors/angiotensin receptor blocker (ARB)	Percentage of diabetes members with microalbuminuria or clinical albuminuria (per ADA Guidelines) taking ACE inhibitors or ARB.
A1C level at target	Percentage of diabetes members with an A1C level ≤ 7.0% in the past year. (ADA Guideline)
LDL level at target	Percentage of diabetes members with LDL levels < 100 mg/dL within the past two measurement years. (use last measure to report) (ATP III Guideline)
BP at target	Percentage of diabetes members with BP < 130/80. (Use last measure to report) (ADA and AHA/ACC Guideline)
Dilated retinal exam*	Percentage of members with diabetes who had one examination in the measurement year.
Diabetic Nephropathy screening*	Percentage of members with diabetes who had one screening test in the measurement year or receiving treatment for existing nephropathy.
A1C	Percentage of members with diabetes who had at least two A1C tests in the measurement year.
A1C level*	Percentage of diabetes members with the most recent A1C in the past year that is > 9.0%.* (use last measure to report)
Fasting lipid panel	Percentage of members with diabetes who completed one test in the measurement year.
LDL level*	Percentage of diabetes members with LDL < 100 mg/dL (Current ADA/ACCA guideline) within the past two measurement years. (use last measure to report).
ASA	Percentage of diabetes members > 30 years of age taking an aspirin each day.
Smoking quit rate	Percentage of diabetes members who reported smoking at the beginning of the measurement period who at the time of measurement had quit smoking
Flu vaccination	Percentage of all diabetes members who received a flu vaccination within the last 12 months.
Pneumococcal (pneumonia) vaccination*	Percentage of all diabetes members who have ever received a pneumococcal vaccine.
Depression screening	Percentage of all diabetes members who had a depression screening in accordance with United States Preventive Services Task Force (USPSTF).

*HEDIS Standard

METRIC	ASTHMA - DEFINITION OF METRIC
Hospital admissions	Rates (number per 1000 asthma members): 1. Hospital admissions for asthma and 2. Hospitalizations for any cause for asthmatics (denominator defined as per 2007 DMAA guideline).
Inhaled corticosteroid use for uncontrolled asthma	Percentage of uncontrolled asthma members with one dispensed inhaled corticosteroid within 30 days of identification. Uncontrolled asthma is identified as one ED visit or one hospitalization for asthma or three or more dispensed prescriptions of short-acting beta agonists within three-month period, or $FEV_1 < 80\%$ predicted.
Smoking quit rate	Percentage of asthma members who reported smoking at the beginning of the measurement period who at the time of measurement had quit smoking.
Flu vaccination	Percentage of all asthma members who received a flu vaccination within the last 12 months.
Appropriate use of long-term control medication*	Percentage of asthma members with at least one dispensed prescription for inhaled corticosteroids, nedocromil, cromolyn sodium, leukotriene modifiers or methylxanthines in the measurement year.
Spirometry testing	Percentage of asthma members with documented spirometry testing.
Emergency department visit	Percentage of asthma members with an ED admission for asthma in the past 12 months.
Personal action plan	Percentage of asthma members with personal action plan for managing their asthma. (Self-report)

*HEDIS Standard

METRIC	COPD - DEFINITION OF METRIC
A course of systemic corticosteroids for acute exacerbation of COPD	Percentage of members with an acute exacerbation of COPD who were treated with systemic corticosteroids. (ICD-9 code 491.21).
Oxygen therapy	Percentage of members who meet CMS requirements for continuous O_2 therapy and who are receiving therapy.
Smoking quit rate	Percentage of COPD members who reported smoking at the beginning of the measurement period who at the time of measurement had quit smoking.
Flu vaccination	Percentage of all COPD members who received a flu vaccination within the last 12 months.
Spirometry testing	Percentage of members with documented spirometry testing.
Oxygen status	Percentage of COPD members with FEV_1 less than 40% predicted with documentation of oxygenation status (Oxygen saturation or blood gas).
Quality of life	Percentage of COPD members with improvement in Quality of Life (QOL)■ assessment compared to baseline. ■Examples of QOL assessments include SF12 or SF36.
30-day readmit	Percentage of COPD members readmitted to the hospital with COPD as primary diagnosis within 30 days of hospital discharge for COPD.
Pneumococcal (pneumonia) vaccination*	Percentage of all COPD members who have ever received a pneumococcal vaccine.
Depression screening	Percentage of all COPD members who had a depression screening in accordance with United States Preventive Services Task Force (USPSTF).

■ HEDIS Standard

*Duncan [52], Fettterolf [59] and Porter [166]

PART 2

ACTUARIAL ISSUES IN CARE MANAGEMENT INTERVENTIONS

6 UNDERSTANDING THE ECONOMICS OF DISEASE MANAGEMENT PROGRAMS[1]

6.1 INTRODUCTION

As managed care and health insurance organizations struggle to control their enrollees' utilization of medical resources, they seek less obtrusive and more cost-effective ways to reduce costs and improve patient outcomes. As discussed in Chapter 2, Disease Management (DM) is a widely proposed solution for cost-reduction and quality improvement. Despite the interest in DM and the number of programs that have been implemented in different health plans, the reaction to DM on the part of health insurers and other payers remains skeptical. Vendors and carriers seldom discuss their programs without claims of positive financial results, yet somehow the buyers seem unconvinced. Some of the skepticism arises because it is difficult to reconcile savings claims with health plan cost trends that seem to move inexorably upwards.

Two important meta-analyses of DM outcomes have recently been completed. In Chapter 3, we defined a meta-analysis as a re-analysis of results from comparable studies reported in the literature for the purpose of generating sufficient amounts of data to enable statistical and significance testing. The product of a meta-analysis is a summary of the reported outcomes. Weingarten et al. [209] examined over 100 studies of clinical outcomes from DM programs. David Krause's (unpublished) study [111] examined financial outcomes from a number of DM programs. The conclusions from the two meta-analyses appear to be inconsistent: the Weingarten study found a preponderance of studies that showed significant improvement in the clinical outcomes of participants in DM programs; the Krause study found little or no evidence of financial improvement to the payer. The Krause conclusion is similar to that of a Congressional Budget Office study of Disease Management Outcomes [4] which finds evidence of improvement in health outcomes, but little evidence of cost savings. Our own review of the literature as discussed in Chapter 4 resulted in a similar conclusion: there is evidence of improvement in health outcomes, but limited evidence of savings in published, peer-reviewed studies of disease management. What evidence exists is seldom from commercial applications to large populations. As we noted before, it is an axiom of the industry (even taken up by candidates for the 2008 presidential nomination) that higher quality reduces cost. The evidence for DM improving quality outcomes is stronger than the evidence of financial savings. Why is this? Why is it difficult to demonstrate the link between quality and cost improvement? What is the source of the apparent inconsistency between health outcomes and financial savings?

[1] Although this chapter discusses Disease Management programs, the techniques and methods discussed are applicable to any intervention program.

We suggest three possible causes for these inconsistent outcomes:

1. The measurement of financial outcomes is not sufficiently stable (for example, subject to variation or external factors that have been inadequately controlled), or our measurement techniques are not sufficiently sensitive to be able to detect positive financial outcomes. Chapters 7 and 8 discuss rigorous measurement methods.

2. Programs (particularly early DM programs) were either not focused on financial outcomes, or were not structured to optimize the financial outcomes. Programs were often implemented by the Medical Management Department, or were established to achieve clinical improvement. For example, many programs are designed to improve HEDIS scores or improve patient clinical outcomes. The achievement and measurement of financial outcomes was an afterthought in these early programs, so it should not be surprising that they do not produce financial results as favorable as the later programs.

3. Program sponsors do not understand the economics of DM programs and therefore do not optimize the programs for financial return.

Three factors may help to resolve the contradiction:

1. A better understanding of the economics of DM programs. This may allow those who are responsible for designing and implementing programs to set reasonable expectations.

2. More rigorous measurement of financial outcomes. We believe that the core problem with measurement is not the methodology employed to measure outcomes, since measurement methodologies are, for the most part, reasonably well understood. Rather, it is the way a methodology is applied to a particular analysis, the assumptions made and decisions taken with regard to data that will affect the outcomes. Factors that potentially influence the outcomes range from the way that claims data completion is handled to who is included in and excluded from measurement. How these issues are addressed in a study will impact the final outcomes, sometimes significantly. Chapter 12 will assess the impact of some key factors on actual outcomes, using actual health plan data.

3. Reconciliation between program savings, overall claims costs and cost increase trends. A number of issues concerning Trend, defined as the percentage change, period over period, in per member per month cost (or other metric such as inpatient hospitalizations per 1000 members per year) are addressed in Chapter 11.

Before we address the economics of DM programs and the factors that must be considered to achieve optimal financial returns, we first consider the question of the appropriate measurement of financial returns from a program.

6.2 What Is the Appropriate Financial Statistic to Measure?

Return on Investment (ROI) is the metric favored by the DM industry for reporting the value of a DM program. Unfortunately, it can be a misleading metric for many reasons, making conclusions and comparisons between programs difficult to draw. ROI is the total savings attributable to a program divided by the total cost of the program. In Appendix 6.1 we further define the components of the numerator and denominator of the ROI calculation. As we discuss in this Appendix, there is no agreement in the industry regarding the calculation of savings (numerator) or the components that should be included in cost (denominator). So comparison between program and vendor ROI measures could be misleading.

There may be divergence between *planned* and *actual* ROI as well. ROI, as defined in Appendix 6.1 is the *ex ante* or planned ROI. Planned ROI is a helpful metric to use in deciding whether to proceed with a program, or how large a program to implement, or what level of staffing is optimal for a program. The *ex post,* or actual measured ROI will be subject to the operational and stochastic factors that will cause actual ROI to diverge from the planned level. Because of definitional issues and the random variability in the components that are used in its calculation, ROI can also be misleading for comparing actual program outcomes to what was expected.

6.2.1 Return on Investment

In assessing whether to implement a DM program, the projected ROI is an appropriate metric. A DM program requires investment, and like any investment, should provide a measurable return. A health plan uses a "hurdle rate" (Minimum Rate of Return on Investment required for a viable project) against which the planned or projected return on a DM program should be assessed. This hurdle rate could be 15 percent post-tax, for example. This post-tax rate can be converted to a pre-tax rate, using the corporation's effective tax rate, as follows:

$$\text{Pre-tax Hurdle Rate} = \frac{15\%}{(1-0.35)} = 23\%$$

(assuming that institutions pay a 35 percent corporate tax rate).

Because DM outcomes are subject to uncertainty as well as statistical fluctuation, they may represent additional risk, compared with other projects that a company is assessing for investment. A risk-margin, or addition to the minimum risk-free hurdle rate, is sometimes added to the hurdle rate of return when assessing a proposed project. The pre-tax, risk-adjusted hurdle rate is unlikely to exceed 30 percent to 35 percent. A higher planned return (implying a planned ROI of greater than 1.35) results from one (or both) of two causes:

- A very high risk-margin has been used, indicating that the company estimates a high risk of the proposed project not being able to achieve the expected return due to high variation around the expected return; or
- The project has been planned to a sub-optimal scope. Because of the diminishing returns of additional interventions and penetration into the population, penetration at only the highest risk-level in a population returns high savings relative to cost. As penetration increases, additional interventions could be performed that increase savings, but at a decreasing rate. As long as penetration can be increased at a marginal return greater than the hurdle rate, absolute savings can be increased while maintaining an average return above the hurdle rate, implying that unexploited savings opportunities exist.

In the early years of DM, reported returns of multiples of fees (5 times, six times or even more) which translate into ROI measures of 500% or more were claimed (proudly) by vendors and those who promoted programs in health plans. (These claims appeared even more unrealistic when they were reported in the first year of a program, despite the length of time required to implement a program, enroll members, and change their behavior.) More recently, the industry has reduced its claimed returns to lower levels (returns between 1.0 and 2.0 times fees, or ROI of 100% to 200% are now more usual, particularly in the first year of a program). The tendency of the industry to report total returns as multiples of fees makes it more difficult to comprehend what is being claimed, but a 2 to 1 ROI, if correctly measured, implies a return, over and above the cost of the program, of 100% of fees. This is clearly a sub-optimal program in a plan with a hurdle rate of 15% (post-tax), because the plan should be investing more dollars in DM. Faced with two investment opportunities – a DM program with a return of 100% above program cost, and an alternative investment with a return of 15% above cost, the profit-maximizing health plan should be moving resources from the lower-yielding investment into DM.

6.2.2 Total Savings Measures

Although both DM organizations and health plans focus discussion on ROI, a more important measure to a health plan is total savings. After all, if a plan achieves a high ROI but manages only 100 members, the total savings will have negligible impact on health plan trend, and probably will not cover the fixed costs of implementation. Total savings is the appropriate bottom-line measure for the health plan to aim to achieve.

A further distinction needs to be made between marginal and average savings. Average savings (which equals total savings net of program cost, divided by the total population) tells the sponsor how profitable a program is overall. Marginal savings (the increase in savings net of program cost due to intervention on the marginal population, divided by the number of members of the marginal population) is critical for deciding what kind of program to implement, how large it should be, and whether the marginal intervention is economically justifiable.

In the following example, the use of ROI as a measure suggests that Program 1 is the better investment. Use of net savings as the basis of comparison suggests that ROI is a misleading measure, and that the health plan is better off investing in Program 2.

TABLE 6.1

	Program 1	Program 2
Number of health plan Members	10,000	10,000
Number of Chronic Members	100	500
Annual Cost	$50,000	$250,000
Annual Gross Savings	$150,000	$400,000
ROI	3.0	1.6
PMPM[2] (net)	$0.83	$1.25

[2] Per member per month. Per chronic member per month is abbreviated as PCMPM. Per member per year is abbreviated as PMPY.

Using the information from Table 6.1, Table 6.2 illustrates the calculation of the terms Average Savings and Marginal Savings.

TABLE 6.2

	Program 1	Program 2
Average Net Savings	$\frac{150,000-50,000}{10,000}$ = \$0.83 PMPM	$\frac{400,000-250,000}{10,000}$ = \$1.25 PMPM
Average Net Savings per chronic member per month	$\frac{150,000-50,000}{100}$ = \$83.33 PMPM	$\frac{400,000-250,000}{500}$ = \$25.00 PMPM
Marginal Net Savings per chronic member per month: first 100 members	$\frac{150,000-50,000}{100}$ = \$83.33 PMPM	$\frac{150,000-50,000}{100}$ = \$83.33 PMPM
Marginal Net Savings per chronic member per month: next 400 members		$\frac{250,000-200,000}{400}$ = \$10.42 PMPM

It is generally impossible to determine whether high reported ROI results are the consequence of high savings, low costs (either because of DM organization efficiency or because of failure to include all costs), sub-optimal program design or random fluctuation. Savings measured on a per member (or per chronic member) per month basis may provide more insight into program value than does an ROI measure.

Reporting savings on a per-health plan member per month basis allows us to determine whether a program delivers meaningful savings (absolutely or on a per member per month basis). Actuaries and others responsible for the financial management of a health plan, monitor health cost trend as a key metric for whether the plan is able to control its costs. For a program to be of value to financial management, it must contribute positively to the control of health care trend. An absolute level of savings that is significant (relative to the underlying claims cost of the health plan) will positively impact trend, and may be worth pursuing—provided its cost and expected variability of outcomes are not excessive. This is the point at which cost-benefit analysis, or ROI calculation, becomes meaningful.

6.3 THE RISK MANAGEMENT ECONOMIC MODEL

In order to achieve the optimal financial measures, a Risk Management Economic Model can be constructed to examine the link between DM program risk, cost, and savings. We refer to this as the Risk Management Economic Model because it is not limited to DM and can be applied to any area of medical management. It is particularly well suited to the broad populations included in DM. We will next define the model, discuss the considerations and metrics for designing the Model, and examine the factors of DM programs that impact financial outcomes.

The Risk Management Economic Model was developed to help program sponsors and vendors of programs understand the interaction between risk level, program cost and potential savings. The model aims to achieve several practical goals. It has been successfully used in a number of practical client situations to understand the economics of DM programs, develop a common framework for use in discussions of programs and their economics, understand contribution of different factors that influence economic outcomes, as well as to plan the scope of a program. In addition, the Risk Management Economic Model helps to facilitate discussion of the distribution of member-risk.

The model depends, fundamentally, on the fact that risk is highly variable within a population. Members evidence different degrees of risk at a point of time, as well as from period to period. Table 6.3 below illustrates this, using population data.

TABLE 6.3

Example of Pareto Principle in Healthcare Claims

	Population Distribution				
Population Cohort	0.0% - 0.5%	0.5% - 1.0%	0.0% - 1.0%[3]	Top 5%	TOTAL
Number	67,688	67,688	135,376	676,881	13,537,600
Total Cost ($'000)	$ 3,204,434	$ 1,419,804	$ 4,624,238	$ 9,680,580	$21,973,586
Average PMPM Cost	$ 47,341	$ 20,976	$ 34,158	$ 14,302	$ 1,623
% of Total Cost	14.6%	6.5%	21.0%	44.1%	100.0%

This table, with data drawn from a large commercial healthplan database, illustrates the well-known concept (sometimes referred to as the Pareto Principle) that a small percentage of any population accounts for a disproportionately high percentage of expense. The highest-cost 0.5% of the population account for 14.6% of total cost, while the next highest-cost 0.5% account for less than half of the cost of the highest-cost cohort – on average, they cost $20,976 compared with the highest-cost cohort's $47,341. As we see, the marginal cost of additional members or groups of members declines quite rapidly from the highest cost. Although it is not illustrated here, the lowest-cost cohort consists of a large number of members who cost very little.

When planning a DM program, historical costs (such as those in Table 6.3), while interesting, are not as useful as *predicted* cost. While there is a certain amount of consistency in costs between time periods, a large percentage of a population transition from one cohort to another, from year to year. Table 6.4 illustrates this concept, using data from a different commercial health plan. In this table we see how member status changes as members transition from their Historic Period status to their status in the Projection Period. Some 28% of the highest cost group's members continue to be in the highest risk group in the next period. 46% of the high-cost cohort's members fall to the intermediate group, and 26% fall to the lowest-cost cohort. Predictive modeling plays a key role in the process of being able to predict which members will fall into which cohort. Analyzed slightly differently, a predictive model will assign a probability of a particular outcome to groups of members.

[3] The shaded column summarizes the two columns to the left.

TABLE 6.4

Transition Between Risk Levels over Time[4]				
	Distribution of Members and Claims Projection Period			
Historic Period Group	Historic Period Cost	$0 - $2	$2 - $25	$25+
$0 - $2 87%	$ 324	$ 327 90% 90%	$ 5,368 10% 64%	$ 46,836 0% 40%
$2 - $25 12%	$ 5,658	$ 668 55% 10%	$ 6,599 40% 34%	$ 47,811 40% 40%
$25+ 1%	$ 49,032	$ 847 26% 0%	$ 9,609 46% 2%	$ 58,489 28% 20%
TOTAL	$ 1,230	$ 355	$ 5,851	$ 49,377

In Figure 6.1, we illustrate the concept of the "decreasing risk – increasing population penetration" trade-off. Using a predictive model, we rank members of a population according to their probability of having a hospital admission in the next 6 to 12 months. In this example, we apply the principle illustrated in Table 6.1 to the entire population.

Probabilities in Figure 6.1 are presented on a cumulative basis. Thus the top 0.2% of the population (or in a population of 50,000, the 100 members predicted to have the highest cost) has approximately 70% probability of experiencing an admission (that is, of the 100 members in this cohort, we predict that approximately 70 will experience an admission). As we have discussed previously we would expect the cumulative probability of an admission to fall quickly as we move down the risk curve, as indeed it does. The highest risk 1% of the population (or 500 out of a population of 50,000) has a probability of an admission of only 40%.

Decreasing Risk with Increased Population Penetration

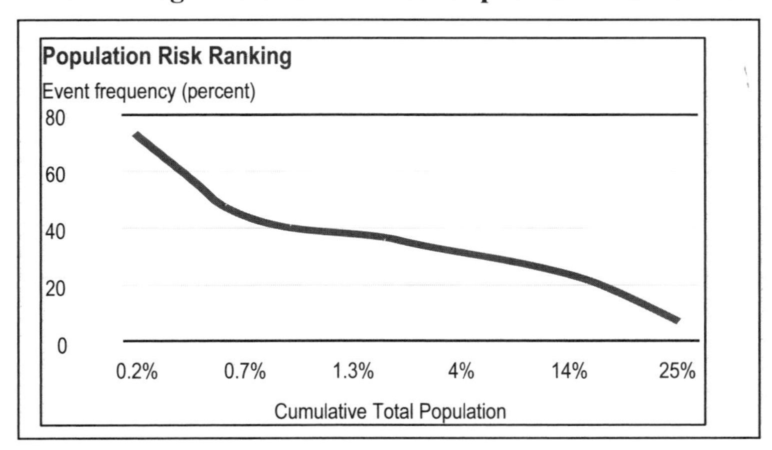

FIGURE 6.1

[4] In this table, unshaded percentages represent the distribution of the population in that row (the historic period group); the shaded percentages represent the distribution of the population in the column (the projection period group).

Table 6.5 below shows an application of the key concepts in the Risk Management Economic Model:

- Risk varies within populations as well as over time;
- Patients can move between risk categories; and
- A small percentage of the population will account for a disproportionately large percentage of expense.

This model applies the population risk ranking, in combination with various assumptions about the expected event rate, cost per event, and program effectiveness (events avoided) achieved by the DM program, at different penetration levels. The DM economic model provides a systematic way of quantifying the potential for gross and net savings at different points in the risk distribution.

This example includes both fixed and variable costs. Because of the fixed costs, ROI initially rises, and then falls, as the marginal cost of additional interventions is greater than the marginal savings achievable from those interventions. A graphical example of the effect of penetration of a population by risk-rank on savings is shown in Figure 6.2.

TABLE 6.5[5]:

Application of the Risk Management Economic Model to the Analysis of Inpatient Admission Events

Penetration %	No. of members (Cumulative)	Event Rate	Expected Events	Cost/ Event	Events Avoided	Gross Savings	Cumulative Gross Savings	Cumulative Expenses	Cumulative Net Savings	ROI
2%	18	75.0%	13	$30,000	40%	$159,763	$ 159,763	262,130	(102,367)	0.61
7%	68	55.0%	37	27,000	33%	332,01	491,779	437,130	54,649	1.13
12%	118	45.0%	53	25,000	25%	331,176	822,955	612,130	210,825	1.34
17%	168	40.0%	67	22,000	20%	295,243	1,118,198	787,130	331,068	1.42
22%	218	33.0%	72	17,000	15%	183,238	1,301,436	962,130	339,306	1.35
27%	268	30.0%	80	15,000	15%	180,732	1,482,168	1,137,130	345,038	1.30
32%	318	25.0%	79	12,000	15%	142,988	1,625,156	1,312,130	313,026	1.24
37%	368	22.0%	81	10,000	15%	121,358	1,746,514	1,487,130	259,384	1.17
42%	418	18.0%	75	9,500	15%	107,153	1,853,668	1,662,130	191,537	1.12
47%	468	16.5%	77	9,000	15%	104,192	1,957,859	1,837,130	120,739	1.07
52%	518	15.4%	80	8,500	15%	101,661	2,059,520	2,012,130	47,390	0.02
57%	568	13.6%	76	8,250	15%	93,445	2,152,965	2,187,130	(34,166)	0.98
62%	618	12.5%	77	8,000	15%	92,663	2,245,627	2,362,130	(116,503)	0.95
67%	668	10.6%	71	7,750	15%	82,284	2,327,911	2,537,130	(209,219)	0.92
72%	718	9.0%	65	7,500	15%	72,672	2,400,583	2,712,130	(311,547)	0.89
77%	768	8.3%	64	7,250	15%	69,299	2,469,882	2,887,130	(417,248)	0.86
82%	818	7.9%	65	7,000	15%	67,832	2,537,715	3,062,130	(524,415)	0.83
87%	868	7.5%	65	6,750	15%	65,895	2,603,610	3,237,130	(633,520)	0.80
92%	918	7.3%	67	6,500	15%	65,321	2,668,931	3,412,130	(743,199)	0.78
97%	968	7.1%	69	6,250	15%	64,416	2,733,347	3,587,130	(853,783)	0.76
100%	1,000	7.0%	70	6,000	15%	63,000	2,796,347	3,700,130	(903,653)	0.76

[5] Hypothetical data for illustrative purposes.

6.4 DESIGNING A PROGRAM

A more sophisticated Risk Management Economic Model would include details of different types of interventions, as well as different utilization (drug therapy, outpatient, and Emergency Room utilization, for example). Applied to an entire population, the Risk Management Economic Model allows the user to test the sensitivity of the return from different types of interventions, at different penetration levels in the population. The results may be summarized graphically in a form similar to Figure 6.2. The design of the proposed program will affect the economics through both inputs and results. The Risk Management Economic Model provides a way for users to recognize different factors that influence the economic outcomes. Program metrics that should be explicitly recognized include:

- The number and risk-intensity of members to be targeted. The number of target members is important because without critical mass, a program will not achieve sufficient savings to justify its implementation. As Table 6.3 shows, not all members are equally likely to experience adverse events, and a point is reached at which targeting more members with a costly, nurse-based program will not be economic.
- Types of interventions to be used in the program, such as mail, automated outbound dialing, or outreach through physician offices. Some interventions are less personalized, but may still be successful at reaching some members and having an effect on behavior. Some interventions are more appropriately targeted at some populations (for example, mail reminders to lower-risk populations). A successful program will combine multiple interventions of different types, cost-structures, and results.
- The number of nurses and other staff required to deliver the program and their cost, and other program costs (such as materials, data processing, or equipment). One fact of life in these programs is that clinical staff are costly and can only manage a relatively small patient load. For example, if we assume that the fully-loaded annual cost (including salary, benefits and other indirect staffing costs) of a nurse is $100,000, and 200 is the caseload that can be managed by a telephonic intervention nurse at one time, the annual cost of the nurse component is $500 per member managed. Assuming further that the frequency of events in the managed population is 25 percent and that nurses manage to avoid 25 percent of these events, this implies a nurse cost of $8,000 per member whose event is avoided. This amount is significant, compared to the cost of the hospital admission that is avoided. Some proponents of programs look for savings in areas other than hospital admissions and these may be obtained (for example, in Emergency Room visits). Since the objective of many programs is increased compliance with physician-ordered treatments, we would expect increased physician, lab test, and pharmaceutical drug costs to result. The largest component of program savings is achieved through reduced hospital admissions and length-of-stay. It is a good idea to look at the admissions experience and costs of the target population, since this, effectively, is the base of expense that any program can affect.
- The methodology for contacting and engaging or enrolling members (telephone, provider, internet, mail, etc.). The methodology for reaching and engaging members is critical. Each method has its own cost structure and statistical outcomes in terms of the engagement rates (and behavior change) achieved. Encouraging a member, over the telephone, to participate in a program aimed at changing behavior is difficult. (Think about the analogous problem of persuading the member to change his long distance carrier or credit-card company with a telephone call.) Unpublished research

by Duncan indicates that those members who are more likely to participate in such a program tend to be those who have lower event rates and costs, while the higher utilizers tend to have lower participation rates. Mail programs have low participation rates, while telephonic programs have higher rates, particularly when the caller is a nurse. Unfortunately this is an area in which there is little published data (in part because companies consider their results to be proprietary, and in part because of a lack of consistent definition in the terms eligible, engaged, etc.) The economic model needs to include very specific assumptions and data for the number of members targeted, the number reached, allowing for data issues like incorrect or outdated telephone numbers, members with caller ID who will not accept a call, and the number enrolling or engaging in the program.

- The rules for integrating the program with the rest of the care management system. DM programs can refer (triage) members elsewhere for services and accept members who are identified elsewhere, due for example, to provider referral. As we discussed earlier, clinical resources are costly and cases should be referred to the appropriate level of management quickly and cost-efficiently. This includes members who, because they are controlling their own conditions or who clearly are not ready to comply, need to be referred to a lower-cost, "maintenance" program.
- The timing and numbers of program members to be contacted, contacts, engagements and interventions.
- The predicted behavior of the target population, absent intervention and the predicted effectiveness of the intervention at modifying that behavior. In particular, if the program is designed to reduce medical admissions among the target population, how successful is the program at reducing this admission rate?

The Risk Management Economic Model illustrates the fact of decreasing returns to intervention in a population, as well as the choice of an "optimal" level of penetration, given the availability and cost of resources. The underlying data are shown in Table 6.5. Figure 6.2 shows this data in graphical form, where the gross and net savings and program cost levels are compared with the level of penetration (percentage of population targeted) by quintile.

Illustration of the Application of the Risk Management Economic Model

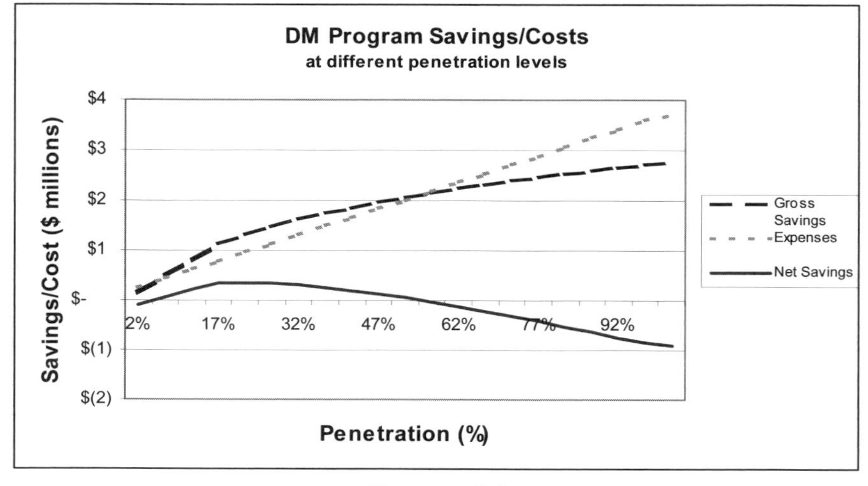

FIGURE 6.2

Figure 6.2 illustrates how the decreasing event rate curve can be combined with a cost per event and an assumed behavior change rate (or estimate of events avoided as a result of the intervention) to produce an increasing "opportunity" curve. The opportunity curve increases monotonically, but at a decreasing rate, reflecting the declining event rate with increased population penetration. Assuming that intervention costs increase linearly, we can calculate the difference (or savings) at different levels of penetration. Combining savings with the cost of the intervention we produce an ROI curve (Figure 6.3) for different levels of penetration into the population. In this example, maximum ROI is achieved with a penetration of 17 percent of the population (1.42), while maximum net savings (shown in Table 6.5) is achieved at 27 percent penetration (1.30). If the health plan has a hurdle rate of 1.35, the optimal program would be achieved at a 22 percent penetration rate (1.35). (Lower penetration results in lower absolute dollars; higher penetration results in less than the required rate of return on investment.)

ROI at Different Levels of Population Penetration

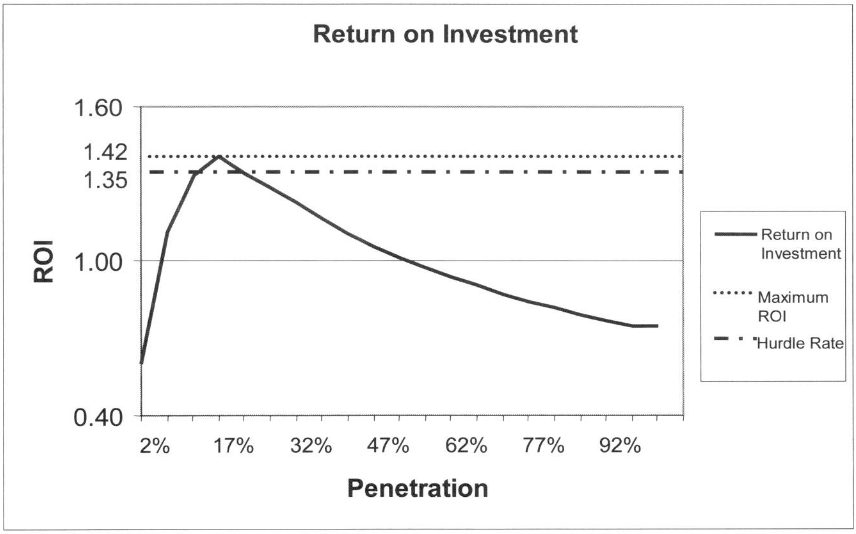

FIGURE 6.3

This simple approach to DM economics ignores many variables such as health plan member turnover, timing (of interventions and events), termination from the DM program, different types of interventions, etc. Nevertheless, understanding the simple model will provide a basis for assessing and discussing more sophisticated structures.

6.5 COMPONENTS OF THE RISK MANAGEMENT ECONOMIC MODEL

A number of factors interact in contributing to financial outcomes of DM programs. We now discuss these factors in more detail.

6.5.1 Prevalence of Different Chronic Diseases

Disease management usually addresses five chronic diseases:

- Ischemic Heart Disease
- Heart Failure
- Chronic Obstructive Pulmonary Disease (COPD)
- Asthma
- Diabetes

For a younger population (such as the commercial members of a health plan), the prevalence of these five conditions is relatively low (rarely more than 5 percent to 6 percent, when double-counting of members with more than one disease is excluded). Prevalence of chronic disease within an older population is much higher. Approximately one-third of Medicare members, for example, will have one or more of these conditions. In a Medicaid population it is not always possible to predict prevalence (or membership) accurately because some Medicaid populations have less stable contact with the health insurance system. Chronic conditions will differ according to the "type" of Medicaid member included. Dual eligibles (Medicare members who are also eligible for Medicaid based on income) will have prevalence similar to Medicare; "CHIP" or child health program participants have high prevalence of asthma; and the disabled population will have a higher prevalence of all conditions than is typical in the commercial age group.

6.5.2 Chronic Disease Cost

Chronic diseases are important financially because of both the prevalence and cost of the diseases. See Chapter 11 for a discussion of the cost of chronic disease.

6.5.3 Payer Risk

While prevalence is important, it needs to be related to the financial risk imposed by the affected patients. A health plan is clearly at risk for commercial patients, as well as any Medicare + Choice (now Medicare Advantage) programs that it offers. An employer, on the other hand, does not assume risk except on a supplemental basis for chronic Medicare patients. Therefore, chronic management programs will benefit health plans financially, but the major portion of the benefit will accrue to Centers for Medicare and Medicaid Services (CMS), not the employer.

6.5.4 Targeting and Risk

The identification and prioritization of target members, and association of different outreach campaigns with member cohorts, is at the heart of the Risk Management Economic Model. With many different programs and interventions possible, it is difficult to prioritize the target members and the programs addressed to them. A necessary component of prioritization is a uniform risk-ranking of the population. An example of such a risk distribution or risk-ranking was shown in Table 6.5. Members are ranked according to their predicted probability of experiencing the "targeted event." In this example, the "targeted event" is an inpatient admission, although any type of utilization may be predicted, such as Emergency Room use, Specialist Visits, or costs in excess of a threshold.

Different programs and health plans rank members differently. For example, some DM companies use a High, Moderate, Low ranking system (in which members with similar risk ranks are grouped into three categories). Other companies may rank by decile. In Table 6.5, we use a more detailed ranking system (quintiles). The highest-risk 2 percent of members have an expected event rate of 75 percent, approximately 10 times the expected event rate for the group as a whole. As a practical matter, a uniform measure of risk is also important. If, for example, members were risk ranked according to two different sets of criteria (for example, by a predictive model that predicted their probability of a hospital admission, and also by a model that predicted risk based on clinical factors such as "gaps in care," or clinical markers observed to be missing on the clinical record) it would still be necessary to find a uniform method of ranking members in order to determine where to assign intervention resources.

6.5.5 Estimated Event Cost

In Table 6.5, which is an analysis of admissions events, the cost per event refers to cost per admission. While the frequency of this event is the primary driver of the financial outcomes, the cost per event is also important; higher cost per event should create more opportunity for savings, provided the events are preventable.

6.5.6 Contact Rate

This is the rate at which the DM company is able to actually make telephonic contact with targeted members.

6.5.7 Engagement Rate

Also called the enrollment rate, this is the rate at which members are selected for ongoing coaching and management. The actual activity between disease management staff and patients consists of evaluation, education and "coaching" or encouragement of the member to change behavior and take better care of the condition. The engagement rate will be less than 100 percent because nurses who assess members will find members with non-intervenable conditions or members with good member self-management skills, none of whom will be good candidates for enrollment in an ongoing DM program.

6.5.8 Member Re-stratification Rates

"Stratification" refers to the process of assigning a risk rank to an individual member. Initially, the risk rank is based solely on claims data available to the health plan, and is therefore objective. The nurse interacts with the member, allowing the risk ranking to be varied subjectively, based on the nurse's assessment of risk factors, as presented in Table 6.6.

TABLE 6.6

Subjective Re-stratification factors	
Factor	**Effect on Re-stratification**
Accuracy of diagnosis	Did the identification algorithm correctly identify the member's conditions?
Risk factors	Risk factors may include gaps such as absent prescriptions or tests, potential drug interactions, or a pattern of sporadic prescription refills. If the claims history identifies gaps in prescription refills, for example, was this due to the member failing to fill the prescription, or because the member obtained the drugs from the VA hospital or Canada? Another source of prescription fills that is not captured in the claims system is the increasing use of chains (Wal-Mart, CVS, for example) that offer an array of generic prescriptions for a $4 or $10 co-pay.
Intervenability of condition(s)	Chronic conditions such as heart failure or diabetes are highly intervenable, because members may be educated to attend to their own conditions. Other conditions-- some cancers for example– are not as amenable to the methods of DM.
Receptivity/Readiness to change	Members, particularly those who have had a recent hospitalization, are ready to take charge of their health care, while others may not be ready to change behavior.
Self-management skills	Because risk rank is initially identified from claims, some members will have a high risk ranking, even though they are well aware of their condition and its control, and do the "right thing," such as having regular check-ups and ordering regular prescription refills. Based on the nurse's interaction with the member, members who are inaccurately diagnosed, or who are good at managing their own conditions will be re-stratified with a lower risk rank, while members with a lower risk rank, who indicate problems in these areas, will be assigned a higher rank as a result of the nurse interaction.

6.6 CONCLUSION

Optimizing ROI and Total Savings can result in different program designs. Yet a different program design may also be required if the objective is to optimize clinical outcomes. Because there are many parties involved in implementing a DM program, it is possible that a single, compromise design will be selected in a particular client situation that optimizes no single objective – achieving adequate ROI without maximizing it, for example—in favor of higher penetration and higher clinical scores. What is important is that all professionals understand the factors that influence the *financial* outcomes, and how those results are affected by the choice of program design, and the specific values of those variables in a particular health plan situation.

APPENDIX 6.1: CALCULATING RETURN ON INVESTMENT

Definitions

Savings: The estimated reduction in health care claims costs due to the program or intervention being evaluated.

Cost: The economic value of resources committed to the program or intervention being evaluated.

ROI: $$\frac{\text{Total Savings Attributable to the Program}}{\text{Total Program Cost}}$$

In other financial applications, rate of return is generally expressed on a Net basis (i.e. as the difference between gross savings and cost, divided by the cost of the program). In Disease Management applications it is traditional to express the rate of return in gross terms, that is, as gross savings divided by cost. It is important when quoting an ROI that the user of this information clearly define and understand the basis of the calculation.

Rate of Return on Investment (i) is found by solving for i in the following expression:

$$i = \sum_{t=1}^{n} \frac{S_t}{(1+i)^t} = \sum_{t=1}^{n} \frac{C_t}{(1+i)^t}$$

where:

Measurement or Evaluation period $= n$ (may be greater than or less than 1 year). When the period of measurement is not one year, adjustments should be made to the formula. This expression applies equally when $t < 1$, although the validity of results becomes increasingly less reliable when $t < 1$.

The following two terms are defined in greater detail below.

$S_t =$ Savings attributable to the program in year t
$C_t =$ Cost of the program attributable to Year t

CALCULATION OF TERMS

Program Cost (denominator): There is no single agreed definition in the industry for program costs, with variation often centering on the treatment of internal or indirect costs. Generally, in a program evaluation exercise, total costs should include:

- Direct costs (salaries of internal staff; vendor fees);
- Indirect costs of internal support activities, such as Information Systems, mail and printing, medical director involvement etc.;

- Management costs: costs of internal management involvement, including program management, medical management and financial management;
- Overhead and other allocated costs: generally, expenses allocated to internal resources for overhead such as rent, employee benefits, senior management load, etc.
- "Set-up" costs: one-time expenses that are incurred prior to and coincident with the start of a program. The formula above, which discounts the pattern of future emerging savings, can accommodate set-up costs as an element of total costs without further adjustment.

Savings Due to the Program (numerator)

Savings (Medical Cost Savings) result from decreased health care resource utilization, in turn resulting from the beneficial effects of a DM program or intervention. Savings are usually calculated (rather than being observed directly) in the reconciliation process, and in turn may form part of an ROI calculation.

Because we are attempting to measure something that has *not* occurred (as a result of the intervention), savings usually cannot be measured directly and, instead, are inferred or estimated from other observations. A robust study design is crucial to the derivation of the observations that are used in the savings calculation. In Chapters 7 and 8, we discuss at length different methods for estimating savings.

Example of a Savings Calculation:

The following is an example of a savings calculation using the actuarially adjusted (or Trended) historical control group methodology. This example has been simplified to illustrate the method (the calculation is limited to a single service category, inpatient admissions only).

This particular example is a Medicare population. The chronic prevalence (33.3 percent) and number of admissions per 1,000 per year (600) are typical of chronic Medicare-eligible populations. Both of these statistics will be lower for Commercial populations, although the principles illustrated here will apply equally to any population.

Basic data:

	Baseline Period	**Measurement Period**
Period	1/1/2001- 12/31/2001	1/1/2002 - 12/31/2002
Average total population	150,000	150,000
Average chronic population	50,000	50,000
Chronic Member months	600,000	600,000
Chronic population Inpatient Admissions	30,000	28,800
Chronic population Inpatient admissions/1000/ year	600.0	576.0
Cost/admission	$7,500	$8,000
Utilization (admission) trend	–	5.3%

Calculation:

Estimated Savings due to Averted Admissions =

$\frac{\text{Baseline Admissions}}{1000} \times$ Utilization Trend	600.0×1.053	= 631.8
Minus: $\frac{\text{Actual Admissions}}{1000}\,yr$		576.0
Equals $\frac{\text{Reduced Admissions}}{1000}\,yr$		55.8
Multiplied by: $\frac{\text{Actual Member Years in Measurement Period}}{1000}$		50.0
Total Reduced Adminssions		2,790.0
Multiplied by: $\frac{\text{TrendedUnitCost}}{\text{Admissions}}$		$ 8,000
Estimated Savings due to Averted Admissions		$22,320,000

In this case, savings are generated by those (estimated) admissions that have not occurred in the observed population, post-intervention. Any estimated savings numbers should be carefully reviewed and reconciled to the underlying expenses of the population. Savings may, accordingly, be expressed in terms of total dollars, dollars per member per month, dollars per chronic member per month, or dollars per chronic member enrolled in a program.

Measurement of both costs and benefits requires a measurement period during which these quantities are calculated. The two periods (cost measurement period and benefit measurement period) need not be of the same duration. Start-up costs, for example are typically incurred prior to the beginning of enrollment and well before the emergence of savings from interventions. Because costs are incurred differently in different time periods, costs may be "annualized" and, for example, start-up costs may be amortized over the life of the program.

7 MEASURING DISEASE MANAGEMENT SAVINGS OUTCOMES

7.1 INTRODUCTION

Controversy over Disease Management outcomes has been part of the industry since its inception. Many authors and researchers have struggled to find a suitable methodology that will give results that are credible, reasonable and acceptable to purchasers. Examples of discussions of general methodological principles for ensuring validity in Disease Management savings outcomes measurement may be found in several papers[1]. More recently the industry trade association, Disease Management Association of America (DMAA) has assembled a number of workgroups of industry experts to address methodological issues, resulting in the publication of three "Outcomes Measurement Guidelines" [154], [155], and [155a]. Several of these references, in addition to discussing measurement principles, provide lists of different study types and designs. This Chapter will address both the theory of measurement design, and provide a practical evaluation of the most common designs for the practitioner.

7.2 EVALUATING A SAVINGS CALCULATION

The actuary may not always have the chance to design a measurement study, and will more frequently be called in to evaluate a vendor's or colleague's results. Of utmost importance is confidence in the validity of the study. Validity is important in research and in commercial applications because it gives an indication of how well a particular study addresses the nature and meaning of the variables involved in the research, and how much reliance may be placed on the results. Internal validity relates to whether the results of the study can be ascribed to the actions taken or whether they are the result of other factors. External validity asks whether the results of a study are reproducible and can be generalized to other populations or settings.

Three questions should be considered when evaluating results:

1. Has the measurement been performed according to a valid methodology?
2. How has that methodology been applied in practice? In other words what assumptions, adjustments and calculation processes have been used to prepare the results?
3. Are the results arithmetically correct? Have data processing, arithmetic or calculation errors been made in the preparation of results?

---

[1] See Wilson & MacDowell [219], Wilson et al. [218], Fetterolf et al. [58], Linden et al. [120], Fitzner et al. [62], and Flynn et al. [64].

This chapter addresses the first issue, namely the assessment of the validity of the methodology. Later chapters provide insight into the second issue of practical application. Audits of actual calculations are, however, beyond the scope of this book. With regard to the third point, calculations may be audited or a parallel test may be performed in which the results of the study are reproduced, in order to confirm that results have been correctly prepared. We assume readers will be able to perform audits to validate the calculations, or, if necessary, a parallel test (although the latter is often highly resource-intensive).

Evaluation requires two concepts defined previously – Causality (see Chapter 3.3.1) and Methodology (see Chapter 3.3.2).

7.3 PRINCIPLES OF MEASUREMENT DESIGN: WHAT CONSTITUTES A VALID METHODOLOGY?

Evaluation of a methodology is a different problem than the evaluation of the results of a study. The former is a question of conformance to evaluation principles, while in the latter case we evaluate whether or not the author's hypothesis is rejected. This chapter is not intended to be a review of the statistical principles of hypothesis testing, but a brief summary is provided in Appendix 7.1.

Whether designing a study from scratch, or evaluating a published study, the same principles determine whether a methodology is likely to be judged acceptable. The principles below are discussed in Chapter 3.

In addition to the requirement for scientific rigor that is necessary for an academic study, commercial purchasers of DM are likely to have additional requirements.

- The methodology must be one that a purchaser (or its consultant) is familiar with, or at least can grasp readily, and that should be perceived in the market-place as sound;
- The methodology must be documented in sufficient detail for another practitioner to replicate the study, and, if required, allow the client to be able to replicate the savings estimates themselves (or at least major components of the calculation);
- The results of the application of the methodology must be consistent with the client's savings expectations, and plausible overall;
- The application should lead to stable results over time and between clients, with differences between different studies and clients that can be explained; and
- The methodology must be practical, that is, it must be possible to implement it cost-effectively, without significant commitment of resources relative to the potential benefit being measured.

7.4 STUDY DESIGNS FOR DM: A SUMMARY

Many of the methodological differences in published studies that calculate savings are the result of the application of different methods of addressing population equivalence. As we survey methodologies, we find it useful to group those with similar characteristics together. So, for example, methods in the Control Group category have in common that they set up a control group; they differ in the way equivalence is achieved between the intervention and reference populations. Our groupings are differentiated by whether or not they incorporate an experimental control or reference group, or use primarily statistical methods for their conclusions. We believe that it is useful to identify similarities and differences this way; other evaluations of methodologies, for example that in DMAA's *Program Evaluation Guide,* simply list methodologies, leaving the reader to determine how each methodology differs from the others. But, as noted above, there is no single, agreed classification in the industry. Our view is that most major methodologies encountered in the literature or in practical commercial analyses may be mapped into the following three classes:

- Control Group Methods
- Population Methods without control groups
- Statistical Methods

7.4.1 Control Group Methods

Control Group methods are those that attempt to match the study subjects with other subjects that are not part of the study. They generally rate higher than other methods in terms of validity, scientific rigor and replicability. The "matching" that takes place in these methods can be random (that is, subjects are selected randomly from the same population) or non-random. (We describe several non-random control groups below.) These methods also have high market acceptance, because it is simple to understand how the methods achieve equivalence. Except for random fluctuations, two large enough samples drawn from the same population will exhibit the same risk factors.

A control group may be:

- *Randomized* (comparing equivalent samples drawn randomly from the same population). It is important that randomization be performed prior to any interventions, if the results are to be generalizable to the population from which the groups are drawn. Equivalence between the intervention and control groups is also not assured and should be demonstrated. This methodology is encountered more in academic than commercial studies, although the new Medicare Chronic Care Improvement Program requires randomized evaluation in large-scale implementations, so it may become more prevalent commercially.

- *Geographic* (comparing equivalent populations in two different locations). Unlike randomized controls, in which the control group is subject to the same forces as the intervention group, the risk profile and market forces present in different geographies may cause differences that obscure ("confound") the true difference in the intervention and reference populations. In many cases, these differences may be anticipated and adjustments made in the study. See, for example, "Actuarial Adjustment" in *Dictionary of DM Terminology*, Duncan [51]. This adjustment is easier to make when there is no dynamic effect on the reference population over time.

Consider the following example:

TABLE 7.1

Application of Actuarial Adjustment to a Reference Population		
	Claims Per Member Per Month	
	Reference Population	Intervention Population
Baseline Period Cost	$90	$100
Intervention Period Cost	$105	$102

In this example, (assuming that the Intervention Population represents a population before and after the implementation of a program) there appear initially to be no savings: costs increased by $2 PMPM between the Baseline and Intervention periods. This result is due to the confounding effect of healthcare cost trend. Comparison with the Reference Population experience shows that trend at the rate of 16.7% was present in the Reference Population. The obvious adjustment to the Intervention population data is to multiply the Intervention period cost by $100/$90, or $\$105 \times 1.11 = \$116.67$. Then the estimated savings from the intervention would be: $\$116.67 - \$102.00$ or $14.67.

This savings estimate may, however, be subject to forces that impact the two populations in the intervention period differently (for example, benefit design changes or changes in provider contracts), something that should be further explored before the results are accepted.

- *Temporal* (also known as the Historical Control Design). This design compares equivalent samples drawn from the same population before and after the intervention program. This is the most common approach used in the Disease Management industry, and uses a medical Trend adjuster to project the historical experience to the same time period as the intervention data.

- *The Product Control Methodology* compares samples drawn from the same population at the same point in time, but differentiating between members who have different products, such as HMO vs. PPO, or indemnity vs. ASO. Clearly the introduction of product differences introduces the potential for confounding effects of product selection, different medical management, included benefits or providers (often a factor with ASO groups) and reimbursement, and this approach should be treated with caution. The mathematics of this methodology are similar to those of the Geographic methodology (see above).

- "*Patient as their own control*" (*Pre-post Cohort Methodology*) This method differs from the "temporal" method described above, in which the intervention and comparison populations are re-sampled in each period to ensure equivalence. Applying the same rules of identification to create an equivalent population in a different time period is somewhat analogous to the "with replacement" and "without replacement" problems with which actuaries are familiar from introductory statistics courses, where problems are often stated in terms of a number of red and black balls present in an urn. In the "Patient as their own control" method, the comparison group is the population as initially defined, but measured post-intervention. In this design, there is no equivalent reference population. One conclusion from our discussion in Chapter 3 is that regression to the mean is potentially present in the post-intervention population (often because candidates are identified for intervention based on recent claims experience). If the extent of the regression were known, an adjustment could be applied to the population. In most cases, however, the extent of regression is not known.

- *Participant vs. Non-participant studies.* In this method, the experience of those who voluntarily elect to participate in a program is compared with the experience of those who choose not to participate. The participants represent a group with potentially different risk-factors to that of the non-participants (we already know that they differ with respect to the important factor of willingness to take control of their own health by engaging in a program). Some authors appear to believe that it is possible to adjust the reference population (non-participants) to bring them into equivalence with the intervention population. It does not appear to us, however, that the effect of selection can be estimated. In any event, the existence of selection bias is known in the industry and this methodology is not assigned a high credibility, with or without adjustment.

- *Other types* of control group methods are cited in the literature. An example of a "staggered roll-out." method used in examining diabetes outcomes can be found in the literature [204]. These methods, however, can be de-constructed to fit one or more of the above five categories.

Randomized control methods exhibit a high degree of validity. Other types of control methodologies (including adjusted historical control methods) also achieve high market acceptance because of their intuitive appeal (even though the technical aspects of achieving equivalence in non-random controls may be daunting). Methods using other controls (geographic or product) are less practical to implement and may require a highly sophisticated system of risk-classification and risk-adjustment to ensure equivalence between the intervention group and reference group. The "patient as their own control" or pre-post cohort methodology, as discussed elsewhere in this book, while it is well-known and understood, suffers from potential bias due to regression to the mean. Results produced using this method cannot be considered valid (something that is increasingly being recognized in the market). A similar conclusion is drawn for Participant vs. Non-participant studies, which, while they may be simple to understand and implement, suffer from a fundamental flaw in that they compare a self-selected population with its complement and therefore fail to demonstrate equivalence.

7.4.2 Non-Control Group Methods

- Among non-control group methods, *Services Avoided* methods are commonly used, particularly for case management applications. In this methodology, the intended resource utilization of the member prior to the intervention is estimated because the member calls a health plan to pre-authorize a particular service. Savings are then estimated by performing a cost-estimate of the requested service, and comparing this estimate of cost with actual cost of services used after the intervention. In the specific example of case management, an estimate of the likely resource utilization of the member is compared with actual approved utilization (including any alternative services arranged or approved by the case manager), and the difference is counted as savings due to the case management program. Some applications track the utilization of members who report a change in intent (for example the intent to have surgery) for as long as 6 to 12 months post-intervention to ensure that the change in intent was not later reversed. Because of its wide-spread use, the methodology scores high on familiarity but lacks a reference population. The method also includes a high degree of subjectivity both in selection of candidates and in estimating what utilization would have been, absent of intervention. Case managers are also known to request more resources and services than required, in the expectation that some will be denied, thus over-estimating the savings. For these reasons, the validity of savings calculated by this method is questionable.

- *Clinical Improvement* methods have achieved reasonable market acceptability. In such a method, the change in an objective clinical measure is first observed (for example, the rate of use of a particular medication by members who have a diagnosis for which the medication is indicated). The peer-reviewed clinical literature is searched for studies that indicate how health is improved (and resource utilization is decreased) in the population with the particular diagnosis, as a result of adherence to treatment. A dollar value is assigned to the reduction in resource utilization which is then applied to the observed change in the clinical measure due to the program. This method appeals to some evaluators because it involves objective causal factors: unlike some other methods that measure changes in claims, this method can point to actual improvement in a clinical factor that can cause reduction in claims. Despite its appeal, the methodology rates relatively low because the results are achieved through a subjective process and often lack a reference group – in this case, the subjective element is the estimation of financial savings by inference from published clinical studies (somewhat akin to a benchmark method). To our knowledge, no study has ever been published that compares estimates of savings in a population using a clinical improvement approach with estimates in the same population using a randomized or other control group approach. We should also remember that our review of the literature in Chapter 4 found that the literature does not yet show a strong, demonstrated, link from clinical to financial effects.

7.4.3 Statistical Methods

The term "statistical methods" is used when purely statistical techniques are involved (for example, regression or benchmarks), rather than the construction of an explicit reference population. The term "Statistical Methods", however, should not be confused with the statistical tests that underlie hypothesis testing (see Appendix 7.1). Statistical tests of hypotheses should be applied to any study to determine whether the results are significant.

- *Time-Series Methods.* The objective of these methods is to fit a curve or series of curves to the data over time, and then to demonstrate a divergence from the best-fit line once the intervention is applied. This method is a generalization of the trend-adjusted historical control methodology, which focuses on just one historical period. The difficulty of fitting a curve to healthcare data over time appears to us to be almost insuperable, because of the need to capture in the model the effect of a multitude of factors, both endogenous and exogenous. Because of the difficulty of demonstrating a high correlation between the actual data and the fitted line, demonstrating divergence from that line and assigning causality to the DM program is complicated.

- *Regression Discontinuity*[2] This design may be considered as a special case of the Time Series method. At its core, this method looks for a statistically-significant difference between two similar sub-sets of the population. A regression line is first fitted to data that relates pre- and post-intervention experience. A dummy variable is included in the regression to capture the difference between the intercept of the Intervention Population's regression line at the "cut-off point" and that of the Reference Population. To understand the Regression Discontinuity method, consider Figure 7.1. In this example, we plot the relationship between an individual's risk-score in a baseline period (Year 1) and a cost per member per month in the follow-up period (Year 2). Each point in the scatter represents the pair of observations for a single member. The method requires an objective way to segregate those members eligible for, and those not eligible for, the intervention. The risk-score is a useful variable because intervention programs are frequently targeted at members whose risk-score exceeds some pre-determined minimum. (Risk-score is a preferable measure for the Year 1 variable than cost because, while the group targeted for intervention often includes high cost members, this is seldom the sole criterion for targeting.) An upward sloping regression line implies that members with high Year 1 risk score tend to have high Year 2 costs, as well. The closer this relationship, the closer the data points will be to the line. On the other hand, a line that slopes upward at less than 45° indicates regression to the mean (high-cost year 1 members tend to have lower year 2 costs; low-cost year 1 members tend to have higher year 2 costs).

A regression is fitted to the Year 1 vs. Year 2 data. An example of this regression is:

$Y_i = \beta_0 + \beta_1 X_i + \beta_2 Z_i + \varepsilon_i$, where:

Y = Dependent variable (year 2 cost for the ith person)
β_0 = Regression intercept
X_{1i} = Independent variable (year 1 cost for the ith person)
β_1 = Regression coefficient for variable 1
Z = Dummy variable with value zero (if observation is in the Reference Population) or 1 (if in the Intervention Population)
β_2 = Regression coefficient for dummy variable Z
ε_i = Random error term for the ith person

In some applications the independent variable, X, is transformed so that the Cut-off point intersects the X axis at a value of zero. However, this does not appear to be essential to the successful application or understanding of the method.

[2] This section is adapted from publications of William M.K. Trochim ("Research Design for Program Evaluation" by W.M.K. Trochim. Sage, 1984) and Linden A, J.L. Adams and N. Roberts: "Evaluating Disease Management programme effectiveness: an introduction to the regression discontinuity design". Journal of Evaluation in Clinical Practice, 10 (2004). We wish to thank Dr. Ariel Linden for his helpful discussion on this section.

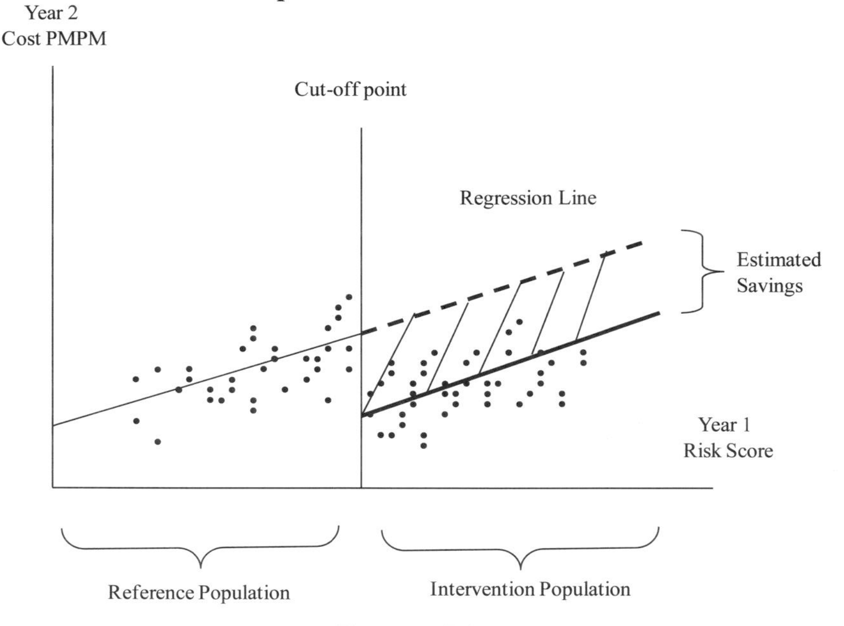

FIGURE 7.1

A significant value for the dummy variable regression coefficient (β_2) implies that there is a statistical difference between the intercept of the basic line (reference population line) and the intervention population line at the cut-off point. The value of this coefficient gives an estimate of the effect of the program at that point. The focus on the cut-off point may seem excessive, but an important feature of this method is that the effect is calculated at a point (the cut-off point) at which the reference and intervention populations are most similar. This overcomes a potential objection that there is not a reasonable "goodness-of-fit" throughout the entire population, particularly at the extremes of the distribution. Second, while this method may have been used to demonstrate a significant effect, clients who are purchasers of care management interventions require an estimate of the savings due to the program, and we are not aware of an actual savings calculation using this method. Savings could, however, be calculated by projecting the expected cost of the intervention population using the regression analysis, and subtracting the intervention population's actual expenses (as in the hatched area above). We have described this method at greater length than some others because there is a considerable interest in its potential application in commercial calculations, and we expect to see the method used more in the future.

- *Benchmark Methods.* Certain key statistics in the population under management are compared with the value(s) of the same statistics in another (benchmark) population. Benchmark studies compare outcomes for a managed population with an independent statistic: either a national, regional or other external benchmark, or a metric available from a published study. It is difficult to demonstrate adequate equivalence between the intervention population and benchmark population in these studies. The principle of equivalence requires consistency between the populations on a very large number of risk factors. While it may be possible to have equivalence in theory, it is unlikely that a published study or benchmark source will provide sufficient detail needed to apply adjustments in such a way that equivalence can be assured. Actuaries, who are used to making adjustments to population data and inferring, from one set of data, conclusions in another (in rating and underwriting applications, for example) will be familiar with the issues that exist in using "external" data sources.

Statistical methodologies are restricted to the scientific community; we have not seen them used in wide-spread commercial application. The more commonly-used control group and non-control group methods are simpler to understand and the calculations are transparent. Statistical methods involve techniques with which most business users are not familiar and may regard with a degree of suspicion (for their "black box" aspect). The Regression-discontinuity Method is often discussed favorably in the literature, but we have yet to find significant analyses using this method. Time series methods have one important advantage in that they draw attention to long-term utilization and cost trends in the population, which provides the evaluator with valuable information about what was happening in the population before the intervention program began. We question the practical usefulness of this method in a health plan environment, where so many variables change over time, making it virtually impossible to control for confounding. Benchmark methods are favored by some authors (and have some appeal to actuaries, who are used to making the type of adjustments required to compare different populations). The sheer number of variables and risk-factors, however, (and lack of information about their values) that could potentially affect a benchmark study will make this another difficult methodology to apply in practice. Statistical methodologies may yet prove useful but none is developed to the point of being practical for implementation in a commercial environment.

Some authors suggest "Propensity Scoring" as a methodology, equivalent to others considered above (Linden et al. [121]). We recognize the importance of Propensity Scoring, a method of identifying or creating populations of the same degree of risk as the intervention population. (Propensity Scoring is potentially of importance to actuaries because of its similarity to Risk Adjustment. See Appendix 7.1.) Because we do not consider Propensity Scoring a methodology, but rather a technique for adjusting other populations or creating matched populations, we do not include it in our comparison.

Comparative Assessment of Methodologies

Table 7.2 summarizes our conclusions concerning effectiveness of different measurement methodologies in meeting our key criteria (above) validity:

- Inherent validity (lack of obvious bias);
- Scientific rigor;
- Familiarity (how commonly used is the methodology in the industry?);
- Market Acceptance (how is the method perceived in the market-place?);
- Ease of replication and auditability;
- Application (how is the methodology applied in practice?), and
- "Other Issues" (other important issues in the application of each methodology).

These criteria for assessing methodologies are our own, and reflect our experience as consulting actuaries in this area. Other actuaries, or practitioners from other disciplines, may have different criteria by which to judge methodologies. The point, however, is that methodologies are not equally valid, and results that are prepared according to a higher-scoring methodology should be given more weight.

TABLE 7.2

	Method Type	Method	Application	Validity/ Scientific Rigor	Familiarity	Replicability/ Auditability	Evaluation of Methodology	Other Issues
	Comparison of Certain Commonly Used DM Savings Calculation Methodologies							
1	Control Group Methods	Randomized Control	Requires Randomized, control group not subject to Intervention. Metric in the intervention group is compared with the same metric in the control group, and the difference is assigned to the effect of the intervention	High	High	Difficult to replicate and audit; need another randomized group	"Gold Standard" method, although requires demonstration of equivalence. Need for incurred claims results in delays in evaluations.	Practical to implement and avoids adjustment issues, although requires sufficient number of members. Viewed by health plans as difficult to implement and potentially unethical. Randomization must occur at the population level if results are to be applied to the population.
2	Control Group Methods	Temporal (Historical) control	Requires population drawn according to identical rules from two periods. Metric from the Intervention period is compared with the same metric from the Baseline period, adjusted with trend. Requires adjustment of the comparison population to be equivalent to the Intervention population.	High	High	Replicable and auditable	Becoming the most widespread methodology in the industry. Need for incurred claims results in delays in evaluations.	Implicit assumption that regression to the mean is uniformly distributed in the Baseline and Intervention periods, and that a robust trend estimate is available. Differs from the Pre-post cohort (Patient as own control) method because a new cohort is used for comparison, including all members that meet the identification criteria in the period.
3	Control Group Methods	Geographic or product line controls	Requires population drawn according to identical rules from two different groups (e.g., geographies). Metric from the Intervention period is compared with the same metric from the control, adjusted for all appropriate risk-factor differences.	High/ Medium	High/ Moderate	Replicable and auditable	Not widely used.	Sometimes difficult to adjust for the many risk factors that affect a population and its utilization (see Chapter 3).
4	Control Group Methods	"Patient as their own control" (Pre-post cohort)	Patients are identified pre-intervention and then followed post-intervention. Pre-intervention metric is compared with post-intervention metric.	Low	High	Replicable and auditable	Widely used, but regression to the mean issues are causing purchasers to re-evaluate (see Chapter 3).	Theoretically possible to correct for the effect of regression, but no method has yet been developed to do so. Differs from the Temporal (historical control) method because the same cohort is used for comparison, and newly identified members are not added.
5	Control Group Methods	Participant vs. Non-participant	Patients are invited to enroll in a program. Those who choose to enroll are subject to treatment; those who choose not to enroll form the control group.	Low	High	Replicable and auditable	Widely used, but selection bias causes this methodology to be highly suspect.	Theoretically possible to correct for the effect of selection bias, the effect of a member's "willingness to change" is unmeasurable.

TABLE 7.2 (Continued)

	Comparison of Certain Commonly Used DM Savings Calculation Methodologies							
	Method Type	Method	Application	Validity/ Scientific Rigor	Familiarity	Replicability/ Auditability	Evaluation of Methodology	Other Issues
6	Non-Control Group Methods	Services Avoided (also called pre-intent/ post-intent)	Record intent of different patients, track for a period of time to determine actual outcome, and assign a dollar value to the avoided event (adjusted for alternative treatment, if any).	Moderate	High	May be difficult to replicate; auditable	Frequently used for small, highly-specialized programs (such as case management).	Two issues; participant bias (participants who are more likely to change their minds seek information and support) and evaluation and recording of intent is subjective.
7		Clinical improvement methods	Measure clinical improvement and estimate financial savings using a model based on the difference in cost of well-managed and other patients.	Moderate	Moderate	Difficult to replicate; difficult to assemble comparable clinical trial data	Useful for small volume studies and when a result is required more quickly than data-based evaluations	Requires review of the significant literature on clinical improvement, and a method for projecting financial from clinical improvement. To our knowledge there is no comparative study of results of clinical improvement and other methods.
8	Statistical Methods	Regression-discontinuity	A regression line is fitted on the relationship between Year 1 Risk Score and Year 2 PMPM costs in a population; a dummy variable is included to indicate membership in the intervention group. The difference at the "cut-off point" between the non-intervention and intervention population regression lines indicates that the intervention has had an effect.	Unknown	Low	Replicable and auditable	Highly-regarded as a theoretical method in the scientific literature, but we are not aware of a specific practical DM application.	To be determined.
9		Time-series	Extension of the Adjusted historical control methodology to multiple periods	Low	Low	Replicable and auditable	Not widely used in commercial evaluations.	The effect of changes in risk-factors (often reflected in variations in Trend) is compounded over a period of years, making it very difficult to control this calculation.
10		Benchmark	Metric in the intervention group is compared with the same metric in another population. The difference is assigned to the effect of the intervention and savings are estimated accordingly.	Low	Low	Replicable; difficult to assemble valid comparison data	Occasionally encountered in commercial applications	Comparison populations are unlikely to be described in sufficient detail to determine their degree of comparability (or the extent to which adjustment is required).

7.5 CONCLUSION

A non-control group methodology is unlikely to be a satisfactory method for calculating DM savings results, except under unusual circumstances. In "The Principles for Assessing Disease Management Outcomes," [61] the DMAA Committee examining appropriate research methodologies concluded that the preferred method for any evaluation is a randomized control study (in our experience, easier to implement and more practical than is commonly believed). As our discussion shows, other forms of non-randomized control group can also be valid (provided equivalence is maintained and can be satisfactorily demonstrated). A non-randomized control group could be temporal, geographic, or product-based, but not based on self-selected members (such as non-participants). The achievement and demonstration of equivalence is an area where actuaries may make a contribution. Actuaries are qualified, through their experience in rating and underwriting of health risks, to perform the process of drawing conclusions and making projections in one population from data or experience of another population. In our next few chapters, we will address issues to consider in order to maintain control of the study data and the achievement and demonstration of equivalence.

In addition to the issues of equivalence that are important in choosing a valid methodology, the application of the methodology needs to be carefully controlled, or the results of the study will be invalidated. In Chapter 8 we turn to the issue of the controls that should be in place as we apply an important methodology, the actuarially adjusted historical control design.

APPENDIX 7.1: PROPENSITY SCORES AND RISK-ADJUSTMENT

Propensity Score methods are not a methodology on a par with others discussed in Chapter 7, but represent a way of identifying or scoring different members for evaluation using another methodology. Because of the interest that Propensity Score methods have raised in the industry, and their similarity to the Risk Adjustment methodologies with which actuaries are familiar, we cover them briefly in this section.

In order to grasp the basics of Propensity Scoring, consider a Randomized Control method. In this method, every member is equally likely to be selected for assignment to the Intervention or Reference population, irrespective of the member's characteristics. In such a method, the outcomes from the Intervention and Reference groups are compared, and, if savings are the statistic of interest, this is estimated from the difference in mean costs of the two groups. In a propensity scoring method, an intervention group is first identified (or may self-identify, as, for example, program participants). A matching reference population is then identified from a population of non-participants, either those who elect not to enroll, or members of a similar population not offered the intervention. Savings are estimated as the difference between the mean costs of the intervention and reference groups. The problem in such a method, of course, is identifying members with exactly the same characteristics as the intervention population. Consideration of the potential risk variables (age, sex, condition, co-morbidities, residence, plan of benefits, etc.) quickly indicates that the likelihood of finding an intervention group member that matches exactly on every one of the risk characteristics is small. The Propensity Score method was developed to reduce the effect of the multiple risk factors to a scalar variable, or single score, using multiple regression. Thus, for example, a reference group member may have different age, sex, co-morbidities, etc. to those of an intervention group member, yet have the same score, allowing the two members to be "matched." The similarity of the score that this method produces to the score produced by a "risk adjustment" methodology is obvious.

Some authors believe that this method holds considerable promise for DM evaluations, because it allows participants to be "matched" with non-participants in a pre-post study, yet apparently overcome the two major shortcomings of this method: selection bias and regression to the mean.

We believe that this method has a place within other methods, but we are less optimistic about its potential than other authors. While it may be true that a propensity score may be calculated for observable (and measurable) variables, the method cannot accommodate non-observable or non-measurable variables. Important examples of the latter are the member's "readiness to change", which influences the member's likelihood to enroll in a program. As we have shown in our previous discussion on selection bias, members who enroll in programs do not have the same claims experience as those who do not enroll in programs. Examples of otherwise non-measurable variables that affect risk include the quality of care provided by the treating physician, the type of care and support that the member receives in the home environment, and so on.

This concept continues to be of considerable interest to the industry and we are likely to see continued research into its application in the future.

8 An Actuarial Method for Evaluating Disease Management Outcomes

This chapter discusses in more detail an actuarial methodology for performing Disease Management evaluations and addresses the challenges raised in earlier chapters in this book.

8.1 Introduction

The actuary may not always have the chance to design an outcomes measurement study, and will more frequently be called in to evaluate a vendor's or colleague's results from an existing study. This chapter describes the (Actuarially-adjusted) Historical Control Methodology for performing DM outcomes evaluations. Many practical solutions are provided for actuarial issues raised in earlier chapters.

Occasionally, adjustments are made by a researcher to correct for risk-factors that differ between reference and intervention populations. Examples of obvious adjustments are the effects of Trend, catastrophic claims, age, and plan design. It is usually possible to identify when adjustments such as these are required and the extent of the adjustment to be made. Where these adjustments are well-documented it should be possible to assess their validity.

Other factors are not as readily identifiable or quantifiable. Examples of the latter include selection bias (the fact that those members who participate in programs are not randomly distributed within a chronic population), regression to the mean or discrete changes in the population being measured (as for example when a new sub-population that is not equivalent to the former population is added to or leaves the program).

This chapter describes an actuarial methodology for evaluating disease management outcomes. We address several important issues in this chapter:

- Control of exposure;
- Identification of measured populations; and
- Ensuring equivalence between baseline and intervention populations.

A fourth actuarial issue, the calculation and application of healthcare cost trend, is addressed separately in Chapter 11.

The principles of an actuarial adjustment methodology may be applied to any study design in which the results of an intervention group are compared with those of a comparison group.

The **Actuarially-adjusted Historical Control Methodology** for assessing Managed Care outcomes discussed in this chapter is one frequently used by health plans and Disease Management (DM) vendors to assess their financial outcomes, and is an example of an adjusted historical control design. An example of the methodology is described in American Healthways/Johns Hopkins [188]. Although the American Healthways paper does not assign a name to the methodology, it is effectively an adjusted historical method. We begin by describing the calculation in more detail.

8.2 THE ACTUARIALLY-ADJUSTED HISTORICAL CONTROL METHODOLOGY

Under this design, objective criteria are used to define members for inclusion in either reference or intervention population. Certain outcome statistics are measured for that population during the historical period (often referred to as a "baseline" period). Examples of statistics measured in the baseline period include admissions per 1000 of the population, per member per month costs, or clinical markers such as the number of patients receiving beta-blockers, and so on.

The measurement period may be adjacent to the baseline period, or not; it is one of the strengths of the actuarial-adjustment methodology that the periods need not be continuous. There may be some overlap between the populations (i.e., the same members will be identified in both baseline and measurement periods) identified in the baseline and measurement periods, as long as the overlap is not complete. This methodology is not a cohort study, however, because we are not following a population identified in the Baseline period through to the end of the Intervention period, but rather two populations in two periods, identified according to the same criteria. Equivalence between the baseline and intervention period populations is assumed to result from the symmetrical treatment of members in each period - that is, applying exactly the same rules for population selection in each period.

Generally, the intervention program begins before, or simultaneously with, the measurement period. A naïve observer would measure the effect of the intervention program as the difference between the statistic being measured in the baseline and measurement period. It is an empirical fact that most healthcare utilization statistics change over time, even in stable populations. Health insurance actuaries and underwriters allow for this effect by applying "healthcare trend" to their projections (after specifically controlling for directly controllable factors). We discuss the selection and application of a trend assumption in more detail in Chapter 11. In the Actuarially-adjusted Historical Control Methodology, savings are not directly measurable. Instead, they are derived as the difference between an estimated statistic and the actual statistic from the measurement period. The estimated statistic is the corresponding historical statistic from the baseline period, projected for a period of a few months or years to the intervention period.

Table 8.1 shows a simple example of the application of the **Actuarially-adjusted Historical Control Methodology** to the estimation of savings in a population. The outcome being measured is the cost of admissions. The methodology could instead be applied to net paid claims, emergency room visits or any relevant measure of utilization. Baseline medical admissions are recorded for a chronic population (numbering 50,000 chronic members, or 600,000 member months of exposure, assuming every member is continuously enrolled for

12 months). The baseline medical admission rate is projected one year to the first measurement period, applying an annual trend of 5.3%. In this particular example, the applicable trend is derived from the comparable, non-chronic member experience of the same health plan (externally derived and not shown in the example). We refer to this population in Table 8.1 as the "Index" population, because it is used to create an index trend to be applied to the chronic population utilization. Whether the Index population experience is in fact comparable to that of the chronic population is a matter for study and debate, and we return to this topic in Chapters 9 and 12. Ultimately it is not equivalence between the Index and study populations that we care about in this case, but rather whether a trend calculated from the Index population is a suitable proxy for the trend in the study population, absent intervention. Any external source of trend experience may be used, provided the experience on which it is based is not affected by the intervention that the methodology is attempting to calculate.

TABLE 8.1

Simple Example of the Actuarially-Adjusted Historical Control Methodology Applied to Inpatient Admissions[1]

Basic data used in the calculation		
	Baseline Period	**Measurement Period**
Period	1/1/2001- 12/31/2001	1/1/2002 – 12/31/2002
Average total population	150,000	150,000
Average chronic population	50,000	50,000
Chronic Member months	600,000	600,000
Chronic population Inpatient Admissions	30,000	28,800
Chronic population Inpatient admissions/1000/year	600.0	576.0
Cost/admission	$7,500	$8,000
Utilization (admission) trend (Derived from an external source, e.g., the "Index" population)	–	5.3%

Example of a Savings Calculation:

In the following example, we apply the data assembled in Table 8.1. The avoided admissions (equal to measured period admissions less baseline period admissions) are multiplied by an average cost per admission to generate overall dollar savings. The average cost per admission may be observed directly from the Index Population in the measurement period, or may be estimated by trending forward an average cost per admission from the Baseline period, using a suitable admission unit cost trend.

[1] This is an example of a Medicare population. The chronic prevalence (33.3%) and number of admissions/1000/year (600.0) are typical of chronic Medicare populations. Both of these statistics will be lower in commercial populations, although the same principles illustrated here will apply.

Estimated Savings due to Averted Admissions =

$\frac{\text{Baseline Admissions}}{1000} \times$ Utilization Trend	600.0×1.053 =	631.8
Minus: $\frac{\text{Actual Admissions}}{1000} yr$		576.0
Equals $\frac{\text{Reduced Admissions}}{1000} yr$		55.8
Multiplied by: $\frac{\text{Actual Member Years in Measurement Period}}{1000}$		50.0
TOTAL REDUCED ADMISSIONS		2,790.0
Multiplied by: $\frac{\text{TrendedUnitCost}}{\text{Admissions}}$		$ 8,000
Estimated Savings due to Averted Admissions		$22,320,000

Once the calculation has been completed, we recommend validating and reconciling the savings to the underlying cost. As a test of reasonableness of the result, the underlying cost of a Medicare population ranges between $6,000 to $8,000 per member per year, or (for 150,000 members) a total cost of $900,000,000 to $1.2 billion. While estimated savings of $22.3 million from a program in the chronic population may seem high in absolute terms, relative to the total cost of the Medicare population the savings represent 1.9% to 2.5%, which is consistent with results from other studies of this type. For an example of PMPM savings from a population study see a study by Cousins & Liu [33].

8.3 PRACTICAL APPLICATION OF THE "ACTUARIALLY-ADJUSTED HISTORICAL CONTROL" METHODOLOGY

The key component of the actuarial methodology is the application of the trend factor that adjusts historical experience to an estimate of current period experience, absent intervention. "Healthcare trend" is the term applied to the empirical observation that most healthcare measures (utilization, unit cost, per member per month costs, etc.) tend to change over time. Generally, but not always, trend results in increases in healthcare measures. The choice of an appropriate healthcare trend assumption to apply to the baseline experience for calculating savings is discussed later in this chapter, and Chapter 11 explores the practical issues of the application of this methodology in a population subject to Disease Management Interventions.

The Actuarially-adjusted Historical Control Methodology is an "open group" method, in which a comparable population is selected according to the same criteria in each period. This methodology contrasts with a closed group or cohort methodology (such as the Johns Hopkins/ American Healthways methodology) in which, to be included in the measured population, a member must have been continuously eligible for at least 24 months of the baseline and intervention periods). With regular enrollment, termination and identification of new members that is found in most groups, it is reasonable to expect that the open group method will produce a stable population, year-to-year (at least with respect to common risk-factors such as age, gender and disease prevalence). A closed-group methodology, by contrast, will produce a group that is subject to the effects of aging and disease progression. The theory and practice of trend calculation for use in projecting historical costs is covered in more detail in Chapter 11. In summary, when projecting experience from a baseline to an intervention period, it is important to separate the trend measure used between ongoing factors that may be included directly (such as the effect of aging and disease progression, or the effect of benefit design features and their changes) from other one-time factors such as increase in intensity, changes in medical practice or changes in provider contracts. For the purposes of this chapter, we assume that it is possible to find an unbiased estimate of chronic population trend, without the effect of the intervention (and unaffected by the identification algorithm used to select the chronic population).

8.4 EXPOSURE

If outcomes of interventions are to be rigorously measured, it is critical that members and their associated claims be tracked, allocated, associated and summarized appropriately. Actuaries know this issue as the topic of "Exposure to Risk." In Disease Management, Exposure has two meanings. Firstly, a patient is "exposed" to an intervention by being a member of a group selected for intervention or a program. Secondly, for measurement or actuarial calculations, "exposure" has a meaning synonymous with "denominator," and refers to the entire group eligible for an intervention, or included in a study. The risk-unit is often the member month, and the total "exposure to risk" is the total number of member months measured between the start and end dates of the study. Actuaries familiar with underwriting and pricing will recognize that establishing appropriate baseline and intervention period membership populations is similar to the problem of identifying enrolled populations for underwriting and pricing. In this section we assume that a valid scheme exists for defining who is in which category. We view the importance of defining and controlling the "exposure" as one of the most critical components of a study, and for that reason we discuss the issues involved in some depth. We will return later to the definitions of each category.

8.4.1 Managed Vs. Measured Populations

The population to be measured need not be the same population being managed. This may not seem obvious, but a few examples will explain the differences. A DM program may be offered to all chronic members of a health plan. Some of these members may not be good candidates for management (for example, if the member is institutionalized, or suffers from a terminal disease). Conversely, the program may be offered to members who self-identify with a chronic disease, even when they do not have a claims history that would objectively identify them as having the disease. All of these members represent a potential for confounding the DM company's results, in the first example because the member represents a chronic individual who will not contribute to savings, while in the second example, the self-identified member will have no counterpart in the baseline period (because members are only self-identifying in the intervention period, destroying the necessary symmetry of the identification process). Although the DM company will be managing the care of these members, the DM company and health plan may agree to ignore these members in the actual evaluation. The treatment of non-measured members is independent of the particular methodology chosen to measure results, and may apply, for example, to members in a randomized controlled study.

8.4.2 Eligible Members

For measurement purposes, we first determine eligibility for health plan membership, then eligibility for DM services (the program, for example, may not be available to self-insured groups). While this step may seem simple and obvious, anyone familiar with health plan data will know that determining unambiguous eligibility is not a simple task, and is a task often subject to multiple revisions on a monthly basis. In Figure 8.1 below, which illustrates the member classification schematically, we have assumed that all eligible health plan members are also potentially included in the DM program.

8.4.3 Member Months

The basic unit of measurement for any evaluation is the member month. In any month, a member is placed into a single classification category. Members can move between categories from one month to the next, although movements between some categories may not be possible. The number and types of categories used depends on the type of evaluation, the level of detail sought in the study and the types of risk that the study is monitoring.

In the examples that follow, we list a number of different categories that we have used to classify members in studies of DM measurement. Subsets of membership classes may be combined. The application of the classification rules is in most cases hierarchical.

8.4.4 Chronic and Non-Chronic ("Index") Members

Within the eligible membership population, we assign members according to their chronic status. Some companies refer to these members as "suitable," meaning suitable for the intervention program. The assignment of chronic status is determined continuously (i.e. monthly). Any set of definitions needs to be objective and applied consistently within both the Baseline and Measurement period. Those members who do not qualify as Chronic are, by definition, Non-chronic, a group we define as "Index" (because we will use their experience as the source of our trend estimate). Members may be assigned to the chronic population based on the date of first satisfying the chronic criteria, or they may be retroactively assigned to the first of the year if they satisfy the criteria at any time in the year. These two methods produce different results (in terms of identification, trend and estimated savings) as we shall see in the next chapter.

Initial Member Classification*

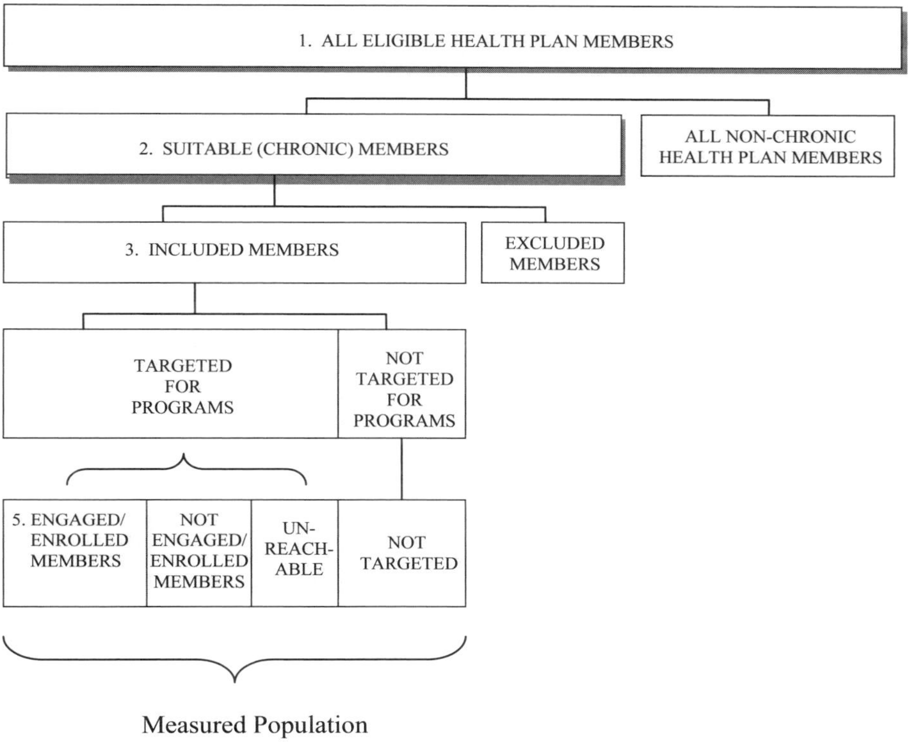

1. ALL ELIGIBLE HEALTH PLAN MEMBERS

2. SUITABLE (CHRONIC) MEMBERS

ALL NON-CHRONIC HEALTH PLAN MEMBERS

3. INCLUDED MEMBERS

EXCLUDED MEMBERS

TARGETED FOR PROGRAMS

NOT TARGETED FOR PROGRAMS

5. ENGAGED/ ENROLLED MEMBERS

NOT ENGAGED/ ENROLLED MEMBERS

UN-REACH-ABLE

NOT TARGETED

Measured Population

* The boxes in this graphic are not drawn to scale.

FIGURE 8.1

8.4.5 Excluded Members

In determining the population for measurement, some members will be excluded. We assign an exclusion status to those members who, while eligible for health plan membership, may not be eligible for inclusion in the program population or the measurement population. The question of which members to exclude, and when, is a significant issue in any program measurement. An issue that appears to cause confusion in both customers of DM programs and those who measure outcomes is the difference between the managed and measured populations. This will be particularly true of health plans that use multiple vendors to manage different conditions. A managed population may be whatever the DM company and the customer agree should be managed. It is not necessary, for example, that members who are excluded from the measurement be excluded from the management services. These members may be eligible for some or all of the DM services and still be excluded from measurement. The measured population, however, will be identified by objective criteria and its outcomes will be tracked and measured in order to assess the effectiveness of the program. Exclusions are generally made from the measured population for one of the following reasons:

- The member class is not receptive to Disease Management. Examples of this category include those members who are residents of long-term care, hospice or other institutions, who are often under the care of resident clinical personnel.

- The member is a candidate for a program, but the program is administered by another vendor, such as mental health, maternity or substance abuse or behavioral conditions.
- The pattern of claims that the member exhibits is subject to sharp discontinuity, and can thus distort a trend calculation. This issue is addressed in greater detail in Appendix 8.1.
- The member's claims are significant, relative to other claimants in the class, and the experience of this particular member is likely to dominate the group, or introduce "noise" to the calculation.

When a member is excluded it is important to consider the effect of the member exclusion on trend calculations (either in the Intervention or Index population). Trend calculations can be affected by the prospective elimination of an excluded member at the point of identification. More detail about member claim patterns and their potential impact on trend may be found in Appendix 8.1.

8.4.6 Measured and Non-measured members

At the next level, we separate measured from non-measured members. Tests for inclusion in the Measurement population may include:

- *Continuous Coverage Test.* In order for a member to be eligible for inclusion in the Measurement Population (either Chronic or Index) the Member must satisfy a continuous coverage condition. A continuous coverage test is applied to exclude those health plan members who have less than 12 months of continuous coverage in the plan in any year, either because they are new members during the year, or because they terminated during the year. Because members are identified through administrative claims data, the identification of newly-chronic members itself takes several months due to claims processing and operational lags. In addition, newly-identified or new health plan members require a start-up period to be contacted, enrolled, and begin the program. For all these reasons, a six-month continuous eligibility criterion is usually applied to all members. Different periods of continuous coverage are possible; in Chapter 12 we will empirically examine the effect that varying the continuous coverage requirement has on measurement results.
- *"Claim-Free Period."* Another test, particularly important for the newly-identified members, is the claim-free period test. This test is applied as a way of addressing the issue of regression to the mean in the newly-identified chronic population. Regression to the mean is covered in greater detail in Chapter 3. Including incident chronic members from the month of identification, when the identifying event is a hospital admission, potentially builds-in regression to the mean (generally a reduction in claims) because the hospital admission usually represents the highest point of utilization for that year. Failure to eliminate the reduction in claims due to the natural course of recovery risks assigning causality and savings to the program that result from the natural course of the event. Defining a comparable population that includes newly-identified members, and separately tracking prevalent and incident members can address this issue. Since failure to satisfactorily address regression to the mean in claims data is probably the single most significant source of criticism by health plans,

the conservative approach of completely eliminating the identifying event and its reversal is recommended here. Another reason for excluding newly-identified members in the first four months since their identifying event is that inclusion of the event itself makes the DM vendor effectively responsible for that event. While there may be ways of identifying members at risk of events who have no prior history of the condition, we doubt that most vendors would agree to be held accountable for reducing events in a population with no prior history of the event. Consistent with the principle that we should measure what we have agreed to manage (and for which we have agreed to be held accountable) we recommend excluding these events unless the DM vendor explicitly agrees to manage and be held accountable for them.

8.4.7 Engaged/Enrolled, Targeted And Reachable Members

In the final line of Figure 8.1, we illustrate several different outcome states in the "Measured" member category: enrolled, not enrolled and unreachable members. Because this is a population methodology, we measure the outcomes of all members, whether enrolled, not enrolled, reachable or unreachable and targeted or not targeted for intervention.

The issue of "reachability" is an important one for program management and comparison of outcomes. In our experience the typical PPO health plan lacks accurate, up to date contact information on 30% to 40% of its membership. Restricting measurement only to those members with valid contact information potentially introduces bias into the measurement, and we do not recommend excluding unreachable members. We do, however, recommend reporting data on contact information as part of the reporting of outcomes. Limiting measurement to enrolled members only similarly introduces bias to the results. For comparison purposes the enrollment rate (as a percentage of reachable members) may be reported as part of the reporting of outcomes. Finally, we recognize that not all members may be "targeted" for a program. Some may not have a sufficiently serious condition (based on the identification criteria used for the program) to warrant management by clinical resources. As with other states, however, all members (whether targeted or not) who meet the identification criteria should be measured.

8.5 TIME PERIODS

The adjusted historical methodology incorporates the following time periods:

- *The Lookback Period:* Baseline members are selected through claims identified in the 12 months prior to the beginning of the Baseline Period, or Lookback period.
- *Baseline Period:* The period prior to the start of a program in which the reference population is identified. This period also forms the Lookback period for identification of members in the first Measurement Period.
- *Measurement or Intervention Periods:* The periods during which the program outcomes will be measured. Measurement periods need not be sequential, or sequential to the Baseline period, although they are usually close.

Sometimes, a ramp-up period is also imposed, during which measurement does not take place, allowing the program to become established and enrollments to be performed.

8.6 CHRONIC MEMBERS AND CHRONIC PREVALENCE

There is no unique way of identifying who has a chronic disease. In order to be useful for measurement, however, an identification algorithm needs to be objective, stable over time, and cheap to apply. These criteria rule out many of the methods that involve clinical resources and chart review, and result in administrative claims-based criteria being used in most population studies. Many different claims-based definitions of chronic condition exist (e.g., Duncan [52], HEDIS [92]). Many health plans use risk-adjuster methods to classify and rank members by risk class, and many actuaries are familiar with these (Cumming et al. [35], Dove et al. [47] and Winkelman & Mehmud [220]).

8.6.1 Data: Available Sources

Chronically ill members are often identified from claims data, so data is a central issue. Unfortunately, there is no ideal source of data. Each source has its advantages and drawbacks, which must be weighed against each other. Five types of data commonly available to the health care analyst are Medical Charts, Survey Data, Medical Claims, Pharmacy Claims and Laboratory Values.

Generally, we favor identification using integrated medical and pharmacy claims, although care needs to be taken with PPO and other commercial plans where employers often carve out pharmacy benefits. Claims data are not as rich or accurate as survey or medical chart data, but are always available and are generally of sufficient quality to drive risk management programs.

When using claims data for chronic identification, the actuary should consider the problem of false negative and false positive identification.

8.6.2 The Problem of False Negatives

False negatives are chronic members who are "missed" by an identification algorithm. These members are more of a problem for program management than for program measurement. To the extent that a member has a condition that is untreated, claims data will be unavailable and the member will be unidentified. A more difficult false negative problem occurs when the member's provider is not part of the data-submission system (for example, when a member obtains drugs from the Veterans Administration system, or buys them in Canada). Eventually, even these members will have claims for a service that is included in the data-reporting system, and thus will be identified. But until this happens, the member will be classified as non-chronic for the purpose of measurement. Different results are obtained, depending on the specific definitions used for identifying chronic members. Table 8.2 illustrates the identification of chronic prevalence using three different sets of criteria applied to the same data.

TABLE 8.2

Chronic Prevalence* According to Different Criteria			
Prevalence of 5 Chronic Conditions			
	Narrow	Broad	R_X
Medicare■	24.4%	32.8%	30.8%
Commercial	4.7%	6.3%	6.6%

*Duplicates (i.e., incidence of members with more than one disease) have been removed.

Definitions:

Narrow: Hospital Inpatient claims, using the primary diagnosis on the claim or face-to-face office visits only (excluding tests and other services that are not face-to-face)

Broad: Hospital Inpatient claims, using any recorded diagnosis on the claim, plus any professional services, including tests

R_X: Narrow + Outpatient prescription drug claims

■ Medicare represents a Medicare Risk population with drug benefits.

8.6.3 The Problem of False Positives

False positives are members who are falsely identified as having a chronic condition, when they do not have that condition. There are two types of false positives: clinical and statistical. Clinical false positives, as the name implies, are those members who are identified with the condition and later found not to have it. Statistical false positives, on the other hand, arise because the administrative claims used for identification will never be complete, unambiguous, or correctly coded. When identification of chronic conditions takes place from administrative claims data, there is a chance of "statistical" false positives (which may be different than clinical false positive identification). We define statistical false positives as those members who meet a chronic definition in Year 1, but who do not "re-qualify" according to the same set of definitional criteria in Year 2. This issue is important for Disease Management outcomes evaluation because false positives who do not have the condition according to the claims data are less likely to have high costs. Their continued inclusion in the chronic population, although they no longer meet chronic definition criteria, will be likely to reduce the average cost (and therefore the trend) in the chronic population, resulting in apparent reduction in cost due to the program.

We should also note that a set of criteria appropriate for identifying members for one purpose may not be the most appropriate for another. For example, one application of identification criteria may be to find members for a management program, while another might identify members for measurement. In the first instance, specificity is not as important as sensitivity (we need to identify as many members as possible with the condition to implement a successful program). For measurement (or other examples involving financial objectives, such as reimbursement of providers) we need to be reasonably certain that the identified population actually have the condition.

Table 8.3 illustrates the results of the three different sets of identification criteria used in Table 8.2, applied to populations in successive years.

TABLE 8.3

Prevalence of Statistical False Positives in a Chronic Population

	Year 1	Narrow	+ Broad	+ R_X	TOTAL
Year 2	Narrow	75.9%			
	+ Broad		85.5%		
	+ R_X			92.9%	
	Not Identified	24.1%	14.5%	7.4%	
	TOTAL	100.0%	100.0%	100.0%	100.0%

Members who are "not identified" in Year 2 are those who no longer meet the identifying criteria through claims in Year 2, and who are defined as statistical "false positives." Including these members in the chronic population in Year 2 even when the member does not meet the chronic criteria in Year 2 risks including members whose claims are lower than the average for the group (they will have lower claims by definition since they do not have chronic claims). Excluding members in Year 2 when they do not meet the chronic criteria risks excluding false negatives. On balance, we recommend re-qualifying members annually, excluding statistical false positives.

8.6.4 Included and Excluded Claims

A DM program aims to intervene with members of a health plan who are at risk of experiencing medical events (Emergency Room visits, specialist visits and admissions) for their condition. In any system these members could also consume resources for conditions that are not subject to management by the DM program, such as trauma, accident, psychiatric, substance abuse or maternity conditions. It is customary in DM evaluations to exclude those conditions that are specifically outside the program, because they are subject to random fluctuation and can introduce "noise" into an evaluation, potentially swamping the effect of the intervention. An example of a list of excluded claims, based on ICD-9 codes, is included in Appendix 8.2.

8.7 RESULTS AND USE

Once members are appropriately assigned to categories, monthly numbers may be aggregated into measurement years, and calculations may be performed with the resulting totals. Below, we illustrate an actual application of the Actuarially-adjusted Historical Control Methodology.

We first summarize data according to the chosen categories for the analysis. In each month of observation, we record the number of total, chronic and index measured members (chronic and index non-measured members are not shown). The corresponding cost per member per month for each group is also summarized, allowing us to calculate the Index trend used in the savings calculation. In this example, data are accumulated over two periods: the program Baseline period which begins in August, 2000, and the first program measurement period which begins in the month of October, 2001. Note that for this analysis, a two-month measurement-free period (to allow for program start-up) has been applied in the months of August and September, 2001.

We use the data from Table 8.4 in a savings calculation below:

Estimated Savings due to reduced PMPY =		
Baseline Cost PMPY × Cost Trend		$\$6{,}000 \times 1.12 = \$6{,}720$
Minus:	Actual Cost PMPY	$6,300
Equals:	Reduced Cost PMPY	$420
Multiplied by:	Actual Member Years in Measurement Period	20,000
Estimated Savings		$8,400,000

8.8 CONCLUSION

In this chapter we have described the Actuarially-adjusted Historical Control Methodology for performing DM outcomes evaluations. This methodology provides practical solutions to many of the actuarial issues raised in earlier chapters. Previously, we have highlighted the issues of ensuring equivalence within a control group, regression to the mean, reconciliation to the source data, and effect of different member types on the trend and savings calculations. The techniques outlined in this chapter are designed to control for many of these problems. We believe that our work provides a framework to address most issues that the actuary is likely to encounter in practice.

TABLE 8.4

Example of a Data Summary

		January	**February**	**March**	**April**	**May**	**June**
Members	2000						
	2001	100,000	100,000	100,000	100,000	100,000	100,000
	2002	100,000	100,000	100,000	100,000	100,000	100,000
Chronic Measured Members	2000						
	2001	100,000	100,000	20,000	20,000	20,000	20,000
	2002	100,000	100,000	20,000	20,000	20,000	20,000
Index Measured Members	2000						
	2001	100,000	100,000	60,000	60,000	60,000	60,000
	2002	100,000	100,000	60,000	60,000	60,000	60,000
TOTAL COST Chronic Measured	2000						
	2001	$10,000,000	$10,000,000	$10,000,000	$10,000,000	$10,000,000	$10,000,000
	2002	$10,500,000	$10,500,000	$10,500,000	$10,500,000	$10,500,000	$10,500,000
TOTAL COST Indexed Measured	2000						
	2001	$12,500,000	$12,500,000	$12,500,000	$12,500,000	$12,500,000	$12,500,000
	2002	$14,000,000	$14,000,000	$14,000,000	$14,000,000	$14,000,000	$14,000,000
COST PMPM Chronic Measured	2000						
	2001	$500	$500	$500	$500	$500	$500
	2002	$520	$520	$520	$520	$520	$520
COST PMPM Indexed	2000						
	2001	$208	$208	$208	$208	$208	$208
	2002	$233	$233	$233	$233	$233	$233

for Use in Savings Calculation

July	August	September	October	November	December	Base Line	Interven-tion
		100,000	100,000	100,000	100,000		
100,000			100,000	100,000	100,000	1,200,000	
100,000	100,000	100,000					1,200,000
	20,000	20,000	20,000	20,000	20,000		
20,000			20,000	20,000	20,000	240,000	
20,000	20,000	20,000					240,000
	60,000	60,000	60,000	60,000	60,000		
60,000			60,000	60,000	60,000	720,000	
60,000	60,000	60,000					720,000
	$10,000,000	$10,000,000	$10,000,000	$10,000,000	$10,000,000		
$10,000,000			$10,500,00	$10,500,00	$10,500,00	$120,000,00	
$10,500,000	$10,500,000	$10,500,000					$126,000,0
	$12,500,000	$12,500,000	$12,500,00	$12,500,00	$12,500,00		
$12,500,000			$14,000,00	$14,000,00	$14,000,00	$150,000,00	
$14,000,000	$14,000,000	$14,000,000					$168,000,0
	$500	$500	$500	$500	$500		
$500			$520	$520	$520	$6,000	
$520	$520	$520					$6,300
	$208	$208	$208	$208	$208		
$208			$233	$233	$233	$2,500	
$233	$233	$233					$2,800
							12%

APPENDIX 8.1: MEMBERS EXCLUDED FROM MEASUREMENT

When determining whether to include or exclude a member, we assess whether the member inclusion or exclusion will contribute to a significant discontinuity in claims. For example, if a member were to be excluded only after the member's claims amounted to $100,000 in a year, the member's claim of $100,000 would be part of the baseline experience, while the member would contribute zero to the intervention period, thus potentially affecting the measured trend between the two periods.

Here we show some examples of individual claims patterns. The reader may extend the principles, however, to any other claim pattern.

The following are examples of specific exclusionary conditions, and how they may be handled:

- *End-stage Renal Disease (ESRD):* The course of ESRD is progressive over time, and management of the condition, while it may delay cost, cannot ultimately reduce or postpone those costs. Claims tend to follow the example below.

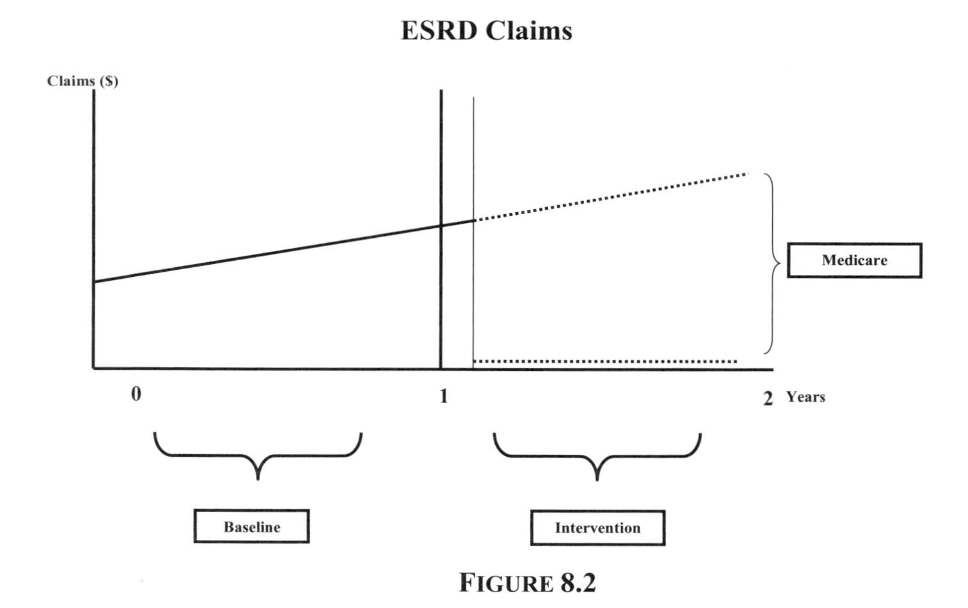

FIGURE 8.2

A secular upward trend in claims is insufficient reason to exclude these members. A more compelling reason (for Commercial members) is the discontinuity that occurs at 33 months after first dialysis treatment when Medicare accepts payment for these members as part of the Medicare End-stage renal disease program. This pattern is illustrated above, as the health plan's responsibility falls to near-zero at the point that the member is eligible for the Medicare program. Failure to recognize this discontinuity may distort the comparison of experience and trend over time. In our work, we exclude these members permanently and retroactively from measurement because the condition is permanent. For Medicare members, where the discontinuity does not exist, the member may be left in the group or retroactively excluded. Retroactive exclusion obviously reduces any potential distortion.

- *Transplants:* Members who have a transplant often experience high and rising claims up to a period shortly after the transplant, at which point the claims are reduced and stabilized. The claims pattern is similar to that of the member above, although for different reasons. A member who undergoes a transplant should probably be excluded. We recommend retroactive exclusion in order to avoid potential distortion.
- *HIV/AIDS, Mental health and other conditions* for which privacy issues make it difficult or impossible for a vendor to receive complete data feeds, or manage the member. Claims for these members may follow a reasonably regular pattern, and are likely to be lower than the claims of a member with End-stage renal disease, as demonstrated in Figure 8.3. For these members, exclusion can occur either prospectively from the point of first identification or retroactively to the beginning of the baseline period.

HIV/AIDS Claims

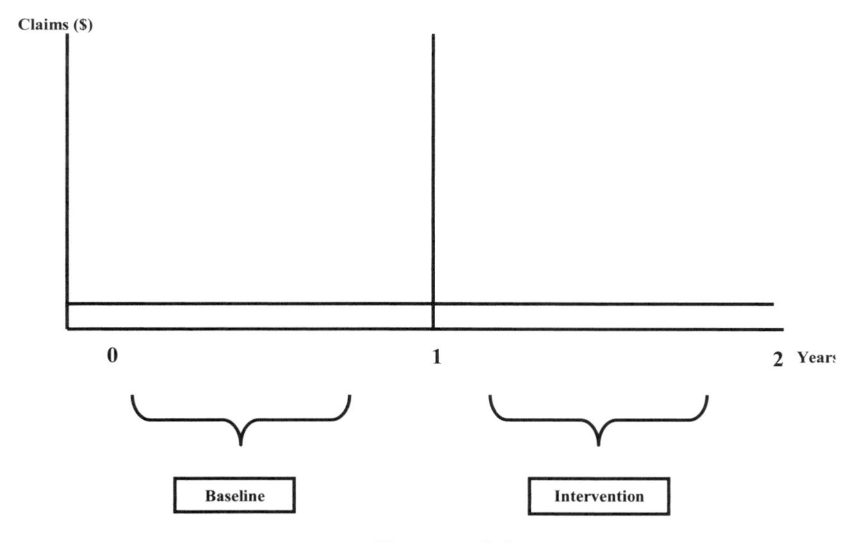

FIGURE 8.3

- *Members who are institutionalized* or who have a history of institutionalization (mental health, hospice, or nursing home) are examples of Members who are not reachable or who may not be able to benefit from disease management interventions. These members are also excluded permanently from measurement because their condition or status is more likely to make them permanently unsuitable for the program. These members often have high costs prior to identification with the exclusionary condition, so we recommend exclusion permanently and retroactively.
- *Members with catastrophic claims* are not manageable by the DM program, and are often subject to management by another program (for example, catastrophic case management). Figure 8.4 illustrates an example of a member with a random, catastrophic claim in the Baseline period that is not repeated in the Intervention year. These claims tend to be excluded above a stop-loss point, or through the exclusion of

the entire member experience for the year. Because these events tend to be acute, traumatic or accidental in nature, members who are excluded in one period are eligible for inclusion in measurement in a subsequent period if they recover and continue to be eligible members. In some instances, a health plan may purchase specific stop-loss coverage. In this case, the specific stop-loss attachment point may be an appropriate level at which to impose a cut-off for evaluation purposes.

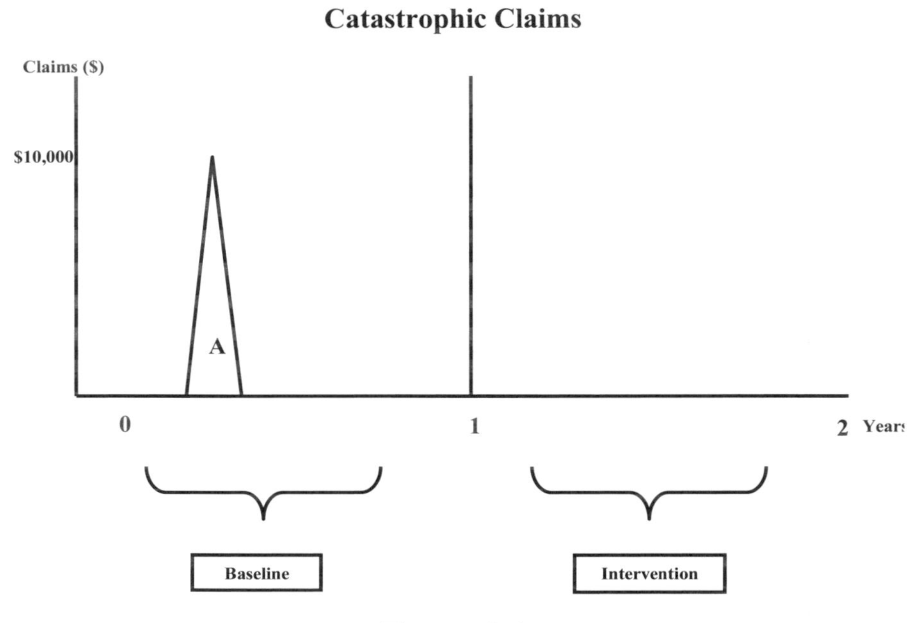

FIGURE 8.4

There is a common belief in the industry that a chronic population must be at significant risk of catastrophic claims, because average member cost is high. It is true that chronic patients are more likely to experience high costs, but the incidence of these claimants in a chronic population is still relatively rare. As an example, some data on the distribution of claims by amount within a commercial HMO is provided below.

Distribution of Members within Each Sub-population

Group	< $1,000	$1,000 -$9,999	$10,000 - $49,999	$50,000 - $99,999	$100,000 +	TOTAL
Chronic	52.04%	39.07%	8.42%	0.41%	0.06%	100.00%
Non-Chronic	82.33%	16.62%	1.01%	0.03%	0.00%	100.00%
Excluded[2]	83.91%	13.33%	0.27%	0.04%	0.03%	100.00%
TOTAL	81.00%	17.35%	1.52%	0.09%	0.04%	100.00%

[2] Members who have exclusionary conditions such as those discussed in this appendix.

Distribution of Costs within Each Sub-population						
Group	< $1,000	$1,000 -$9,999	$10,000 - $49,999	$50,000 - $99,999	$100,000 +	TOTAL
Chronic	6.61%	37.94%	46.21%	6.77%	2.47%	100.00%
Non-Chronic	25.37%	52.43%	19.30%	2.12%	0.78%	100.00%
Excluded	9.44%	24.06%	29.98%	12.70%	23.82%	100.00%
TOTAL	19.46%	44.81%	25.46%	4.85%	5.43%	100.00%

This data has been taken from a Disease Management analysis, and accordingly, members who have an excluded condition (End-stage renal disease, HIV/AIDS, transplant or institutionalization) are identified separately ("Excluded" members above). We do not have a break-down of these members by chronic/non-chronic status, but the fact that the member has an excluded condition implies that the member's cost is largely driven by that condition. Of note is the fact that the percentage of all chronic members whose costs exceed $100,000 is less than 1% (0.06%). Relatively few Excluded members have high costs as well because members may be excluded for reasons other than condition (insufficient months of eligibility, for example).

The percentage of chronic member costs that arise from members with costs in excess of $100,000 is 2.47% for chronic members. Thus a health plan with specific stop-loss above $100,000 is not likely to be much affected by the catastrophic claims exclusion. Even an employer with a lower stop-loss limit will not find much of his costs excluded. At the $50,000 level, 9.24% of claims are for claimants in excess of $50,000. The percentage of claims in excess of $50,000 will be less than this percentage.

- *Members who are eligible for other management programs*, such as members who are participating in case management, or eligible for another disease management program (not part of the measurement program): these members should be excluded based on objective criteria, prospectively from the point of identification as eligible for the program. Members in Case Management represent a particularly difficult issue for measurement. Because of the selection that exists in the enrollment of patients in such programs, the exclusion of enrolled Case Management patients would result in bias. Ideally, a set of objective, claims based criteria would exist that would allow the identification of a Case Management eligible population that may then be excluded as a class from the measurement population. Well-defined, objective criteria exist for many targets for case management (many of the categories discussed here are candidates). Many candidates are referred by providers rather than identified through claims, making objective identification difficult. A compromise solution may be to include all members in the measurement, irrespective of the program and who is performing the management. The outcomes so measured would be those for the combined programs. The overall savings may then be split into those from different programs on a reasonable basis agreed between the parties.

TABLE 8.5

Member Exclusions: Summary			
Type of Condition	Why Exclude?	Whether to Exclude	When to Exclude?
End Stage Renal Disease	High and increasing claims period to period. Claim discontinuity when CMS becomes responsible for claims	Medicare: No Commercial: Yes	Medicare: may be included, if the ESRD population is large. Commercial: exclude retrospectively.
HIV/AIDS	Claim discontinuity (increase) post-diagnosis.	Yes	Retrospectively or Prospectively
Transplants	Claim discontinuity (reduction) post-transplant.	Yes	Retrospectively or Prospectively
Institutionalized	Data not always available (psych) and population difficult to manage. Population may already be under full-time management (hospice; long-term care)	Yes	Prospectively
Members with catastrophic claims (e.g. > $100,000)	Significant utilization relative to other members; creates noise and potentially distorts comparison	Yes	Retrospectively for current period only; alternatively exclude claims above a stop-loss point.
Members eligible for other programs	Often the responsibility of another program or vendor.	Yes	Retrospectively (if pre-identification claims are significant) otherwise prospectively; alternatively, include in population and measure overall effect of multiple programs.

APPENDIX 8.2: EXAMPLE OF CLAIMS EXCLUSION CRITERIA

Caveat

The identification of claims for exclusion should take into account the availability of detailed information in the claim system. The level of diagnosis information that is retained within the claim system is a carrier decision. Some carriers will retain multiple diagnoses; others may retain only the primary diagnosis.

In the event that it is demonstrated that an exclusionary condition is related to the chronic condition, (for example an accident or trauma event that results from a hypoglycemic episode in a diabetic), the actuary may choose to include a claim that would otherwise be excluded.

Claims with a primary or secondary diagnosis within the following ranges are excluded from measurement.

1. Trauma and Accident
   Typical trauma exclusions include bone fractures, injuries, and burns. These claims cover the range of 8xx.xx and 9xx.xx ICD9 series.

Condition	Codes
Fractures	800 - 829
Dislocations	830 - 839
Sprains & Strains	840 - 849
Injuries & Open Wounds Traumatic Complications	850 - 904, 910 - 939, 950 - 959
Late Effects of Injuries, Poisonings, Toxic Effects & Other External Causes	905 - 909
Burns	940 - 949
Poisoning by Drugs, Medicinal & Biological Substances	960 - 979
Toxic Effects of Substances Chiefly Nonmedicinal as to Source	980 - 989
Other and Unspecified Effects of External Cause	990 - 994
Complications of Surgical & Medical Care NEC	995 - 999

2. Behavioral and Substance Abuse Diagnoses
   As we discussed earlier, members who have a psychiatric or substance abuse diagnosis are not good candidates for a DM program. A health plan often carves-out these services and places them with a specialty vendor. It is sometimes difficult to obtain the full history of psychiatric or substance abuse claims in this instance. Members with a history of institutionalization may be under full time care of a provider, or may not be at the point in recovery where self-care is an option. Nevertheless, this exclusion is likely to be controversial, particularly when the customer and the vendor explicitly agree that the DM program should cover these members.

3. Malignant Neoplasms

   Excluded claims are those with diagnosis codes in the range greater than or equal to 140 and strictly less than 210. In addition, claims in the range V10.x are excluded. Cancer is another condition that DM programs are not generally able to manage, and members are often subject to management by a specialty program. We do not, however, argue for complete exclusion of members with a cancer diagnosis. Depending on the specific criteria used to identify patients, this could represent a large subset of the chronic population, particularly if the criteria identify members who have a prior history of cancer but who are now in remission. These members often represent appropriate candidates for chronic disease management and their measurement is appropriate.

4. Maternity and Childbirth Claims
   Unless the DM program targets maternity, maternity should be excluded because a standard chronic program will not cover these conditions. Maternity exclusion criteria are based on primary diagnosis codes within the standard maternity-related ranges identified as normal delivery and "Complications of Pregnancy, Childbirth and the Puerperium" (Diagnosis codes 630 - 679). These codes include:

   - Ectopic and Molar Pregnancy
   - Other Pregnancy with Abortive Outcome
   - Complications Mainly Related to Pregnancy
   - Normal Delivery and other Indications for care in Pregnancy Labor and Delivery
   - Complications Occurring Mainly in the Course of Labor and Delivery
   - Complications of the Puerperium

   In addition, maternity exclusion criteria include appropriate "V" codes associated with pregnancy management. These codes include:

   - V22 Normal Pregnancy
   - V23 Supervision of High Risk Pregnancy
   - V24 Postpartum Care and Examination
   - V26 Procreative Management
   - V27 Outcome of Delivery
   - V28 Antenatal Screening

5. Pharmaceutical Drugs
   The exclusion of outpatient pharmaceutical drug claims (retail and mail-order) is probably the most controversial category of potential exclusion. Pharmaceutical drug claims may be a candidate for exclusion, particularly in a large employer or self-insured environment, because this coverage is highly volatile due to changes in benefits design, provider, etc. on a more frequent basis than hospital or physician coverage.

APPENDIX 8.3: AN EXAMPLE OF MEMBER CLASSIFICATION OVER TIME

In this example we show a member with no exclusionary conditions who experiences the first chronic identification event (an Emergency Room visit for Chronic Obstructive Pulmonary Disease (COPD)) on 3/15/2002. The member is continuously eligible 2001 through 2005.

Example of Application of Member Classification over Time

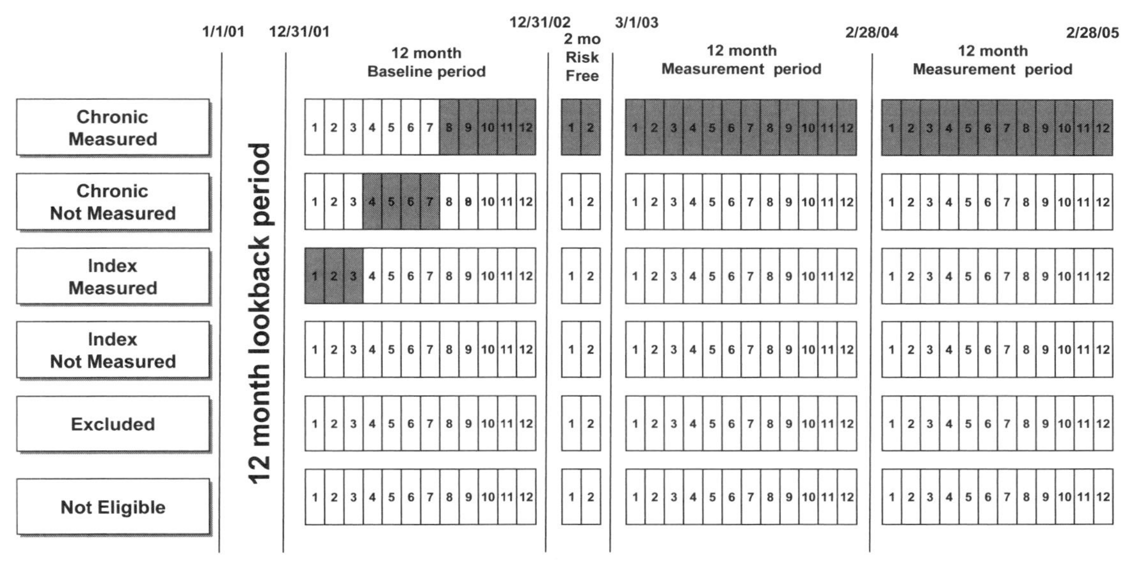

FIGURE 8.5

Figure 8.5 is an example of the application of the exposure classification to this member. In the grid, the member's progression over time between classifications may be clearly seen. In this example the member was enrolled in the plan prior to the Baseline period (which begins 1/1/02). The member was initially non-chronic and had more than 6 months of prior eligibility, so was classified as Index Measured for the first three months of the Baseline period. (The member does not have any evidence of exclusionary conditions that would result in the member being included in the Excluded category.) The Member was then identified as Chronic due to a claim in the third month of the Baseline period. The member is therefore Incident (newly-identified) Chronic Non-Measured for the four months required for the member to reach the claim free status that allows the member to be classified as Chronic Measured. The member will be Chronic Measured for the balance of the measurement period, and (assuming no requirement to re-qualify under the chronic definition and no change in eligibility) will continue in this segment until eligibility ceases.

Several optional choices for a health plan are illustrated by this example: is the definition of chronic condition "once chronic always chronic" or is some form of regular re-qualification required? Will members who terminate eligibility and then re-join the health plan receive credit for prior membership (to qualify as measured) or claims/chronic status (to qualify as chronic)?

9 UNDERSTANDING PATIENT RISK AND ITS IMPACT ON CHRONIC AND NON-CHRONIC MEMBER TRENDS

9.1 INTRODUCTION

The Actuarially-adjusted Historical Control Methodology (as described in Chapter 8) remains the most popular method for demonstrating the value of DM in commercial programs. One key characteristic of this methodology is that it is a population-based technique, in which the experience of the entire chronic diseased population in a baseline time period is compared to the entire chronic disease population in an intervention time period. The methodology relies on an often-implicit assumption that equivalence between baseline and intervention period chronic populations is maintained by a combination of large populations, with a stable distribution of risks between high and low-risk members. An important aspect of the use of this methodology, therefore, is the assessment and demonstration of the equivalence between baseline and intervention years, particularly in populations subject to shifts in size, composition and/or benefit structures.

Another challenge in an actuarially-based disease management savings calculation is the projection of the baseline cost of the entire chronic population to the intervention period in order to estimate the costs that *would* have been incurred had the DM program not been implemented (Bachler, Duncan & Juster [8]). The challenge is to find a trend estimate that appropriately estimates what would have happened in the chronic population, absent the intervention. Since chronic members in a program period are subject to management by DM, any estimate of trend from the chronic members will be influenced by program impacts, thus distorting the estimated impact of the program. A trend external to the chronic population is an essential component of a population based pre-post method. One such external trend can be estimated from the non-chronic members.

Regarding trend, DMAA in its Measurement Guidelines recommends using 2 or 3 years of data (pre-intervention) to compare chronic trend with non-chronic trend for the same population as being intervened currently, and applying this relationship prospectively as an adjustment to the non-chronic trend used for the savings calculation[1]. While this is a useful comparison, it may be impractical because the data are not available, and because changes in commercial populations over time render the comparison suspect.

[1] See Outcome Guidelines Report [155].

9.2 TRANSITION STATES AND THEIR EFFECT ON EQUIVALENCE AND TREND

In a typical DM evaluation, the chronic population "matures" between the baseline and intervention periods simply because one more year passes. Maintaining the same mix of "illness duration" is typically not considered in studies of financial outcomes. In a typical DM evaluation, only three years of data are available, making it difficult to analyze duration since initial diagnosis. Instead, population studies typically assume that the baseline and intervention period populations contain members of the same degree of severity. Nevertheless, when the mix changes significantly, it is possible to separate "select" (incident, or newly-diagnosed members) from "ultimate" members (those identified with the condition before the baseline period), analyze these members separately, and apply a weighting to the results of each group.

9.2.1 Transition States (the Markov Model)

A potentially interesting area of future research is the application of transition state analysis. This is similar to a select and ultimate analysis, except that movement is allowed both upward and downward. The following diagram illustrates the effect of transition probabilities (in this case, the probabilities result in stable risk stratification). In this example, for simplicity, we assume a closed group, with members transitioning between states but neither leaving nor entering the group. Chronic members are distributed between High Risk, Medium Risk and Low Risk groups in Period 1, each of which has its own average cost per member per year. Different transition probabilities apply between different risk levels, tracking the tendency of members to transition to other states in the following year.

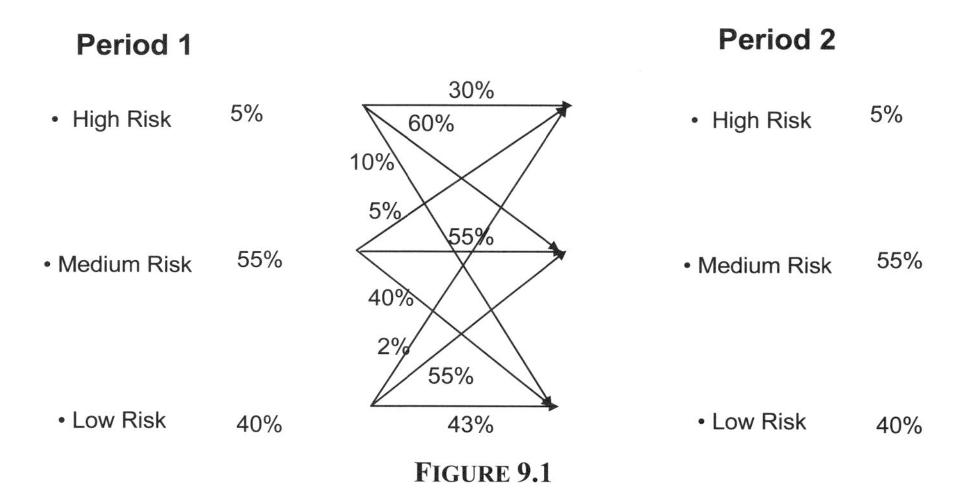

FIGURE 9.1

Very small changes in the transition probabilities can result in relatively large changes in cost. The following example applies transition probabilities to costs, in an example where transition probabilities result in slight changes in risk stratification.

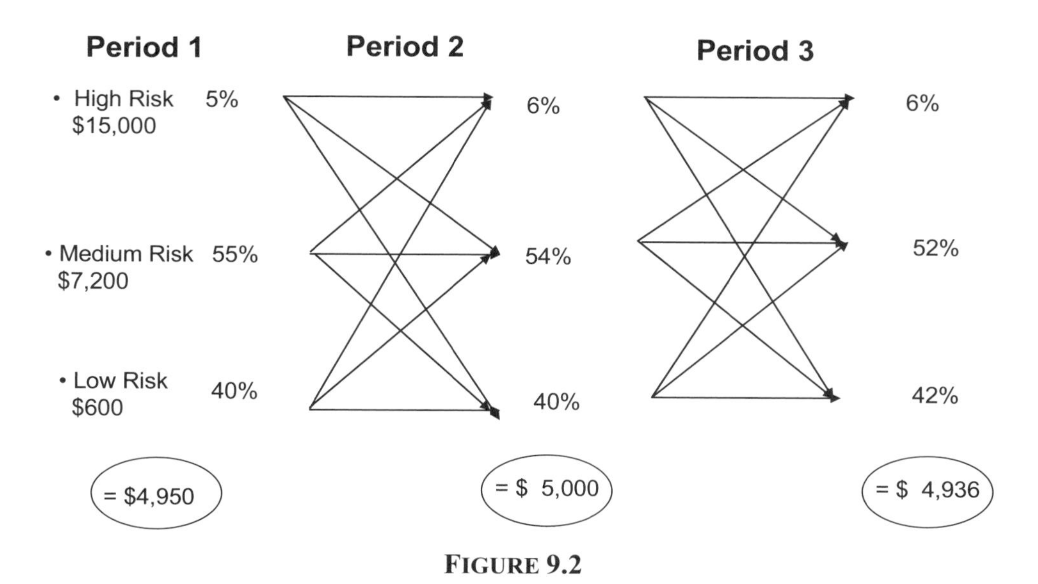

FIGURE 9.2

This analysis may be expanded by increasing the number of states to include disease free, formerly diseased (those members who meet the identification criteria in one year but fail to qualify the following year) and newly-diagnosed. Termination is obviously another state not considered here for simplicity. It is possible to demonstrate that, under certain transition probabilities, the system converges rapidly and results in a stable distribution by state, year after year. A completely stable population will result in constant per member per year costs (absent any underlying trend effects such as changes in utilization or unit cost increases). In our example, Year 2 costs increase by 1.7% from Year 1 because of the change in risk-mix or profile, while Year 3 represents a 2% reduction from Year 2 costs, again because of change in risk-profile. In a typical DM outcomes study, this change in risk-profile will not be isolated and will, instead, contribute to the overall measured trend in the population.

The transition probabilities and time to convergence lend themselves to further analysis and could help us to understand how closely any one-year state is to a stable state. Probabilities that indicate slow convergence of the model would lead one to conclude that the underlying hypothesis (that the baseline population is a reliable control for the intervention population, except for the utilization and unit cost trends) should not be accepted.

While no work has been published (to our knowledge) in the disease management field on this topic, it represents a potentially fruitful area for actuarial analysis.

This chapter explores the circumstances under which it is reasonable to use the non-chronic trend as a proxy for the trend that would have been experienced by the chronic group. To account for potential confounding changes in chronic population mix, a risk adjustment method is suggested that assures equivalence between the baseline and intervention period chronic populations without distorting programmatic impacts.

9.3 EQUIVALENCE, TRANSITION STATES, AND TREND

9.3.1 Using Trend In DM Calculations

A claim sometimes made by practitioners of DM evaluation is that the use of trend in a DM calculation "inflates" the results. This claim is untrue, as the following example illustrates. Here, units per 1000 represents the utilization of the population. The utilization trend, or increase in units per 1000 between the baseline and intervention years is 2%. In the example the reduction in admissions per 1000 between the baseline and intervention years due to the intervention is 3 admissions per 1000. While this is valuable information and helps to convince DM program purchasers of the efficacy of a program, it does not satisfy the needs of most clients, who need dollar savings numbers (for ROI calculations or guarantee evaluation purposes, for example).

TABLE 9.1

	Units per 1000
Baseline	100.00
Utilization Trend	1.02
Trended Baseline	102.00
Actual	99.00
Reduction	3.00

We therefore need to convert the calculation from a utilization unit basis to a cost basis, by multiplying by an average cost per unit.

TABLE 9.2

	Units per 1000	Unit Cost	Cost PMPM
Baseline	100.00	$8,000.00	$66.67
Trend	1.02	1.10	1.12
Trended Baseline	102.00	$8,800.00	$74.80
Actual	99.00	$8,800.00	$72.60
Reduction	3.00	$8,800.00	$2.20

In terms of the standard DM methodology, the effect of the program is estimated as Baseline PMPM cost ($66.67) multiplied by Cost Trend (1.12) less actual PMPM cost ($72.60). We should note, however, that the same result is achieved by calculating the reduction in admissions (3.00) multiplied by the Intervention period Unit Cost ($8,800) and then converting to a PMPM cost by dividing by 1,000. ($3\times\frac{8,800}{(12\times1,000)}=2.20$.) The same result may also be achieved by using the Baseline period unit cost ($8,000) multiplied by the unit cost trend (1.10), multiplied by the change in utilization. The key conclusion from this table, however, is the demonstration of equivalence between a utilization-unit based calculation of savings converted to dollars using a unit cost, and a PMPM-based calculation of savings. More important, this analysis disproves the hypothesis that the use of cost trend to adjust Baseline PMPM costs in a calculation somehow exaggerates the savings.

9.3.2 What is an Appropriate Trend To Use for Adjusting a Population's Experience?

Equivalence, a basic necessity for evaluating DM outcomes, requires stability in the underlying population risk between periods or populations. The issue of trend cannot be divorced from population identification and risk. Within a chronic population, an important contributor to trend is the change in overall members' risk-classification or status. Table 9.3 provides a simple example of the effect of changes in risk-mix on measured trend. In this example, 15% of the population is high risk in the Baseline year, 33% of the high-risk population remains high risk into the next (intervention) year, and the remainder (67%) transitions to a lower-risk status. The effect of different transition rates, even within a fixed population with constant costs per member per year is a decrease in PMPY, or a – 6% trend.

TABLE 9.3

	Baseline Year				Intervention Year	
	Prevalence	Transition Probability Up	Transition Probability Down	Cost	Prevalence	Cost
High Risk	15%	33%	67%	$5,000	13%	$5,500
Low Risk	85%	10%	90%	$500	87%	$500
	100%			$1,175	100%	$ 1,105
					Trend	–6%

The concept of the probability of transitioning between risk categories is an important underpinning of the trend-adjusted or standard methodology, which relies on stability of costs year-to-year (except for the effect of utilization and unit cost trends). The implicit assumption underlying this method is that the transitional probabilities result in a stable risk-mix. We have applied constant unit costs to demonstrate that the effect of change in risk-mix is to produce a (negative) trend. Our simple example shows that stability, period to period, may be difficult to achieve. In this particular example, the change in mix leads to an absolute reduction (-6%) in cost, which would tend to be attributed to an intervention program, had one been in place. These spurious savings would be further exaggerated by the application to the baseline period's costs of a trend adjuster calculated in the traditional way (for example, by using the non-chronic trend as an estimator). Table 9.4 illustrates the effect of this exaggeration in savings.

TABLE 9.4

	Baseline Year				Intervention Year	
	Prevalence	Transition Probability Up	Transition Probability Down	Cost	Prevalence	Cost
High Risk	15%	33%	67%	$5,000	13%	$ 5,500
Low Risk	85%	10%	90%	$ 500	87%	$ 500
	100%			$1,175	100%	$ 1,105
		Trend Adjuster		1.07		
		Adjusted Baseline		$1,257	Actual	$ 1,105
		"Program Effect"				$ 152
		Effect of Population Mix				$ (70)
		Reduction in Cost Due to Program				$ 82

Alternatively, knowing that the effect of population mix on trend is –6%, we could adjust the observed trend adjuster (7%) for this effect and use a net adjuster $7\% - 6\% = 1\%$ in the calculation.

9.3.3 Requirements That Must Be Met to Apply the Trend-Adjusted Method

We apply a trend adjuster to the baseline cost PMPY in order to allow for the utilization and unit cost increases that we observe or estimate. It is appropriate to apply a utilization and unit cost trend adjustment, as discussed above. Provided the underlying chronic population risk mix is stable (no underlying change in risk resulting in changes in cost) the application of a trend adjuster to correct for changes in utilization and unit cost trends will not bias the savings estimate. On the other hand, applying a trend adjustment to a chronic population with non-stable risk mix may result in a biased savings estimate.

9.3.4 Risk Adjustment

Actuaries have always practiced a form of risk adjustment by allowing for the effect on expected cost of changes in age and sex of the population. More recently, models have been developed that add the effect of a member's condition on risk and cost, recognizing that the condition (and its severity) will impact member resource use.

Risk Adjustment in DM is one practical method to ensure equivalence between populations with respect to their underlying risk. Risk Adjustment has to be used carefully because with DM there are occasions when non-equivalence (as measured by risk of the population) will be the product of an intervention program, so one does not wish to adjust-out the effect that one is attempting to measure. Risk Adjustment is appropriately applied when developing an index or adjuster trend from a reference population. If it is believed, however, that there is a change (not due to the intervention) in the chronic population, it may be difficult, if not impossible, to use Risk Adjustment to separate the effect of the intervention from other chronic population changes.

Risk Adjustment may be performed using any adjuster model, provided that the model is stable period-to-period and produces a reasonably high correlation between projected and actual costs. Models are available in the Public Domain (such as Medicare's Hierarchical Condition Categories (HCCs) or the Medicaid payment model (CDPS) from the University of San Diego). Commercial models (for which users pay license fees) are also available. The Society of Actuaries (SOA) performs regular analyses and comparisons of commercially-available risk-adjuster products (Cumming et al. [35] and Winkelman & Mehmud [220].

9.3.5 Risk Adjustment of Trend

Risk Adjustment is an appropriate technique to consider in a situation where an external trend adjuster is being developed (for example the population or non-chronic trends discussed above). Earlier, we examined the factors that affect trend, and noted that among them is change in the underlying risk-pool (population changes). The trend that is used to adjust from the baseline year of a chronic population to the intervention year of the chronic population should be net of the effect of any population changes. The paper referred to earlier (Bachler, Duncan and

Juster [8]) demonstrates one technique for risk-adjusting trend. In Table 9.5, the average population risk increases by 1% from baseline to intervention year, contributing to the measured trend. Observed trend is 6%, but allowing for change in average population risk, trend is reduced to 5%.

TABLE 9.5

Non-Chronic Population		
	Baseline Year	Intervention Year
PMPM	$100.00	$106.00
Trend (unadjusted)		6%
Average Risk Score	1.01	1.02
Risk Score Trend		1%
PMPM/Risk Score	$99.01	$103.92
Trend (adjusted for change in population risk)		5%

9.4 PRACTICAL APPLICATIONS

9.4.1 Adjustment for Risk Mix in the Chronic Population

The technique illustrated in Table 9.7 cannot be used in the intervention population without neutralizing the effect of the intervention. We therefore have to find a different method for correcting for changes in intervention population risk. Below, we discuss two alternative methods for assessing the effect of risk-change on cost, and test these methods by applying to a specific population.

9.4.2 Study Population

The study population was drawn from a state Medicaid plan that has purchased disease management for the chronic conditions of Asthma, Chronic Obstructive Pulmonary Disease (COPD), Coronary Artery Disease (CAD), Diabetes, and Congestive Heart Failure (CHF). A **Chronic** member was defined as any member who met one of the above five conditions based on the contract for either the baseline time period or the first program period. The contract specified a pre-baseline time period for identification of members that would then be part of the baseline calculations.

Although the data for this study is from a state Medicaid plan, the methods and rationale may readily be applied to other populations, for example commercial or Medicare (although results reported here may not be directly comparable). Medicaid programs are similar to other types of commercial indemnity programs, in that services are defined for eligible members (clients) and providers are reimbursed at contracted rates. Each state sets its own guidelines regarding eligibility. These guidelines may include a person's age, pregnancy status, disabled status, income, and other resources (see for example, U.S. Department Health and Human Services, available from the Centers for Medicare and Medicaid Services web-site). Medicaid poses analytical challenges in that many clients fail to enroll when first eligible and are therefore retroactively enrolled when services are rendered. Other clients are provided coverage (and managed by a DM program), only to have their eligibility terminated retroactively as the State Medicaid administrator becomes aware of other coverage for which the client qualifies. Clients are sometimes eligible for limited periods (because of eligibility rules) with multiple discrete eligibility periods within a year. Clients (particularly disabled and dual-eligible members) may also transfer between programs as their disability status changes. The members' disadvantaged socioeconomic backgrounds generally mean that their health status is poorer and that the prevalence of chronic conditions is higher than members of commercial health plans. Eligibility categories which provide temporary assistance exhibit high rates of "churn" - that is, individuals enter and leave the Medicaid program relatively more frequently than in commercial populations. Low income families with children often qualify for temporary assistance, as do disadvantaged individuals with disabilities. In eligibility categories with large proportions of children, the prevalence of asthma is very high.

9.4.3 Classification of the Study Population

For the study population, we performed five classification tests to determine if the member:

1. Qualified in the 12 months before the baseline (i.e., the pre-baseline period);
2. [Re-]qualified in the 12 months of the baseline;
3. [Re-]qualified in the 12 months of program Year 1;
4. Terminated in the baseline; or
5. Terminated in program Year 1.

"Qualified" means that the member was identified with a chronic condition based on the contractual identification criteria. "Terminated" means that the member was chronic at some point in the period (whether or not they [re-]qualified), but was not chronic at the end of the period or in any of the 12 months after the period. This could happen only by virtue of a clinical exclusion, a loss of Medicaid eligibility, or both.

These five classification tests were applied to the population to arrive at the tree structure in Figure 9.3. When these tests were applied to the population, each member was placed into one and only one of the tree's 16 terminal nodes. Cost and member month information for each node was then summarized separately for the baseline and program year periods.

Given the 16 terminal nodes, a "Traditional" DM methodology baseline chronic population can be defined as the population in terminal nodes 1 through 9 (all of which qualified in the pre-Baseline period) and nodes 12 through 16 (newly identified in the baseline year).

Similarly, given the 16 terminal nodes, a "Traditional" DM methodology program period Year 1 population can be defined as the population in terminal nodes 3 through 6, 8 through 11, and 13 through 16.

Study Population Determination and 16 Terminal Nodes

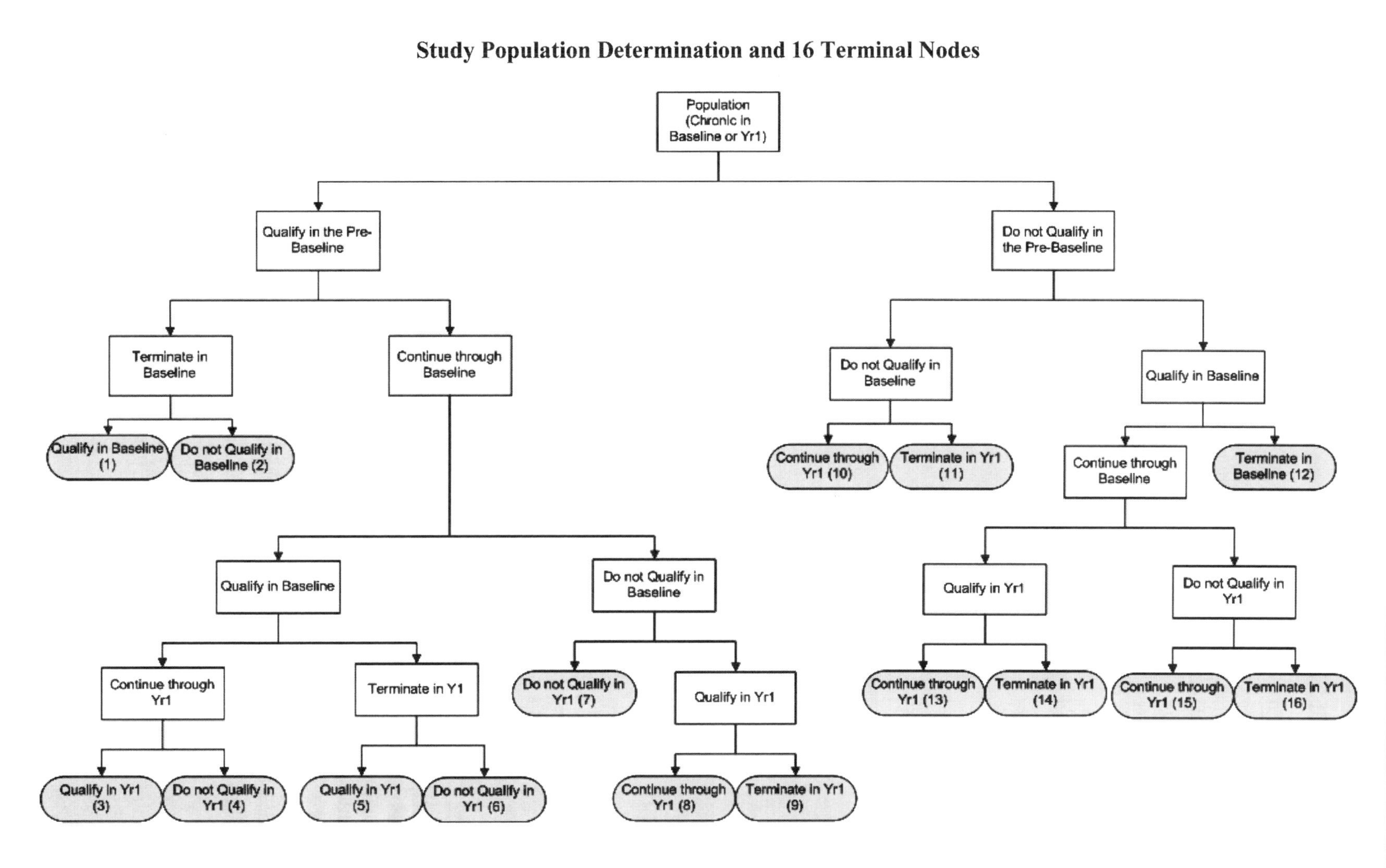

FIGURE 9.3

9.4.4 Risk Adjustment and Stratification

A population's change in risk (such as changes in the covered population's age, gender, geographic, co-morbidity, or employment mix) can distort a measured trend. The use of risk-adjustment, applied to the non-chronic population, normalizes that population's change in risk between periods. Thus, the measured trend, adjusted for the change in risk-level, is an estimate of the true, underlying effect of those trend factors that should be applied to a non-chronic population's cost in a baseline period when performing a study. The effect of risk changes on trend is illustrated by Figure 9.4.

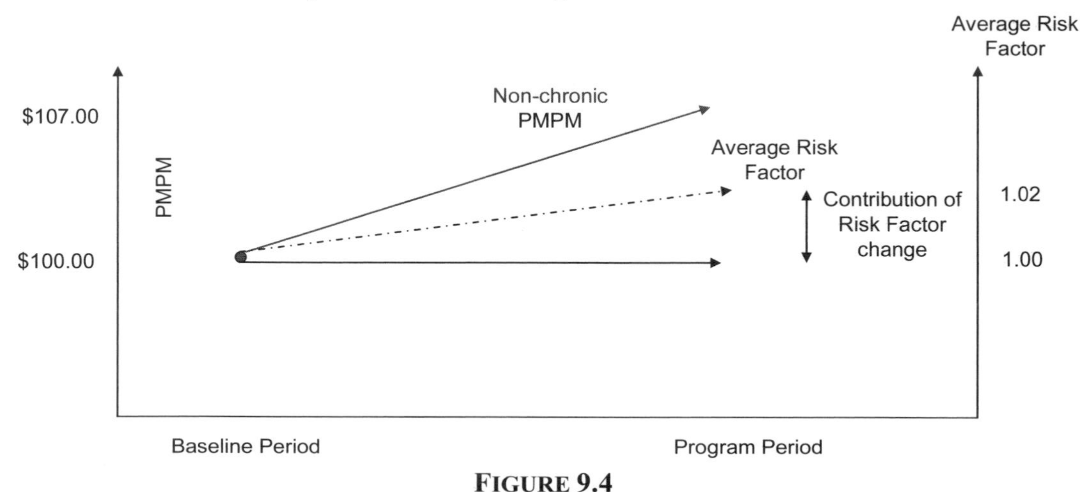

FIGURE 9.4

In Figure 9.4, the increase in non-chronic cost per member per month (left-hand scale) is 7% (from $100.00 to $107.00). The increase in the average risk-factor (right-hand scale) is 2% (from 1.00 to 1.02), which is a contributing factor to the 7% increase in average cost. In deriving a non-chronic trend for adjustment purposes, the increase in cost in a constant-risk population is required. Thus, we need to discount the 7% increase by the 2% increase in the average risk factor, which leaves a "constant risk" trend of 1.07/1.02 or 4.9%.

When projecting the chronic population's cost from the baseline period to the intervention period, an adjustment for (unbiased) trend is appropriate. Other changes may take place in the risk profile of the chronic group, independent of those due to the intervention. For example, if seriously ill members terminate as a result of the member's death or entry to a long-term care or hospice care facility, or new members enter who represent a less-severe risk than the baseline population, the average risk level (and cost) of the chronic population will fall. The trend adjuster that we apply is appropriate to a constant-risk population, but in order to apply it, we would need to demonstrate that the chronic population risk has not changed due to external factors.

One simple way to analyze these effects is to divide the chronic population into risk strata. One such stratification is to put people into one of three categories, continuing, new, or terminated. The risk strata are selected with high **inter-group** variance, while minimizing **intra-group** variance.

The strata are also selected in such a way that they may be measured objectively and without confounding the calculation (by including factors that are subject to the intervention). It is crucially important that risk adjustment for a chronic population does not distort the impact of the intervention. For example, if an intervention decreases diabetes emergency department visits, and diabetes risk is affected by emergency department visits, then (if the intervention is effective) the average risk of the chronic population will be reduced by the intervention. Making an adjustment for the reduction in chronic population risk will neutralize the effect of the intervention.

9.4.5 Transition States

Given the three risk strata of continuing, new, or terminated, there are some possible transition states as illustrated in Table 9.6.

TABLE 9.6

Stratification of the Chronic Population

	Baseline	Year 1	Year 2
Identified in Baseline, Continuing			
Identified in Baseline, Terminated in Baseline			
Identified in Baseline, Terminated in Year 1			
New in Year 1, Continuing			
New in Year 1, Terminated in Year 1			

The chronic population in any year consists of the non-shaded boxes in the table. Thus the average cost per member per month of the entire chronic population is an average of members in different transition states.

Our hypothesis is that the average cost of the different sub-groups varies significantly from the group average and that changes in the mix of sub-groups within the overall population can affect the overall average cost per member per month (PMPM) and therefore chronic trend. The sub-groups are not the only way to look at differential risk within the population, but they are a convenient means for analysis.

In our example from Table 9.5, different states are defined as follows:

- *Identified in baseline, continuing*: members who meet the chronic criteria in the Baseline period and who continue through Year 1.
- *Identified in baseline, terminated in baseline*: members who are identified as chronic during the Baseline period but who terminate prior to the start of Year 1.
- *Identified in baseline, terminated in Year 1*: members who are identified as chronic during the Baseline period but who terminate prior to the start of Year 2.
- *New Year 1, continuing*: Members who are identified as chronic in Year 1 who continue through to Year 2.
- *New Year 1, terminated in Year 1*: Members who join during Year 1 and who do not continue to Year 2.

9.4.6 Calculation of Savings

The challenge in a DM savings calculation is to project the baseline cost to the intervention period, as a valid estimation of the costs that would have applied had the program not been implemented. A risk adjustment method as described above would allow the Intervention Period Projected Cost to be estimated, as follows:

Intervention Period Projected Cost =

BaselinePeriod Cost PMPM *Continuing Population*
$\times(1+T)\times\#$ Member Months of Continuing Members *plus*

BaselinePeriod Cost PMPM for the *Terminating members* in the Baseline Period
$\times(1+T)\times\#$Member Months of Terminating Members in the Intervention Period *plus*

Baseline Period Cost PMPM *Newly – identified* members
$\times(1+T)\times\#$ Member Months of Newly – identified Members in the Intervention Period.

Where $(1+T)$ is the trend adjustor used to project the Baseline Period cost to the intervention period.

Such a calculation would normalize the population for changes in "mix" of new, terminating, and continuing members without distorting the DM programmatic impact.

We tested the hypothesis that sub-groups (selected based on their status) are a proxy for differential risk in the chronic population and that changes in the mix of these sub-groups affect the average cost PMPM of the chronic population, independent of any care management program.

9.5 RESULTS

9.5.1 Risk Normalizing by Continuing, New, and Terminating

The five classification sets described earlier consist of:

1. Qualified in the 12 months before the baseline (i.e., the pre-baseline period);
2. [Re-]qualified in the 12 months of the baseline;
3. [Re-]qualified in the 12 months of program Year 1;
4. Terminated in the baseline; or
5. Terminated in program Year 1

These rules were applied to the population and result in the tree structure with 16 terminal nodes in Figure 9.1.

The member months and PMPM results of all 16 nodes are shown in Table 9.7. As can be seen, the PMPMs between the baseline chronic group and the year 1 chronic group are different. The baseline chronic group had a PMPM of $705.19. In the program period, the chronic group had a PMPM of $620.80 reflecting a 12% decrease.

Summarizing the PMPM results into one of the three risk strata of terminating, continuing, or newly identified is shown in Table 9.8.

TABLE 11.4

Comparison of Chronic and Non-Chronic Service Cost PMPM and Service Mix

	ALL YEARS	Claims PMPM								ALL SERVICES
	Mem Mons	Inpatient	Outpatient	Presc Drug	Emerg Rm	Laboratory	Phys Ofc	Rehab	Other	TOTAL
NON-CHRONIC	10,964,214	$67.32	$68.53	$33.47	$5.24	$4.46	$40.90	$0.91	$7.58	$228.40
CHRONIC	750,281	$294.02	$197.69	$158.37	$9.69	$10.64	$99.34	$6.29	$35.10	$811.15
ALL	11,714,495	$81.84	$76.80	$41.47	$5.52	$4.86	$44.64	$1.25	$9.34	$265.72
	ALL YEARS	Service Category Weights								ALL SERVICES
	Mem Mons	Inpatient	Outpatient	Presc Drug	Emerg Rm	Laboratory	Phys Ofc	Rehab	Other	TOTAL
NON-CHRONIC	10,964,214	29.5%	30.0%	14.7%	2.3%	2.0%	17.9%	0.4%	3.3%	100.0%
CHRONIC	750,281	36.2%	24.4%	19.5%	1.2%	1.3%	12.2%	0.8%	4.3%	100.0%
ALL	11,714,495	30.8%	28.9%	15.6%	2.1%	1.8%	16.8%	0.5%	3.5%	100.0%

Table 11.4 above shows that the PMPM cost and relative service category utilization of Chronic and Non-chronic members is different, with chronic members being heavier utilizers of inpatient hospital, prescription drug, and rehabilitation services. These are all service categories that, for chronic members, have relatively low trends.

Table 11.5 compares the trends in Chronic and Non-chronic populations, by major service category. Trends are 3-year average annualized rates, calculated over the 4-year period. Different trends by service are observed in each sub-population and in the population as a whole, with non-chronic member trends generally higher than those of chronic members.

TABLE 11.5

Comparison of Chronic and Non-Chronic Trends by Service Category

	3-Yr annualized	Service Category Trends								ALL SERVICES
	Mem Mons	Inpatient	Outpatient	Presc Drug	Emerg Rm	Laboratory	Phys Ofc	Rehab	Other	TOTAL
NON-CHRONIC	10,964,214	12.3%	15.4%	11.0%	19.4%	10.8%	16.5%	12.8%	9.0%	13.8%
CHRONIC	750,281	6.6%	8.3%	1.1%	12.1%	0.6%	8.9%	– 9.5%	– 1.7%	5.7%
ALL	11,714,495	15.8%	17.2%	13.7%	20.0%	11.4%	17.7%	12.6%	11.3%	16.0%

Here it can be seen that the aggregate PMPM of the chronic population in the baseline of $705.19 is the result of aggregating the three risk strata PMPMs. The cost of the continuing population is close to the average in both periods, but both the newly-identified and terminating member costs vary considerably from the average. Comparing to this aggregate PMPM of $705.19, the terminating strata had a higher PMPM of $929.75, the continuing strata had a slightly higher PMPM of $706.53, and the newly identified strata had a lower PMPM of $601.71. A similar pattern and relationship for program period Year 1 was also noted between the aggregate and the individual strata.

For the purpose of calculating DM savings, let us assume that the non-chronic trend adjuster is 5%.

The standard DM calculation using the PMPM rates from Table 9.8, the aggregate PMPMs, the 5% trend adjuster, and the chronic member months in year 1 would be:

$$\$705.19 \times 1.05 - \$620.60 = \$119.65 \text{ PMPM}$$

Number of chronic member months in Year 1: 299,042

$$\text{Estimated Savings} = 299{,}042 \times \$119.65 = \$35{,}780{,}832$$

Taking into account shifts in risk mix as discussed above (using the three strata – terminating, continuing and new), we would normalize the baseline population to match the risk-mix of the Year 1 population as shown in Table 9.4. The aggregate baseline PMPM is still $705.19, but the re-weighted PMPM is now higher at $724.15. This re-weighted PMPM was calculated from the three individual risk strata PMPMs weighted by the Year 1 member months. In this case, the re-weighted PMPM ($724.15) was calculated as

$$(\$929.75 \times 18\%) + (\$706.53 \times 60\%) + (\$601.71 \times 22\%).$$

The weights are the program Year 1 member months for each of the three risk strata.

TABLE 9.8

PMPM Re-weighted by Risk Group

Group	Average Cost Baseline PMPM	Year 1 Member Month Percent	Average Cost Year 1 PMPM
Terminating	$929.75	18%	$721.73
Continuing	$706.53	60%	$623.80
Newly Identified	$601.71	22%	$528.11
Total	$705.19	100%	$620.60
Re-weighted	$724.15		
Trended	$760.36		

Using Table 9.8 as the basis of the standard calculation and the aggregate re-weighted baseline PMPMs, year 1 PMPMs, the 5% trend adjuster, and the chronic member months in year 1, results are:

Basic savings: $119.65 PMPM or $35,780,832 in total

Using re-weighted average cost:

$$\$724.15 \times 1.05 - \$620.60 = \$139.56 \text{ PMPM}$$

Number of chronic member months in Year 1: 299,042

$$\text{Estimated savings} = 299{,}042 \times \$139.56 = \$41{,}733{,}554$$

When applying the distribution of members from year 1, the re-weighted PMPM as well as the savings PMPM both increase. Thus, risk adjustment using the three strata of continuing, new, or terminated does have significant impacts on measured savings from the DM program. The savings without risk adjustment is $35,780,832 whereas the savings with risk adjustment is $41,733,554.

9.5.2 Risk Normalizing by Changes in Chronic Condition

Another source of change in chronic population risk over time is changes in conditions and co-morbidities. A similar calculation to that above could be done at a condition category level. With 5 chronic conditions, there are 31 condition categories, as shown in Table 9.9.[2]

[2] This table excludes one eligibility group. Hence the totals do not correspond to preceding tables.

TABLE 9.9

PMPM by Condition Group				
Chronic Condition	**Average Cost Baseline PMPM**	**Member Months Baseline**	**Average Cost Year 1 PMPM**	**Member Months Year 1**
Asthma	$587.43	45,279	$606.75	45,521
CAD	$521.51	17,219	$525.47	14,641
CHF	$574.26	4,333	$553.47	3,618
COPD	$595.08	13,852	$525.82	12,485
Diabetes	$495.50	66,742	$521.55	59,047
Asthma & CAD	$698.99	2,205	$688.11	1,791
Asthma & CHF	$938.22	829	$1,211.46	728
Asthma & COPD	$858.41	15,748	$763.01	14,143
Asthma & Diabetes	$696.14	7,513	$662.64	6,337
CAD & CHF	$890.73	4,878	$857.00	4,061
CAD & COPD	$833.78	5,624	$703.62	5,308
CAD & Diabetes	$762.71	22,786	$791.20	18,987
CHF & COPD	$979.51	1,898	$950.95	1,554
CHF & Diabetes	$797.94	5,275	$736.61	4,228
COPD & Diabetes	$712.71	6,187	$806.86	5,846
Asthma & CAD & CHF	$1,026.22	597	$917.79	719
Asthma & CAD & COPD	$947.81	2,564	$898.94	2,521
Asthma & CAD & Diabetes	$921.92	2,089	$916.60	2,091
Asthma & CHF & COPD	$1,172.99	1,513	$1,156.95	1,152
Asthma & CHF & Diabetes	$1,046.79	1,044	$788.90	761
Asthma & COPD & Diabetes	$1,003.77	5,242	$869.19	4,863
CAD & CHF & COPD	$1,269.28	3,929	$1,219.22	3,142
CAD & CHF & Diabetes	$1,141.84	10,391	$1,009.50	8,036
CAD & COPD & Diabetes	$970.40	3,933	$1,006.26	3,514
CHF & COPD & Diabetes	$1,055.43	2,082	$981.09	1,532
Asthma & CAD & CHF & COPD	$1,708.55	2,017	$1,456.85	1,533
Asthma & CAD & CHF & Diabetes	$1,264.14	1,375	$1,276.83	935
Asthma & CAD & COPD & Diabetes	$1,065.95	2,257	$1,235.85	1,906
Asthma & CHF & COPD & Diabetes	$1,487.47	2,086	$1,404.62	1,304
CAD & CHF & COPD & Diabetes	$1,640.84	5,430	$1,440.18	4,257
Asthma & CAD & CHF & COPD & Diabetes	$1,799.27	3,765	$1,716.11	2,510
Total	**$725.99**	**270,682**	**$697.04**	**239,071**
Re-weighted	**$709.94**			

Using the observed data, the savings calculation is:

$$\$725.99 \times 1.05 - \$697.04 \;=\; \$65.25$$

Using the Year 1 distribution of conditions to re-weight the Baseline PMPM the savings calculation is:

$$\$709.94 \times 1.05 - \$697.04 \;=\; \$48.39$$

By normalizing for changes in the distribution of chronic conditions in the chronic population, the estimated savings are reduced. The PMPM savings without co-morbidity adjustment is $65.25 whereas the PMPM savings with co-morbidity adjustment decreases to $48.39. Total estimated savings without adjustment is $15.6 million ($65.25 PMPM * 239,071 member months) whereas total savings with adjustment is $11.6 million ($48.39 PMPM * 239,071 member months). In this case, adjusting for the effect of change in risk profile represented by member conditions reduces savings by 26%.

9.6 APPLICABILITY TO OTHER POPULATIONS

The methods described in this chapter are applicable to other populations (Medicare, Commercial) as long as data exists that enables the analyst to classify members by duration (new, continuing, terminated, for example) or by condition category. The specific costs for different conditions will be different by type of population, so our results, while indicative, cannot be directly applied to other populations. Other Medicaid populations, too, may differ, depending on state coverage rules and reimbursement contracts, so any extrapolation of results to specific populations should be performed with caution.

9.7 CONCLUSION

The standard DM savings calculation depends for its validity on the comparability of populations between the baseline and intervention years (Year 1). We have examined the effect on the standard DM savings calculation of two typical factors that reduce the equivalence between baseline and intervention chronic populations:

- Change in the mix of new, continuing, and terminating members (and their relative costs); and
- Changes in condition and co-morbidities.

Our hypothesis was that the average cost of the different sub-groups varies significantly from the overall average and that changes in the mix of sub-groups within the overall population can affect the overall average cost per member per month (PMPM) and therefore chronic trend. This hypothesis was confirmed by using risk strata subgroups as well as co-morbidity subgroups.

In both cases we have shown that these factors can have a significant effect on the standard savings calculation. We have also shown that it is possible to correct for the distortion introduced into the calculation in each case by re-weighting the baseline population cost without distorting the DM programmatic impact.

Even if no adjustment is made for these effects, it would be important to test a population for either of them before the results of a savings calculation are accepted.

This chapter has examined the circumstances under which it is reasonable to use the non-chronic trend as a proxy for the trend that would have been experienced by the chronic group. A risk adjustment method is suggested to account for potential confounding changes in the chronic population mix. This thus assures equivalence between the baseline and intervention period chronic populations without distorting programmatic impacts.

10 Random Fluctuations and Validity in Measuring Disease Management Effectiveness for Small Populations

10.1 Introduction

One objective of a Disease Management (DM) program is the reduction of members' claims costs. A considerable amount of effort has been dedicated to standardizing DM outcomes measurement. An area that has not received as much attention is that of random fluctuations in measured outcomes, and the related issue of the validity of outcomes subject to random fluctuation. From year to year, large random fluctuations in claim costs can increase or reduce potential savings from a DM program, as well as confound the measurement of actual savings. Sponsors of DM programs want to know how large a group or sample is necessary so that the effect of random fluctuations does not overwhelm the effect of claims reductions.

In this chapter, we measure the fluctuations in calculated DM savings in a large commercial population using an adjusted historical control methodology (the methodology that has become the industry standard and which is codified by DMAA's Guidelines). We then determine the sample size necessary to demonstrate DM program savings at different levels of confidence, and model the effect on fluctuations in observed outcomes under different methods of choosing trend, different levels of truncation, and for different estimates of program savings.

Some groups, particularly employers, will be smaller than the minimum size required for credible outcomes measurement. For such smaller groups, we suggest a utilization-based outcomes measure that can be used as a proxy. For both claims and utilization-based calculations, we provide confidence intervals to be placed around savings estimates. We do this for group sizes ranging from 1,000 to 100,000 members. We also provide charts of continuous distributions of confidence intervals and group sizes, under different truncation assumptions, that will allow a DM program sponsor to assess credibility for any size of group.

For smaller populations, it may be difficult to demonstrate that observed savings are the result of the intervention rather than the result of random statistical fluctuation. This becomes a particularly difficult problem when the group being measured seeks a guaranteed return on its investment in a DM program. As DM has penetrated deeper into employer groups, even smaller groups with fewer than 1,000 employees may seek guarantees. DM providers need to know at what size the program can comfortably provide such a guarantee.

To help answer this question, we calculate the relationship between employer group size and the confidence intervals around a savings estimate. The larger the group size, the less chance that random fluctuations will overwhelm savings. In addition, the larger the program effect (underlying savings) the less likely that random fluctuations will overwhelm savings. We provide tables of group sizes necessary to demonstrate various confidence levels (68%, 90%, and 95%) and at various levels of DM savings (5%, 10%, and 15% of total chronic costs). We also provide tables of confidence intervals at employer group sizes from 1,000 to 100,000.

Our base measurement method uses a group-specific trend (calculated from the non-chronic members of the employer group) with no truncation of claims for high-cost claimants. We then generate similar results under alternative assumptions:

- Replacing the group-specific trend with a population trend;
- Applying different truncation methods to counter the volatility due to high-cost claims;
- Measuring utilization (admissions) rather than chronic claims costs; and
- Analyzing the variability in single diseases rather than the entire chronic population.

10.2 Methods

Our objective is to measure the confidence interval that may be placed around estimated savings at the 95%, 90% or 68% confidence level for different expected savings levels. To do so, we need to measure the random fluctuations that can occur in the course of the measurement process. Obviously, larger sample sizes produce narrower confidence intervals. From basic statistics, we expect that confidence intervals will decrease proportionally to the square root of the increase in sample size. Said differently, to halve the width of the confidence interval, increase the sample size by a factor of 4.

10.2.1 Data

We use a commercial claims database of over 800,000 members to generate a chronic population in the base year. We follow the claims of groups of these members into the "measurement" year and observe the range of deviations from expected. This range of deviations allows us to calculate the tables providing group sizes and confidence intervals. To maintain the same group size in the base year and measurement year, we add new members in the measurement year. Specific details are provided below in the section "Method of Simulation."

10.2.2 Diseases

We focus on the five most commonly managed chronic diseases of Diabetes, Coronary Artery Disease (CAD), Congestive Heart Failure (CHF), Chronic-Obstructive Pulmonary Disease (COPD), and Asthma. A member was classified as having the disease if there was either one inpatient claim or two other claims with an appropriate diagnosis. Specific details are provided in Appendix 10.1.

10.2.3 The Adjusted Historical Control Method

The adjusted historical control (AHC) methodology is the most widely-used method for estimating DM program savings, and forms the basis of DMAA's Guidelines. In this method, experience of a chronic population is measured in a base year, and again in a program year. In our database, the base year is 2005 and the measurement year is 2006. The AHC model measures savings by multiplying the base year per member per month (PMPM) cost of a chronic condition by a trend and then comparing this product to the measurement year PMPM. If the DM program worked, then there should be a difference between the trended baseline PMPM cost and the actual PMPM cost.

In order to keep the two periods as equivalent as possible, we require re-qualification for each period. Specifically, for a member to be considered to have a chronic condition in the base year there must be a qualifying claim in either the 12 months prior to the base year (the "pre-base year") or in the base year itself. The member is considered as chronic from the month of qualification through the end of the base year.

Similarly, for a member to have a chronic condition in the measurement year there must be a qualifying claim in either the base year or the measurement year. So a member whose only claim was in 2004 would qualify as chronic for all of 2005, but would not qualify as chronic in 2006. For 2006, the member would have to re-qualify by having claims in 2005 or 2006.

Consistent with the DMAA methodology, we excluded certain members from the study based on their having conditions which are not amenable to nurse-telephonic chronic disease intervention, or which are traditionally subject to case management programs. These conditions include Aids/HIV, Dialysis, Cancer, Transplants, Maternity, Infertility, Respiratory diseases, and Hemophilia. Members with these conditions were removed from all periods. Trauma claims were also removed from the study.

The remaining member months were assigned to a chronic condition or "none" based on the descending hierarchy: Diabetes, CAD, CHF, COPD, Asthma, and none. Classification was based on the presence of claims meeting the criteria of Appendix 10.1.

We assume that a disease management program primarily saves costs by reducing the number of hospital admissions. There may be other financial savings (reduced costs for hospital-based physicians, reduced emergency room utilization), but these are smaller in terms of their effect and are to some extent offset by increases in preventive medicine and pharmacy. There may be non-financial benefits (for example quality of life) and non-healthcare-specific benefits (for example lower absenteeism) due to these programs, but these are not considered in this analysis.

Applying the categorization and exclusions described above results in the prevalence shown in Table 10.1. A member who experienced months with more than one condition was placed in the highest category according to the hierarchy above.

TABLE 10.1

Hierarchical Prevalence of Chronic Members in a Commercial Population

Base Year	Number of Members	Percentage of Population
Excluded	25,753	3.09%
Diabetes	25,151	3.02%
CAD	10,014	1.20%
CHF	1,100	0.13%
COPD	972	0.12%
Asthma	18,928	2.27%
Other	751,068	90.17%
Total	832,986	100.0%

Measurement Year	Number of Members	Percentage of Population
Excluded	25,328	3.05%
Diabetes	25,690	3.09%
CAD	9,492	1.14%
CHF	932	0.11%
COPD	924	0.11%
Asthma	18,380	2.21%
Other	750,359	90.28%
Total	831,105	100.00%

Different DM programs will have a different prevalence of chronic members depending on the treated population and definitions of conditions. If the population has a different prevalence because of illness (and not definitions) then the minimum group sizes found in the tables may require modification.

10.2.4 Method of Simulation

For this study we simulate a large number of employer groups by running a large number of samples. The AHC methodology requires equivalence of populations between the base and measurement periods. To ensure equivalence in a simulation, we need to simulate the movement of members into and out of a group. It is important to include the new entrants because new entrants tend to be at a different state in disease progression and have different costs than continuing members.

Consequently, in each sample, we start with a certain number of members in the base period. In some simulations these members have a specific disease state. In others they may be chosen from the broad population. We follow these members into the measurement year. Some of these members will not persist into the measurement year either because of termination or because of the development of a different condition that removes them from the population. These members are replaced by an equal number of members in the measurement year.

The replacement members will have the same health status that is being tested. If CHF is being tested, the replacements will have at least 1 member-month of CHF in the measurement period. The replacement members may not have the same number of member months of exposure in the disease category as the members being replaced. Therefore the number of members is equal in both years although the number of member-months is not.

For each category of disease and sample size, we performed 1,000 simulations to generate sufficient observations to calculate means and standard deviations for each scenario. With a sufficiently large sample size the means should follow a normal distribution. The standard deviation should shrink proportionally to the square root of the increase in size. Thus a sample size of 400 members will have a standard deviation ½ as large as a sample size of 100 members. This is a precise way of stating what we all know intuitively, that a larger sample size gives more reliable results.

Once we have the standard deviation, we use standard statistics to calculate the number of members necessary to be x% confident that we are within y% of the true mean.

10.2.5 One-sided vs. Two-sided Tests of Significance

An important determinant of the selection of an appropriate level of significance is the choice of a one-sided or two-sided test. A one-sided test is appropriate for constructing a guarantee (the guarantee should be at a level, Y, such that, with high certainty, the outcome will exceed Y), while a two-sided test will be appropriate for assessing the confidence that can be placed in a measured outcome.

10.3 TRENDS AND DISEASE MANAGEMENT SAVINGS MEASUREMENT

As noted earlier, choosing an appropriate trend adjuster is always a difficult issue in an AHC model. This analysis focuses on fluctuations, that is, the standard deviation of the measured savings. The choice of trend can affect the mean significantly but has relatively little effect on the standard deviation.

Analysts choose different methods for calculating the trend that is used to project base year claims. Choices include using the overall health plan experience trend, a published industry trend, and the trend of the employer's or health plan's non-chronic population.

There are benefits to using the employer non-chronic ("well") trend: there is the same provider network and this is the trend the employer is actually seeing. On the other hand, there are very significant random fluctuations in non-chronic trends, adding to the difficulty of estimating a reliable measure of effectiveness.

We select a certain number of well base year members and follow their costs through the measurement year. Some of these members are not classified as well in the measurement year because of termination or sickness. We will replace these members by randomly selecting an equal number of well members from the measurement year as described in Section 10.2 above.

Trend is calculated as:

$$\frac{\textit{Measurement Period PMPM}}{\textit{Base Period PMPM}} - 1$$

We repeat this calculation several times using sample sizes of 500, 5,000, 20,000 and 40,000 well members. For each size, we repeated the calculation of trend 1000 times. The results are shown in Table 10.2.

TABLE 10.2

Trends as Calculated from the Well Members of the Population				
Sample Size	500	5,000	20,000	40,000
Mean	13.9%	9.5%	9.4%	9.4%
Standard Deviation	29.7%	10.1%	5.1%	3.6%
Minimum	– 56.6%	– 18.5%	– 7.2%	– 2.7%
10th Percentile	– 18.8%	– 3.0%	2.8%	4.9%
Median	10.8%	9.1%	9.4%	9.4%
90th Percentile	51.4%	22.5%	16.1%	14.0%
Maximum	204.3%	50.4%	25.7%	23.5%

The trend for samples of well members can vary widely, even for large samples.

There is considerable variability, even at the largest group sizes. For 40,000 well members, the average trend is 9.4%. The standard deviation in the trend is 3.6%, which implies that 68% of the time, the trend calculated from group-specific well members will be between 5.8% and 13.0%. This broad range has considerable implication for savings calculations, since even a 1% change in trend has a significant effect on savings (and performance guarantees!). Further, 32% of the time, the trend falls outside of this range.

Theoretically, with the results from the 1,000 runs of 40,000 members, we should be able to predict the results for the larger sample sizes. Table 10.2 supports an assumption that the samples follow a normal distribution, so the standard deviation should diminish proportionally to the square root of the sample size. That is, since 5,000 members is 10 times as big as 500 members, the standard deviation should be $\frac{1}{\sqrt{10}}$ or 0.316 times as large.

The results shown in Table 10.3 show that the theoretical standard deviation is quite close to the actual standard deviation. We conclude that we can predict the standard deviation in the trend for any number of members *X* by using the formula

$$Std\ Dev(X) = Std\ Dev(40{,}000)\left(\sqrt{(x/40{,}000)}\right)$$

TABLE 10.3

Comparison of Standard Deviations of Trends – Well Population				
Sample Size	500	5,000	20,000	40,000
Standard Deviation	29.7%	10.1%	5.1%	3.6%
Predicted Standard Deviation	32.0%	10.1%	5.1%	3.6%

We will take advantage of this idea to complete the tables in the next section.

10.4 THE BASE MEASUREMENT METHOD – EFFECT OF USING GROUP-SPECIFIC TREND

Table10.2 showed the potential variations that can occur in the trend. We examined the effect of this method on group size using our method of selecting a certain number of members and replacing those who dropped out. Trend was calculated for each of inpatient, outpatient, physician, and pharmacy costs separately by comparing the PMPMs for the "well" portion in the base and measurement years. These trends were applied to their corresponding base PMPMs resulting in expected PMPMs for each component. The resulting 4 PMPMs were summed to arrive at projected base year costs. Consequently, different trends were calculated for each sample.

Fluctuations are defined as:

$$\frac{\text{Actual Measurement Year Costs} - \text{Projected BaseYear Costs}}{\text{Projected BaseYear Costs}}$$

To arrive at Projected Base Year Costs, we calculate the costs for the base year for each disease, trended forward, and adjusted for the number of member-months in the measurement period. That is,

$$\textit{Projected Base Year Costs} = \sum \frac{\textit{Trended Base Year Costs} \times \textit{Measurement Year Member} - \textit{Months}}{\textit{Base Year Member} - \textit{Months}}$$

We calculate the standard deviation in the fluctuations as a percent of projected base year costs (See Table 10.10) for 1,000 runs at each sample size. These standard deviations should and do diminish proportionally to the square root of the sample size. Once we have the standard deviation for one size, we can calculate how large an employer group must be in order for the DM program to be a certain percent confident of savings and the width of confidence intervals as a function of the employer group size.

The minimum group sizes are very large as shown in Table10.4.

TABLE 10.4

Minimum Group Size when DM Program Saves 5% of Chronic Costs			
Standard Deviations	1.000	1.645	2.000
One Sided	84.1%	95.0%	97.7%
Two Sided	68.3%	90.0%	95.4%
Group Size	96,100	260,000	384,300
Expected Chronic Prevalence	6,500	17,500	25,900
Minimum Group Size when DM Program Saves 10% of Chronic Costs			
Standard Deviations	1.000	1.645	2.000
One Sided	84.1%	95.0%	97.7%
Two Sided	68.3%	90.0%	95.4%
Group Size	24,000	65,000	96,100
Expected Chronic Prevalence	1,600	4,400	6,500
Minimum Group Size when DM Program Saves 15% of Chronic Costs			
Standard Deviations	1.000	1.645	2.000
One Sided	84.1%	95.0%	97.7%
Two Sided	68.3%	90.0%	95.4%
Group Size	10,700	28,900	42,700
Expected Chronic Prevalence	700	1,900	2,900

Table 10.4 lists two confidence levels, "one-sided" and "two-sided". For a DM program that believes it saves 10% of total chronic costs for an employer group of 23,700 members, the program sponsor can equivalently state that:

- It is 84% confident that the measurement of savings will show that costs were reduced. Conversely, there is a 16% probability that the program will appear to have increased costs. (Note that this is not an estimate of savings, but an estimate of how much random fluctuation affects savings measurements); or
- It is 68% confident that the measurement of savings will show that costs were reduced between 0% and 20%.

Table 10.5 provides the half-width of the confidence intervals. For example, for an employer group of 10,000 members, we can expect that 68% of the time, actual claim costs will be within plus or minus 15.5% of the expected claim costs. If a DM program expects to save 10% of actual costs, then the randomness will frequently overwhelm the savings. This suggests looking for other measurement techniques to smooth these swings and increase confidence in measurement.

TABLE 10.5

Half-Width of Confidence Intervals							
	Employer Group Size						
Confidence Level	1,000	2,000	4,000	10,000	20,000	40,000	100,000
68%	49.0%	34.7%	24.5%	15.5%	11.0%	7.7%	4.9%
90%	80.6%	57.0%	40.3%	25.5%	18.0%	12.7%	8.1%
95%	98.0%	69.3%	49.0%	31.0%	21.9%	15.5%	9.8%

Base Measurement Method - Trends calculated from the non-chronic "well" proportion of 1,000 samples at various group sizes.

10.5 ALTERNATE MEASUREMENT METHOD – POPULATION TREND

As we discussed earlier, one source of variation in DM measurement is the use of the employer population as a source of the trend adjuster. To reduce the potential variation in measurement, we can use a trend adjuster that is less subject to variation than the employer non-chronic trend. Where a larger population (such as a health plan) is available, the use of a trend based on the whole population may be appropriate.

The results (Tables 10.6 and 10.7) indicate that greater credibility is achieved in smaller group sizes. The group size is approximately 30% smaller than in the base measurement methodology and the confidence intervals are also smaller. The minimum group size for credibility is still large for all but a minority of groups.

Table 10.6

Minimum Group Size when DM Program Saves 5% of Chronic Costs			
Standard Deviations	1.000	1.645	2.000
One Sided	84.1%	95.0%	97.7%
Two Sided	68.3%	90.0%	95.4%
Group Size	64,700	175,100	258,800
Expected Chronic Prevalence	4,400	11,800	17,400
Minimum Group Size when DM Program Saves 10% of Chronic Costs			
Standard Deviations	1.000	1.645	2.000
One Sided	84.1%	95.0%	97.7%
Two Sided	68.3%	90.0%	95.4%
Group Size	16,200	43,800	64,700
Expected Chronic Prevalence	1,100	3,000	4,400
Minimum Group Size when DM Program Saves 15% of Chronic Costs			
Standard Deviations	1.000	1.645	2.000
One Sided	84.1%	95.0%	97.7%
Two Sided	68.3%	90.0%	95.4%
Group Size	7,200	19,500	28,800
Expected Chronic Prevalence	500	1,300	1,900

Alternate Measurement Method (Population) – A trend was calculated from the entire population and used in each sample.

TABLE 10.7

Half-Width of Confidence Intervals

	Size of Employer Group						
Confidence Level	1,000	2,000	4,000	10,000	20,000	40,000	100,000
68%	40.2%	28.4%	20.1%	12.7%	9.0%	6.4%	4.0%
90%	66.2%	46.8%	33.1%	20.9%	14.8%	10.5%	6.6%
95%	80.4%	56.9%	40.2%	25.4%	18.0%	12.7%	8.0%

Alternate Measurement Method (Population) – A trend was calculated from the entire population and used in each sample.

10.6 ALTERNATE MEASUREMENT METHOD – USING TRUNCATION TO STABILIZE MEASUREMENT

Large claims can cause significant fluctuations in costs from year-to-year. It is common industry practice to "truncate" these claims, frequently at $100,000 or a lower amount. Truncation at $100,000 does not dampen fluctuation very much in small groups, which are more likely to be at risk of claim frequency (the number of large claims) than a larger group such as a health plan. Consequently, we ran our simulations with truncation levels of $50,000 and $100,000. For the measurement year, these limits were inflated at 10%, the overall population trend.

In addition, we looked at two other methods of truncation:

- Truncation at a level equal to the mean annual claim, plus two standard deviations; or
- Truncation at a level equal to the 90th percentile of the claims distribution. The 90th percentile of the claims distribution is that dollar claims level at which 90% of members had claims of lesser or equal amount.

Table 10.8 shows the results of truncation on trends. Although DM evaluations usually focus on truncation of the chronic claims, the method should be applied symmetrically to the non-chronic claims in developing the trend adjuster. Both methods reduce the variability due to trend significantly.

TABLE 10.8

Effect of Truncation on Trend (40,000 Members)

	Yearly Cap				
	None	$100,000	$50,000	Mean plus 2 Standard Deviations	At 90th Percentile
Mean	9.3%	9.6%	9.6%	7.8%	4.7%
Standard Deviation	3.6%	2.8%	2.3%	2.5%	1.0%
Minimum	– 1.0%	1.0%	3.4%	– 0.5%	0.7%
10th Percentile	4.5%	6.0%	6.6%	4.5%	3.3%
Median	9.3%	9.7%	9.6%	7.8%	4.7%
90th Percentile	13.9%	13.0%	12.6%	10.9%	5.9%
Maximum	21.1%	17.9%	16.9%	13.9%	8.6%

Alternate Measurement Method (Truncation) – In this scenario, we used the claim costs of the non-chronic members to calculate trends.

Limiting claims at a certain percentile has some attraction because it reduces the variability of the highest cost members at a level that is specific to a particular population. In our data, capping claims at the 90th percentile of annual claims cuts trend variability in half, because the 90th percentile occurs at approximately $4,000 of annual costs. This claims level is too low for application to DM claims, because many chronic members' claims exceed this amount. Application of this limit would exclude claims on managed members and reduce the ability to assess the effect of the intervention. As an alternative, we could use the 95th or 99th percentile, but these levels are similar to a flat claim threshold of $25,000.

The "mean plus 2 standard deviations" method does not suffer from the same drawback. In practice, the mean plus 2 standard deviations produced claim limits between $15,000 and $30,000. So this can be seriously considered as a possible method to limit fluctuations, although there are drawbacks. First, if a DM program reduces a member's costs from (say) $100,000 to $25,000, the program would receive no credit. Second, a reduction in costs from $100,000 to $0 would receive only partial credit. At this truncation level, measuring change through admission reduction could be considered as a simpler, valid alternative.

The standard methods of truncation are effective at limiting random fluctuations only if the DM program is confident of reducing chronic costs by 10% or more. If the program can achieve this level of cost reduction, then Table 10.9 shows that using truncation at $50,000 for groups larger than 11,300 members will provide some confidence in the results. It appears that $100,000 is too high a truncation level to limit fluctuations for all but the largest groups.

TABLE 10.9

Minimum Group Size When DM Program Saves 5% of Costs				
	Truncation			
Confidence Level	Mean + 2 SD	$50,000	$100,000	None
68%	28,000	45,300	56,300	96,100
90%	75,800	122,700	152,400	260,000
95%	112,000	181,400	225,200	384,300
Minimum Group Size When DM Program Saves 10% of Costs				
	Truncation			
Confidence Level	Mean + 2 SD	$50,000	$100,000	None
68%	7,000	11,300	14,100	24,000
90%	18,900	30,700	38,100	65,000
95%	28,000	45,300	56,300	96,100
Minimum Group Size When DM Program Saves 15% of Costs				
Confidence Level	Truncation			
	Mean + 2 SD	$50,000	$100,000	None
68%	3,100	5,000	6,300	10,700
90%	8,400	13,600	16,900	28,900
95%	12,400	20,200	25,000	42,700

Alternate Measurement Method (Truncation) – Trends were calculated from the non-chronic "well" proportion of 1000 samples at various group sizes.

10.6.1 Minimum Employer Group Sizes with Truncation

Truncation offers significant advantages for stabilizing measurement. Tables 10.9 and 10.10 show the results for the different truncation methods as well as the results with no truncation. These tables were all calculated with a group-specific trend. We applied truncation both to the chronic members and to determine trend.

It can be seen that truncation can significantly reduce the minimum group size. Moving to a limit of $50,000 reduces the minimum group size by over half.

For a group of 20,000 members, the 68% confidence interval has a width of +/-7.5% even with a truncation level of $50,000. In other words, if savings are measured at x%, there is a 68% chance that true savings fell between x-7.5% and x+7.5% and a 32% chance that true savings fell outside of this range. This is a relatively wide range. Truncation is helpful because it decreases variability but is no panacea for the issues of fluctuations of small groups.

TABLE 10.10

Half-Width of Confidence Intervals, $50,000 truncation							
	Size of DM Program						
Confidence Level	1,000	2,000	4,000	10,000	20,000	40,000	100,000
68%	33.7%	23.8%	16.8%	10.6%	7.5%	5.3%	3.4%
90%	55.4%	39.2%	27.7%	17.5%	12.4%	8.8%	5.5%
95%	67.3%	47.6%	33.7%	21.3%	15.1%	10.6%	6.7%
Half-Width of Confidence Intervals, $100,000 truncation							
	Size of DM Program						
Confidence Level	1,000	2,000	4,000	10,000	20,000	40,000	100,000
68%	37.5%	26.5%	18.8%	11.9%	8.4%	5.9%	3.8%
90%	61.7%	43.6%	30.9%	19.5%	13.8%	9.8%	6.2%
95%	75.0%	53.1%	37.5%	23.7%	16.8%	11.9%	7.5%
Half-Width of Confidence Intervals, mean + 2 SD truncation							
	Size of DM Program						
Confidence Level	1,000	2,000	4,000	10,000	20,000	40,000	100,000
68%	26.5%	18.7%	13.2%	8.4%	5.9%	4.2%	2.6%
90%	43.5%	30.8%	21.8%	13.8%	9.7%	6.9%	4.4%
95%	52.9%	37.4%	26.5%	16.7%	11.8%	8.4%	5.3%

Alternate Measurement Method (Truncation) – Trends were calculated from the non-chronic "well" proportion of 1000 samples at various group sizes.

10.7 ALTERNATE MEASUREMENT METHOD – UTILIZATION MEASURE

The number of hospital admissions is an attractive alternative to total cost as a measure of DM effectiveness. Although a DM program can impact other types of utilization, it primarily achieves its effects through reducing inpatient admissions.

We performed the same analyses replacing costs with the number of admissions. Since, very roughly, admissions must be reduced by 2% to 3% to save 1% in total costs, we examine the number of chronic members necessary when there are possible reductions of 10%, 20% and 30% of admissions. For simplicity we assume that there is no trend in admissions (trends in admissions within health plans tend to be low, of the order of 1% or 2% annually, and may be negative). Tables 10.11 and 10.12 show the results.

TABLE 10.11

Minimum Group Size when DM Program Saves 10% of Chronic Admissions			
Standard Deviations	1.000	1.645	2.000
One Sided	84.1%	95.0%	97.7%
Two Sided	68.3%	90.0%	95.4%
Group Size	17,400	47,000	69,500
Expected Chronic Prevalence	1,170	3,170	4,680
Minimum Group Size when DM Program Saves 20% of Chronic Admissions			
Standard Deviations	1.000	1.645	2.000
One Sided	84.1%	95.0%	97.7%
Two Sided	68.3%	90.0%	95.4%
Group Size	4,340	11,700	17,400
Expected Chronic Prevalence	290	790	1,170
Minimum Group Size when DM Program Saves 30% of Chronic Admits			
Standard Deviations	1.000	1.645	2.000
One Sided	84.1%	95.0%	97.7%
Two Sided	68.3%	90.0%	95.4%
Group Size	1,930	5,220	7,720
Expected Chronic Admissions	130	350	520

Alternate Measurement Method (Utilization) – Admissions were used as a proxy for total costs.

TABLE 10.12

Half-Width of Confidence Intervals							
	Employer Group Size						
Confidence Level	1,000	2,000	4,000	10,000	20,000	40,000	100,000
68%	41.7%	29.5%	20.8%	13.2%	9.3%	6.6%	4.2%
90%	68.6%	48.5%	34.3%	21.7%	15.3%	10.8%	6.9%
95%	83.3%	58.9%	41.7%	26.4%	18.6%	13.2%	8.3%

Alternate Measurement Method (Utilization) – Admissions were used as a proxy for total cost.

The minimum group sizes required for credibility are significantly smaller than when measuring costs. For example, if the DM program reduces the number of admissions by 20%, then an employer group size of 4,340 members can be used to be 84% confident that the measurement will show savings. This number is about one-quarter of the number of members required for the same degree of confidence when the measure is claims-based and not truncated.

Note that the confidence intervals in Table 10.12 are the same magnitude as confidence intervals for the base method. The reason admissions are to be preferred is that the admissions are reduced 10%, 20% or 30%, which is twice as much as costs – there is more room for error.

When admissions are used as the measure, the employer will still want a measure of total dollars saved. A reasonable estimate may be made by multiplying the reduction in the number of admissions by a standardized cost per admission. An admission-based estimate using standardized costs is only a proxy for the effect of a program and could differ from the true program effect for a number of reasons, including:

- A DM program may reduce the severity of admissions exhibited through length of stay rather than through a reduction in admissions;
- A DM program may reduce ER visits (which do not form part of the measurement);
- A DM program may increase physician visits and pharmacy spend (also omitted from the admission-based calculation); and
- The standardized cost per admission may be inappropriate for the avoided admissions.

Despite the shortcomings of the admission-based methodology, this method has the potential to provide estimates at a reasonable level of confidence within smaller group sizes (particularly groups smaller than 20,000) than other methods.

10.8 MINIMUM SAMPLE SIZES FOR SPECIFIC DISEASES

There are significant differences in utilization and costs across chronic diseases. For example, 43% of CHF members have at least one inpatient admission (for any cause) per year compared to 12% of asthma members. We wanted to know how many members in a specific disease state were necessary to be confident that random fluctuations would not overwhelm the effects of a DM program.

We define fluctuations as

$$\frac{\textit{Actual Measurement Year PMPM} - \textit{Base Year PMPM} \times (1+\textit{Trend})}{\textit{Base Year PMPM} \times 1+\textit{Trend})}$$

We chose trend so that the average fluctuation would be 0 since our focus in this section is on fluctuations within the population and not on random effects caused by the choice of trend. This simplification has only a small effect.

For each disease, we chose a certain number of members with the condition in the base year and performed our simulations using the select-and-replace methodology described earlier. In this case, however, members who were replaced had to have the same chronic condition.

Tables 10.13 and 10.14 show minimum group sizes and confidence intervals for each chronic condition.

TABLE 10.13

Minimum Chronic Members when DM Program Saves 5% of Total Costs			
Standard Deviations	1.000	1.645	2.000
One Sided	84.1%	95.0%	97.7%
Two Sided	68.3%	90.0%	95.4%
Diabetes	4,300	11,600	17,200
CAD	3,550	9,600	14,200
CHF	3,170	8,580	12,700
COPD	5,490	14,900	22,000
Asthma	5,870	15,900	23,500
Total	22,380	60,580	89,600
Minimum Chronic Members when DM Program Saves 10% of Total Costs			
Standard Deviations	1.000	1.645	2.000
One Sided	84.1%	95.0%	97.7%
Two Sided	68.3%	90.0%	95.4
Diabetes	1,070	2,910	4,300
CAD	890	2,400	3,550
CHF	790	2,150	3,170
COPD	1,370	3,720	5,490
Asthma	1,470	3,970	5,870
Total	5,590	15,150	22,380
Minimum Chronics when DM Program Saves 15% of Total Costs			
Standard Deviations	1.000	1.645	2.000
One Sided	84.1%	95.0%	97.7%
Two Sided	68.3%	90.0%	95.4%
Diabetes	480	1,290	1,910
CAD	390	1,070	1,580
CHF	350	950	1,410
COPD	610	1,650	2,440
Asthma	650	1,770	2,610
Total	2,480	6,730	9,950

Specific Chronic Conditions – Costs

TABLE 10.14

Half-Width of Confidence Intervals					
		Chronic Population Size			
	Diabetes	10	40	100	400
Confidence Level	68%	104%	51.8%	32.8%	16.4%
	90%	171%	85.3%	53.9%	27.0%
	95%	207%	104%	65.6%	32.8%
	CAD	10	40	100	400
	68%	94.2%	47.1%	29.8%	14.9%
	90%	155%	77.5%	49.0%	24.5%
	95%	188%	94.2%	59.6%	29.8%
	CHF	10	40	100	400
	68%	89.1%	44.5%	28.2%	14.1%
	90%	147%	73.2%	46.3%	23.2%
	95%	178%	89.1%	56.3%	28.2%
	COPD	10	40	100	400
	68%	117%	58.6%	37.1%	18.5%
	90%	193%	96.4%	61.0%	30.5%
	95%	234%	117%	74.1%	37.1%
	Asthma	10	40	100	400
	68%	121%	60.6%	38.3%	19.2%
	90%	199%	99.7%	63.0%	31.5%
	95%	242%	121%	76.6%	38.3%

Specific Chronic Conditions – Costs

Only the largest groups exhibit sufficiently small variation for us to have confidence in the measurement of results for a single condition. Tables 10.15 and 10.16 replace costs with the number of admissions. Table 10.15 shows the number of chronic members necessary when there are possible savings of 10%, 20% and 30% of admissions.

These sample sizes are approximately 30% of the minimum sample sizes for measuring costs.

TABLE 10.15

Minimum Chronic Members when DM Program Saves 10% of Admissions			
Standard Deviations	1.000	1.645	2.000
One Sided	84.1%	95.0%	97.7%
Two Sided	68.3%	90.0%	95.4%
Diabetes	1,470	3,980	5,880
CAD	840	2,280	3,380
CHF	430	1,160	1,710
COPD	620	1,660	2,460
Asthma	2,790	7,560	11,180
Total	6,150	16,640	24,610
Minimum Chronic Members when DM Program Saves 20% of Admissions			
Standard Deviations	1.000	1.645	2.000
One Sided	84.1%	95.0%	97.7%
Two Sided	68.3%	90.0%	95.4%
Diabetes	370	990	1,470
CAD	210	570	840
CHF	110	290	430
COPD	150	420	620
Asthma	700	1,890	2,790
Total	1,540	4,160	6,150
Minimum Chronic Members when DM Program Saves 30% of Admissions			
Standard Deviations	1.000	1.645	2.000
One Sided	84.1%	95.0%	97.7%
Two Sided	68.3%	90.0%	95.4%
Diabetes	160	440	650
CAD	90	250	380
CHF	50	130	190
COPD	70	180	270
Asthma	310	840	1,240
Total	680	1,840	2,730

Specific Chronic Conditions – Admissions

TABLE 10.16

Half-Width of Confidence Intervals for Admissions					
		Chronic Population Size			
	Diabetes	10	40	100	400
Confidence Level	68%	121%	60.6%	38.3%	19.2%
	90%	199%	99.7%	63.1%	31.5%
	95%	242%	121%	76.7%	38.3%
	CAD	10	40	100	400
	68%	91.9%	45.9%	29.1%	14.5%
	90%	151%	75.6%	47.8%	23.9%
	95%	184%	91.9%	58.1%	29.1%
	CHF	10	40	100	400
	68%	65.4%	32.7%	20.7%	10.3%
	90%	108%	53.8%	34.0%	17.0%
	95%	131%	65.4%	41.4%	20.7%
	COPD	10	40	100	400
	68%	78.4%	39.2%	24.8%	12.4%
	90%	129%	64.5%	40.8%	20.4%
	95%	157%	78.4%	49.6%	24.8%
	Asthma	10	40	100	400
	68%	167%	83.6%	52.9%	26.4%
	90%	275%	137%	87.0%	43.5%
	95%	334%	167%	106%	52.9%

Specific Chronic Conditions – Admissions

10.9 PRACTICAL APPLICATIONS IN SMALL POPULATIONS

We have summarized the results of this analysis graphically, presenting the relationships between confidence and population size continuously. These charts will allow sponsors of DM programs to determine the level of credibility for any size of group, under different assumptions about expected savings and truncation levels (interpolating where necessary).

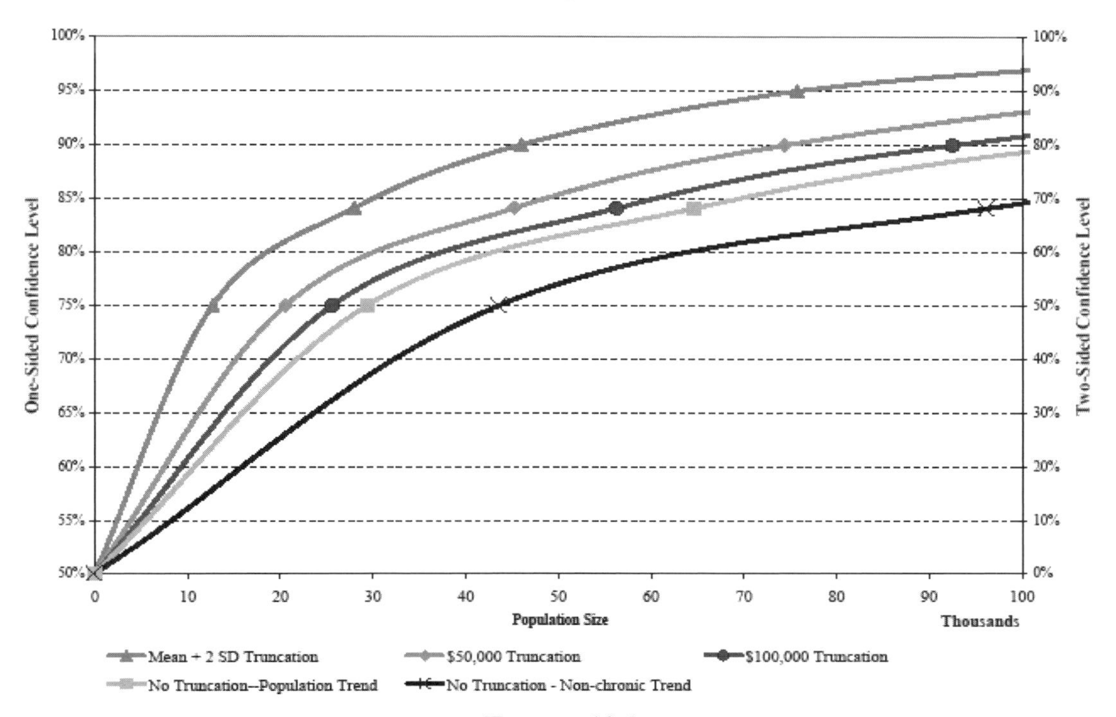

FIGURE 10.1

10% DM Program Effect

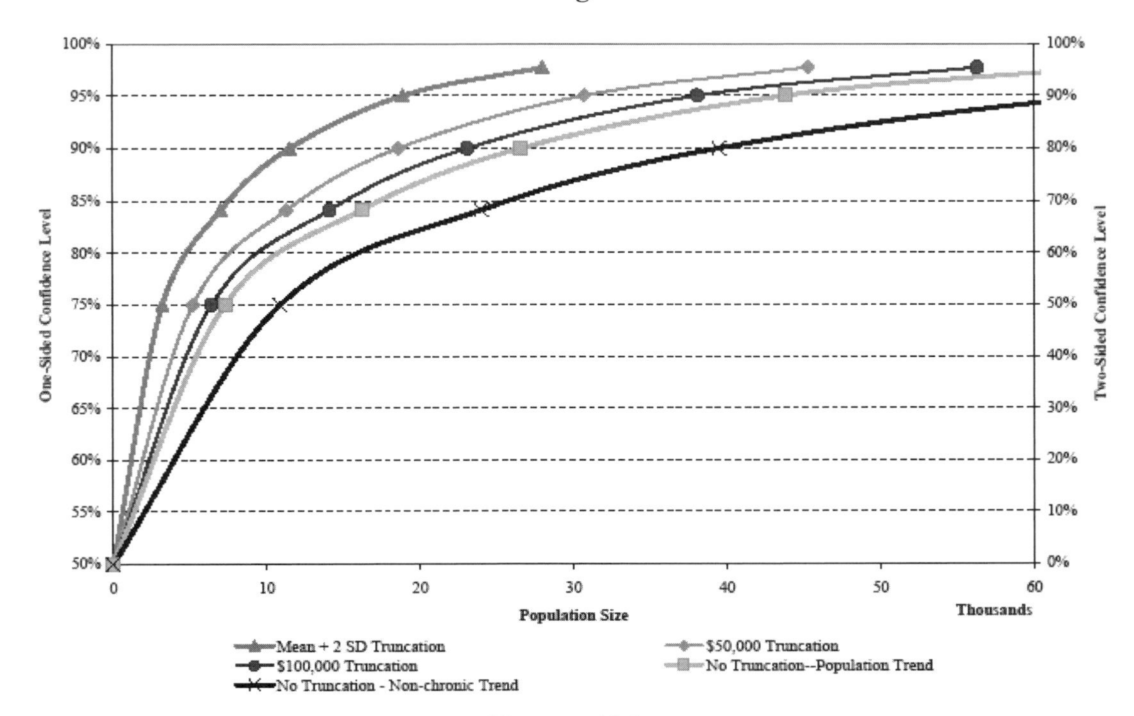

FIGURE 10.2

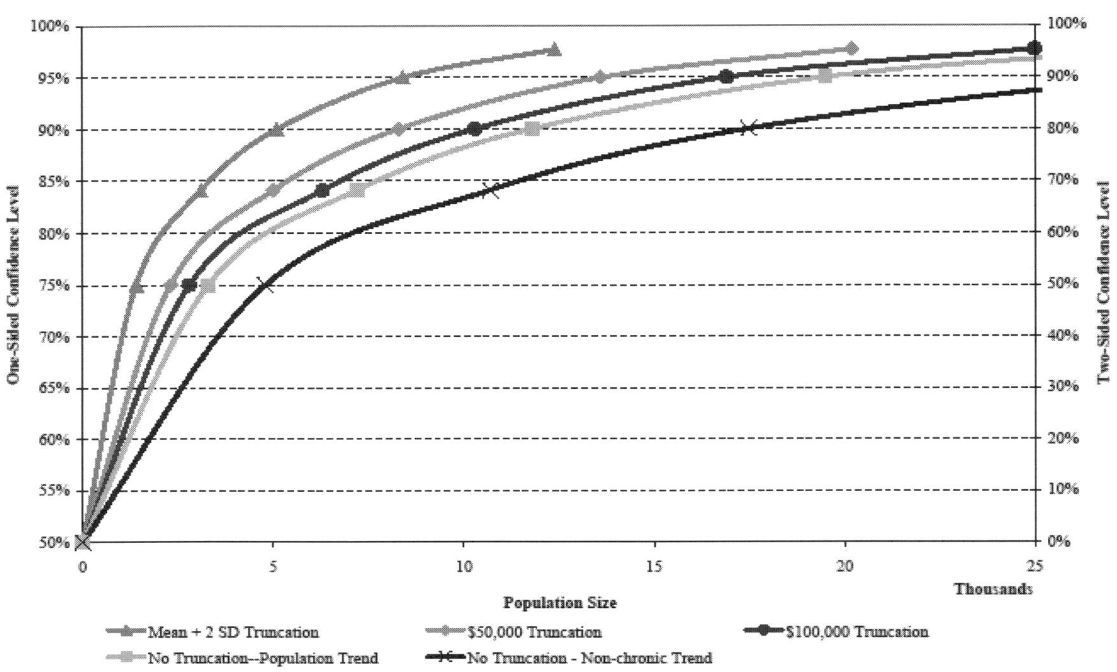

FIGURE 10.3

Using Admissions to Estimate Program Effect

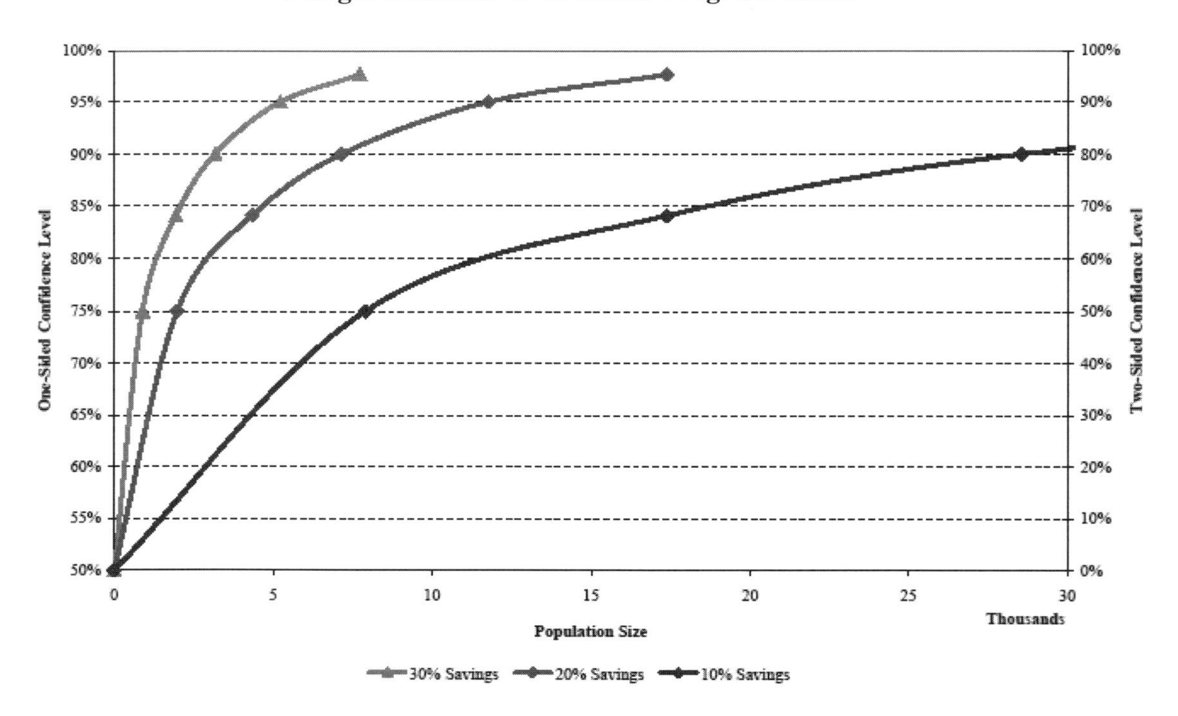

FIGURE 10.4

The final figure illustrates confidence intervals using admissions rather than claims costs. No truncation is applied to these results because it is difficult to translate the stop-loss method to the admissions calculation.

10.10 LIMITATIONS

The confidence intervals or minimum group sizes estimated in this chapter will not necessarily apply to all other commercial populations. Our analysis used one population with one set of provider contracts, utilization and with one set of classification criteria. These factors will change from population to population. Nonetheless, we believe our results are an appropriate first approximation for a commercial population.

10.11 CONCLUSIONS

There are a number of considerations that a DM program sponsor needs to weigh in evaluating its outcomes, including (but not limited to) the financial savings. Almost regardless of the size of the client group, an effective DM program may appear ineffective because of adverse fluctuations. Some general guidelines may be derived from our discussion:

- A 95% confidence interval (+/−2 standard deviations) is widely accepted in other applications as being "almost sure." Reducing the confidence level to ± one standard deviation may be sufficient for commercial purchasers who need to balance their need for credibility with practical considerations. We have provided different results under different assumptions that a sponsor may use to choose a confidence level, keeping in mind the size of group and other considerations.

- A program sponsor should consider whether to use "two-sided" or "one-sided" confidence intervals. For purposes such as assessing fluctuations for constructing guarantees, a DM program is less concerned about fluctuations that cause a program to show greater-than-expected savings. In this situation a "one-sided" test may be appropriate. For example, in Table 10.4 where a DM program managing 24,000 members typically saves 10% of chronic costs, we can be 84% confident that the program will show savings despite random fluctuations. We are only 68% confident, however, that the savings lie within 0% and 20%.

- Our results show that relatively large group sizes are required for confidence in claims-based outcomes. If a program sponsor is willing to use admission-based savings calculations, credibility may be demonstrated at lower group sizes.

- Truncation can be helpful in limiting variation in the measurement of the effect of a DM program. Minimum groups of the size of those in Table 10.9 are required. In cases of programs with moderate success in the 5-10% savings range, small employer groups with fewer that 10,000 members will have a hard time meeting the one standard deviation confidence level, even with the use of aggressive truncation. Our results indicate that the common industry choice of a $100,000 stop-loss limit insufficiently reduces variation in smaller groups and that truncation at $50,000 or at the level of the mean plus two standard deviations should be considered.

- Our results indicate that using the employer non-chronic trend introduces additional variation into the measurement and that, if possible, a source of trend that is less subject to variation (for example, an external consultant trend, a health plan or a book of business trend) should be considered.

- Using the reduction in the number of admissions as a proxy for savings, or as the basis of a financial savings calculation, offers considerable promise for groups that are too small for credible financial savings calculations. If the reduction in admission method is used, the reduction will need to be multiplied by a standardized average cost per admission to estimate savings.

- A DM company that is structuring a guarantee for a client has a related, but different, concern. The DM company must ensure that, with a high probability, the observed savings not be less than the guaranteed savings level. This structure requires assessment under a one-sided test, as discussed in section 10.4. For example, in Table 10.4 where a DM program managing 24,000 members saves 10% of chronic costs, we can be 84% confident that the program will show at least this level of savings despite random fluctuations. In determining the risk that guarantees pose, a DM company may require a higher level of confidence, however.
- A DM program sponsor may consider these results for structuring or assessing savings guarantees. There are many other factors, however, that may affect the structure and pricing of guarantees that go beyond the scope of this chapter.

- Another consideration is the cost of performing a measurement analysis. For a large health plan calculating performance over all groups at once, the cost per employer group may be modest. But performing these analyses for a single group is sufficiently expensive that it may be wise to first determine the probable credibility of results using the methods described in this chapter.

Nevertheless, these results show that, with appropriate caution, many commercial group sponsors of DM programs may be reasonably confident of the calculated financial results of their programs.

APPENDIX 10.1 CRITERIA USED TO CLASSIFY MEMBERS INTO CHRONIC CATEGORIES

We used a database of commercial managed-care members that had membership and claims for calendar years 2004, 2005, and 2006. For both classification purposes and for the measurement of total dollars, claims had to be paid within 3 months of the end of the calendar year, that is with 3 months of runout.

For a member to be included in the chronic measurement period, at least 6 months of continuous plan eligibility is required. The member could be classified as chronic for any number of months.

Members were classified as chronic by ICD-9 code. Members were classified as chronic in the month of service for an inpatient claim or the month of service of the second non-admission claim. Table 10.A-1 lists the ICD-9 codes that were used for each condition.

Members were classified as excluded if there were one or two separate claims, depending on condition. Table 10.A-2 lists the ICD-9 codes that were used for each exclusionary condition. For trauma, only the claims and not the member were excluded from the measurement calculation.

TABLE 10.A-1

Codes Used to Identify Chronic Members

Condition	Codes
Diabetes	ICD-9 250, 250.0, 250.00, 250.01, 250.02, 250.03, 251.1, 250.10, 250.11, 250.12, 250.13, 250.2, 250.20, 250.21, 250.22, 250.23, 250.3, 250.30, 250.31, 250.32, 250.33, 250.4, 250.40, 250.41, 250.42, 250.43, 250.5, 250.50, 250.51, 250.52, 250.53, 250.6, 250.60, 250.61, 250.62, 250.63, 250.7, 250.70, 250.71, 250.72, 250.73, 250.8, 250.80, 250.81, 250.82, 250.83, 250.9, 250.90, 250.91, 250.92, 250.93, 357.2
Coronary Artery Disease CAD	ICD-9 410, 410.0, 410.00, 410.01, 410.02, 410.1, 410.10, 410.11, 410.12, 410.2, 410.20, 410.21, 410.22, 410.3, 410.30, 410.31, 410.32, 410.4, 410.40, 410.41, 410.42, 410.5, 410.50, 410.51, 410.52, 410.6, 410.60, 410.61, 410.62, 410.7, 410.70, 410.71, 410.72, 410.8, 410.80, 410.81, 410.82, 410.9, 410.90, 410.91, 410.92, 411, 411.0, 411.1, 411.8, 411.81, 411.89, 412, 413, 413.0, 413.1, 413.9, 414, 414.0, 414.00, 414.01, 414.02, 414.03, 414.04, 414.05, 414.1, 414.10, 414.11, 414.12, 414.19, 414.8, 414.9
Congestive Heart Failure CHF	ICD-9 398.91, 402.01, 402.11, 402.91, 404.01, 404.03, 404.11, 404.13, 404.91, 404.93, 428, 428.0, 428.1, 428.2, 428.20, 428.21, 428.22, 428.23, 428.3, 428.30, 428.31, 428.32, 428.33, 428.4, 428.40, 428.41, 428.42, 428.43 428.9
Chronic Obstructive Pulmonary Disease -COPD	ICD-9 491.1, 491.2, 491.20, 491.21, 491.8, 491.9
Asthma	ICD-9 493, 493.0, 493.00, 493.01, 493.02, 493.1, 493.10, 493.11, 493.12, 493.2, 493.20, 493.21, 493.22, 493.9, 493.90, 493.91, 493.92

TABLE 10.A-2

Codes Used to Identify Excluded Members or Claims to be Excluded

Condition	Codes	Number of Claims on Separate Dates
AIDS	ICD-9: 042, 079.53	1 claim in 12 months
Trauma	ICD-9: 800 through 815 817 through 825 827 through 832 835 through 840 843 through 844 846 through 909 925 through 995 996.8 through 996.99	1 claim in 12 months
Dialysis	ICD-9: 585-586, v56 series, v45.1	2 claims in 12 months
	CPT Codes: 36145, 36831-36833, 90918-90925, 90935, 90937, 90945, 90947, 90989, 90993, 90997, 90999	
Cancer	ICD-9: 140.x-208.x and 230.x-239.x	2 claims in 12 months
Transplant	ICD-9: v42.0 – v42.9	1 claim in 12 months
	CPT Codes: 32850-32854, 33935, 33945, 33960, 33961, 38230, 38231, 38240, 38241,47120, 47122, 47125, 47130, 47135, 47136,47579, 48152, 48153, 48155, 48160, 48180, 48550, 48554, 48556, 50300-50320, 50340, 50360, 50365, 50370, 50380, 50546-50548, 90935	
Maternity	644-677, v22-v24, v27-v28 series, 648.0-648.04	2 claims in 12 months
Infertility	V26 series	1 claim in 12 months
Respiratory	492-492.8 (emphysema), 518.2 (compensatory emphysema)	2 claims in 12 months
Hemophilia	286.0, 286.1, 286.2, 286.4, 286.7, V83.01	1 claim in 12 months

PART 3

PRACTICAL APPLICATIONS

11 A Comparative Analysis of Chronic and Non-Chronic Insured Commercial Membership Cost Trends[1]

11.1 Introduction

Disease management (DM) is increasingly encountered in health plans and employer groups as a health care intervention targeted to individuals with chronic diseases ("Chronics"). To justify the investment by payers in DM, it is important to demonstrate beneficial clinical and financial outcomes. In the absence of randomized control studies, financial results are often estimated in a pre/post study in which the cost of Chronics in the absence of DM can be predicted by their pre-DM year cost (on a PMPM basis) adjusted for the Non-chronic population's cost trend. The assumption made, not previously tested, is that (absent DM) the Chronic and Non-chronic trends are identical.

We calculated Chronic and Non-chronic trends over 1999-2002 and compared them under different assumptions regarding identification of chronic disease and medical services. Qualification for the Chronic group was defined as having coronary artery disease, heart failure, diabetes, asthma or chronic obstructive lung disease. Our base case used an algorithm that identified a member as Chronic prospectively, (that is, from the point of identification forward), with one or more of the chronic conditions.

We used a data set of 1.5 million commercially insured members.

When Chronic and Non-chronic members are identified and included in the population prospectively, the average 3-year trends over the study period for chronic and non-chronic members adjusted for high cost outliers were 4.9% and 13.9% respectively. Adjusting the population experience for differences in service mix had little impact on the divergence in trends. However, altering the Chronic selection algorithm to eliminate migration between groups (thus classifying a member as always Chronic if identified as Chronic at any point in the four years) caused the trends to converge (Chronics, 16.3%; Non-chronics 17.2%; Total 16.0%).[2] Using the original selection algorithm but risk-adjusting the populations annually also caused their trends to converge (Chronics, 12.5%; Non-chronics 11.9%). Finally, applying an annual "re-qualification" process (in which members who qualify as chronic in one year but not the next are excluded in the year in which they fail to qualify) we see some, although not complete convergence of trends.

[1] Reprinted with formatting changes from *North American Actuarial Journal*, Volume 10 (4) October 2006 with permission from the Society of Actuaries.

[2] A question frequently asked is why trends observed in sub-groups can be higher than the trend observed in the overall group. See Appendix 11.1 for discussion and examples.

Estimating DM program financial outcomes based on the assumption that, absent the program, the chronic population would have had the same trend as the Non-chronic population can lead to erroneous conclusions. Identification of a chronic member and the point at which that member is re-classified from one sub-population to another can significantly impact the observed trends in both sub-populations, implying that great care must be taken over classification and interpretation of the resulting trends, and their use in DM savings calculations. Trends calculated using a prospective identification methodology introduce a bias into estimates of outcomes. We refer to this effect, which has not previously been described or discussed in the literature, as "**migration bias.**" It is critical to understand how trends in a reference population can vary according to selection criteria for disease in the chronic population, service mix, and changes in risk over time.

11.2 BACKGROUND

11.2.1 Disease Management

Disease Management (DM) is "a system of coordinated healthcare interventions and communications for populations with (chronic) conditions in which patient self-care efforts are significant.[3]" DM includes identification of health plan members with chronic diseases, prioritization of members for interventions (often called stratification) by current or predicted risk for worsening illness, and coordination of care between care providers and patients. An important function in DM is measuring the clinical and economic outcomes of DM programs. It is believed that improving clinical outcomes reduces healthcare costs (demonstrated in claims) by reducing the probability of clinical adverse events such as heart attacks, strokes, episodes of heart failure, or complications of diabetes.

Early DM outcomes studies generally compared a cohort, pre- and post-intervention, in which the actually-managed cohort's cost was compared with those eligible for disease management, but not actually managed. This measurement methodology is susceptible to selection bias, in which the experience of the population electing to enroll is different to that of the non-enrolling population, absent intervention. Clearly, selection bias distorts and invalidates any DM savings calculations determined using this methodology. Over time, this pre-post methodology has tended to be replaced by a population methodology in which the experience of the entire chronic population in the historic period is compared with that of the chronic population in the intervention period, thereby eliminating the potentially distorting effect of selection.

A commonly used population method for estimating Disease Management financial outcomes is the Actuarially-adjusted Historical Control methodology discussed in Chapter 8, in which a healthcare cost trend factor is applied to historic chronic member costs (pre-program) to predict the cost of the chronic population in the absence of the program. These costs include all claims costs related to the care of members with specified chronic diseases, not just the costs related to care for the chronic diseases themselves.

[3] As defined by the Disease Management Association of America, (DMAA). See www.dmaa.org.

Cost trend factors are increasingly used in population studies. Because the chronic population is subject to medical management, an estimate of healthcare trend from a source external to the chronic condition (Chronic) population is an essential component of this method. One source of this estimator of trend is the Non-chronic population.

Although the Actuarially-adjusted Historical Cost methodology has been used extensively, the relationship between Chronic and Non-chronic trends is not well understood by those who apply them or by users of the studies. In particular it is often assumed that the Chronic and Non-chronic trends are equal in the absence of intervention, allowing the latter to be a valid estimator of the former. Because many DM savings studies make the assumption that Chronic and Non-chronic trends are identical, this study seeks to examine these trends in a large data set of commercially insured members. We are not aware of the specific disease management programs (if any) that cover the employer groups included in the database.

11.2.2 Previous Studies

Existing healthcare cost trend literature is limited to the cost trends for populations (Strunk & Ginsburg [191], sub-populations (such as the obese), or to costs related to the specific diseases (Thorpe et al. [197]) rather than to that of all payers' costs regardless of cause. The absence of prior studies of healthcare cost trends in chronic populations makes it difficult to benchmark the actual observations in DM studies. We include the Thorpe data because of the paucity of published data in this area. The study by Thorpe, Florence and Joski compares data on chronic disease prevalence and spending from the National Medical Expenditure Survey (NMES) in 1987 and the 2000 Medical Expenditure Panel Survey, Household Component (MEPS-HC). This study does not calculate trends according to the actuarial definition, but the authors provide the data and we report the results of our analysis of the Thorpe et al data in Table 11.1 as these results are important for health actuaries.

The 1987 NMES surveyed 34,459 people (both chronic and non-chronic) and the 2000 MEPS-HC surveyed 25,096. The data used in Table 11.1 are self-reported data from the 1987 NMES and the 2000 MEPS-HC, and include health spending, demographics, use of services and self-reported conditions. The data should be treated with some caution because they are self-reported by patients (rather than collected from the more reliable Disease Management methods of either clinician reporting or claims data analysis). Over time, it is possible that the increased awareness of and testing for chronic diseases in the population may have contributed to the increased prevalence observed. The data are easily summarized in a traditional actuarial trend form (Table 11.1). We have extracted only the cost and prevalence data associated with the traditional conditions managed by chronic disease programs, and converted to an average annual trend over the thirteen year period, 1987 to 2000.

The raw data provided from these two studies allow us to calculate rates of total expenditure, prevalence of chronic disease, and costs per member per year for the chronic population. Having data at two points in time (1987 and 2000) allows us also to calculate an average trend in each of these metrics between 1987 and 2000. Annual trends in the chronic population range from 3.0% (diabetes) to 7.3% (hypertension), with an average annual trend of 4.6%.

Table 11.1

Total Healthcare Spending for Each Condition

Year	Pulmonary	Hypertension	Diabetes	Heart	TOTAL
1987	$11,685	$8,008	$8,661	$30,450	$58,804
2000	$36,477	$23,395	$18,288	$56,679	$134,839
Increase in Chronic Spending	212.2%	192.1%	111.2%	86.1%	129.3%
Annualized Cost Increase	9.2%	8.6%	5.9%	4.9%	6.6%

Number of Chronic Individuals per 100,000 of the Population

Year	Pulmonary	Hypertension	Diabetes	Heart	TOTAL
1987	10,389	9,734	2,961	6,189	29,273
2000	15,526	11,384	4,260	6,226	37,396
Increase in Chronic Prevalence	49.4%	17.0%	43.9%	0.6%	27.7%
Annualized Prevalence Increase	3.1%	1.2%	2.8%	0.0%	1.9%

Healthcare Cost per Member per Year

Year	Pulmonary	Hypertension	Diabetes	Heart	TOTAL
1987	$1,125	$823	$2,925	$4,920	$2,009
2000	$2,349	$2,055	4,293	$9,104	$3,606
Increase in Chronic Cost	108.9%	149.8%	46.8%	85.0%	79.5%
Annualized PMPY Increase	5.8%	7.3%	3.0%	4.8%	4.6%

Data for this analysis are drawn from Thorpe et al., [197] who uses NMES (1987) and MEPS (2000) data.

Other studies of chronic prevalence trends include a CDC study that predicts an annual growth in chronic prevalence between 1998 and 2020 of about 1% annually, somewhat lower than the 1.9% measured in the Thorpe, Florence and Joski study between 1987 and 2002. The CDC study does not project future cost growth. In addition, these studies measured disease-specific cost trends for the entire population, as opposed to trends (as defined by actuaries) at the individual level (see below).

Many of the published studies examine just one chronic condition. Because of the prevalence of co-morbidities in the chronic population, these studies can contribute to over-estimation of prevalence of chronic disease(s) unless double-counting is explicitly eliminated. Hoffman, Rice and Sung [97] report that forty-four percent of all chronic patients have one or more chronic conditions. Hogan et al., [99] writing for the American Diabetes Association, estimate the total cost of care associated with diabetes to be $92 billion in 2002. The historic rate of increase in diabetes expenditures per member per year is estimated in this study as 5.9% over the period 1987-2000. The growth in prevalence of diabetes over this period is estimated as 2.8%. Hogan et al estimate growth of diabetes prevalence between 2000 and 2020 as 2% annually, somewhat lower than the historic experience. The estimated growth in expenditures is 50% (to $138 billion) by 2020 in constant 2002 dollars. The implied annual trend is only 2.3% annually, to which we must add an estimate of future cost of living increases (we estimate 3%) to estimate total future trend (5.3%).

11.2.3 Definition of Healthcare Trend

"Healthcare trend" is the term applied to the empirical observation that most healthcare measures (such as utilization, unit cost, and PMPM costs) tend to change over time. Generally, but not always, trend results in increases in cost-related healthcare measures.

"Trend" is the rate of increase in PMPM cost, or the difference between Year 2 and Year 1 costs per member per month, divided by Year 1 cost per member per month. Trend may be defined on a calendar year or any twelve-month basis, and with appropriate adjustment, any non-12 month period. Trend from period *t* to period *t*+1 is defined as:

$$Trend = \frac{PMPM_{t+1} - PMPM_t}{PMPM_t}$$

$$PMPM = \frac{\sum_{j=1}^{12} \sum_{i=1}^{n_j} C_{ij}}{\sum_{j=1}^{12} n_j}$$

where C_{ij} is the claims (or utilization, or other statistic being measured) of the ith member in the jth month and n_j is the number of members enrolled in the jth month.

11.2.4 Measurement of Trend

For the purpose of the "actuarially-adjusted historical control" design, it is important that trend be derived from a stable population (or from chronic and non-chronic populations that exhibit similar tendencies) that is not subject to changes in risk profile, such as age, gender, or morbidity. At the very least the effect of changes in the underlying population must be isolated and an appropriate correction must be applied when the observed trend is used in a calculation. Otherwise, the effect of underlying population changes will contribute to the trend calculation. If it is known, for example, that the average age of the population increased between year one and year two, the effect of this age increase could be calculated and deducted from the observed trend to estimate the underlying, or "stable population" trend. To the extent that equivalence with respect to risk factors is not achieved in the two periods over which trend is measured, their effect on trend will have to be estimated and an actuarial adjustment applied.

11.2.5 Factors that Affect Trend

As actuaries are aware, unit cost and PMPM cost trends are influenced by many factors: changes in the covered population's age, sex, geographic or employment mix; underlying cost pressures; increases in intensity of services; actions taken as a result of cost-shifting by some payers; provider contract changes; or leveraging due to the interaction between increasing charges and fixed plan design features such as co-pays or deductibles. Utilization trend, on the other hand, is influenced by intensity of services, the propensity of demand for services to be affected by supply, regulations and changes in medical practice (such as increased use of defensive medicine, or the introduction of a requirement for minimum length-of-stay for certain procedures) and the effect of aging or "maturing" of the diseased population, or introduction of new technologies and treatments.

When trends are calculated for a typical health plan, the overall experience of the population is tracked over time. Measurement of disease management outcomes, however, often introduces the need to analyze the experience of sub-populations. Three factors that have a potentially significant effect on trend are the migration of members between categories (such as non-chronic, chronic or excluded members), catastrophic claims and the mix of services used by members of different categories. We discuss each of these factors below.

11.2.6 Factors that Affect Selection of Measured Populations

While a health plan may apply its DM programs to all members identified as Chronic for the diseases of interest, members may choose not to participate. Measuring only the outcomes of volunteers introduces the possibility of selection bias. In order to avoid selection bias, studies now tend to be done including the entire chronic population – that is, considering all members that meet criteria for identification as chronic, whether or not they choose to enroll in a DM program. The population methodology has the additional advantage of potentially avoiding bias due to regression to the mean, provided increases and decreases in costs in the population are random and thus offset each other (Fetterolf, Wennberg & DeVries [58]. How members are selected into the measured chronic population varies. Selection can be broader (one or two claims with ICD codes for the diagnosis), or narrower (scoring systems in which claims for encounters, drugs, procedures, and lab results are taken into account). Broad selection algorithms tend to have high sensitivity (identify most or nearly all members who have the disease) but lower specificity (some members are selected who do not actually have the disease). Narrow selection algorithms tend to have lower sensitivity but higher specificity.

In addition, the literature cites several methods of determining whether a member, once identified, *remains* in the chronic pool in succeeding periods[4]. A member may be identified as chronic either prospectively, implying that the member is included in the chronic population from the month of first identification onward, or retrospectively, in which case the member is retrospectively classified to the chronic population from the beginning of the study (also referred to as "ever/never Chronic"). In addition, an investigator must decide whether chronic members must be re-qualified as chronic year-to-year under the same set of criteria used to identify the member initially ("Re-qualification") or not. A third method that is used in some studies is the cohort methodology, which measures outcomes only on a cohort of (Chronic) members over all measurement periods, with no continuing eligible members allowed in or out across all periods. We explore some of these ideas in this chapter.

11.3 POPULATION AND METHODS

The population used for this analysis consisted of a total of 1.5 million covered lives enrolled under employer health plans from January 1998 to February 2003[5]. No information about specific medical management or disease management programs was included in the dataset, although the incidence of disease management programs in the commercial population is believed to be minor for the years for which we have data. Retired members whose coverage is

[4] It may seem intuitively wrong for a "chronic" member to be re-classified as "non-chronic" after initially being identified as chronic. Identification that is performed based on administrative data and chronic disease algorithms are not 100% infallible, and a percentage of "false positives" is to be expected with any algorithm.

[5] The Ingenix data set is used with permission of Ingenix Inc., Minneapolis, MN.

complementary to Medicare (Medicare Supplemental) were excluded, and the analysis focuses on the active employer-insured (Commercial) population. Risk-bearing payers (generally employer groups) without continuous enrollment over the study period were excluded (although members of continuously-eligible employer groups were allowed to enter and leave the study). Total membership for analysis was slightly lower than 1 million lives each year.

No minimum eligibility requirements were imposed on individual members within payer groups. Claims for members who did not appear in the eligibility file for the month incurred were eliminated from analysis. The population was divided annually into several groups resulting in each member being counted as either Chronic or Non-chronic for one of the five assessed chronic diseases (coronary artery disease, heart failure, diabetes mellitus, asthma, or chronic obstructive lung disease) for each year based on the following criteria:

- A single admission with primary diagnosis for one of the diseases; or
- At least 2 face-to-face encounter claims on separate days for one of the diseases; or
- In the case of diabetes or asthma a prescription fill for a drug specific for that disease could substitute for one or both of the encounter claims.

The diagnostic (ICD-9-CM) and drug (NDC) codes used were consistent with disease codes recommended by the Disease Management Association of America (Duncan [92]).

The claims costs analyzed were the allowed charges (that is, billed charges for allowed health plan benefits before negotiated discounts and before cost sharing with the insured). The per capita claims experience of the Chronic and Non-chronic groups was tracked; incurred claims were associated with the corresponding membership and summed and expressed as per member per month (PMPM). Trends were calculated based on PMPM costs (allowed charges). We did not separate the prevalence, costs or trends of members with different conditions.

All members were identified as Chronic or Non-chronic using the prospective "once chronic/always chronic" criterion. As an alternative, we varied the identification to attribute chronic conditions retrospectively as well.

11.4 RESULTS

Table 11.2 shows costs and trends using the prospective identification methodology and illustrates the contribution of Chronic individuals to total cost over the four years 1999-2002. In 1999, although Chronic individuals accounted for 4.1% of all covered members, they accounted for 14.5% of all costs. By 2002, Chronic individuals had increased to 8.6% of the population and accounted for 23.1% of costs. This increase in Chronic prevalence arises in part because we analyze prevalence using the "Once chronic always chronic" methodology. It also points out an issue with commercial studies of chronic disease: in order for chronic identification to be consistent year-to-year, we would require as many historic years of claim data for the first year of the study (in this case, 1999) as we have for the last (2002)[6].

[6] Members identified in 1999 are identified through claims incurred in one year of historic claims data. When the population is not re-qualified annually, members identified in subsequent years could have incurred their identifying claims several years previously. For example a member counted as chronic in 2002 could have been identified through claims incurred in 1998, and have had no subsequent claims. Symmetry in claims-based identification would require that the 1999 chronic population be identified by claims back to 1995.

11.4.1 Chronic and Non-chronic Members and Costs

TABLE 11.2

Costs and Trends using the "Prospective Identification" Methodology

Year	Chronic Member Months	Chronic Prevalence	Chronic Cost PMPM	Chronic Cost Trend	Total Chronic Cost ($'000)	Chronic Cost as % of Total
1999	463,196	4.1%	$745.87	–	$345,483	14.5%
2000	701,398	6.0%	$746.42	0.1%	$523,538	18.3%
2001	845,883	7.0%	$820.27	9.9%	$693,856	20.3%
2002	990,646	8.6%	$879.71	7.2%	$871,485	23.1%
3-Year Annualized				5.6%		
Year	Non-Chronic Member Months		Non-Chronic Cost PMPM	Non-Chronic Cost Trend	Total Non-Chronic Cost ($'000)	Non-Chronic Cost as % of Total
1999	10,956,779		$186,26	–	$2,040,836	85.5%
2000	11,067,274		$211,41	12.5%	$2,339,693	81.7%
2001	11,241,633		$242,83	14.9%	$2,729,790	79.7%
2002	10,591,169		$274,44	12.0%	$2,906,654	76.9%
3-Year Annualized				13.8%		
Year	Total Member Months		Total Cost PMPM	Total Cost Trend	Total ($'000)	
1999	11,419,975		$208.96	–	$2,386,319	
2000	11,768,627		$243.29	16.4%	$2,863,231	
2001	12,087,516		$283.24	16.4%	$3,423,646	
2002	11,581,815		$326.21	15.2%	$3,778,138	
3-Year Annualized				16.0%		

Effectively, the combination of "once chronic always chronic" and four historical years of data (in the case of 2002) means that the Chronic population is identified based on a total of five years of claims data. To replicate this identification protocol in each year would require that data be available from 1995 to 1998 to identify 1999 chronic members with the same number of historical years of claims. To analyze trends we need as many years of PMPM costs as we can assemble, which requires us to use all available years of claims. The consequence of this constraint, however, is that by 2002, more years of historic data exist to identify chronic members than were available for 1999.

For the entire population, PMPM cost increased at an annualized rate of 16.0% over this period. If Chronic prevalence remained at 4.1% throughout the study period, the average annualized increase would have been only 12.7%; implying that approximately 3.3% of the annual increase was due to the increase in chronic prevalence. This observation is derived from Table 11.3.

TABLE 11.3

Average Cost PMPM Without the Effect of Prevalence Creep					
Year	Chronic Member Months	Non-chronic Member Months	Total Member Months	Chronic Prevalence	Cost PMPM
1999	463,196	10,956,779	11,419,975	4.1%	$208.96
2002	990,646	10,591,169	11,581,815	8.6%	$326.21
2002 (re-stated)	469,760	11,112,055	11,581,815	4.1%	$298.99

The relative chronic and non-chronic trend results in Table 11.2 may at first appear counter-intuitive. First, the chronic trend is lower than either the total or Non-chronic trend, which appears anomalous, given that Chronic members are high cost (their cost PMPM is between 3 and 4 times that of Non-chronic members). Second, the overall population trend is higher than that of either sub-population. These apparent anomalies, however, are due to migration in membership between the relatively low-cost Non-chronic population, as newly-identified Chronic members transfer to the relatively high-cost Chronic population. The members who leave the Non-chronic are relatively high-cost, while they are relatively low-cost members of the chronic population. In each case the trend of the respective populations is reduced below the underlying rate. Finally, we note that the observed chronic trend (5.6%) is reasonably consistent with the trend observed for similar chronic conditions (4.6%) between 1987 and 2002 by Thorpe et al., (op. cit.)

The growth in the Chronic member population (more than doubling between 1999 and 2002) results from increasing identification of chronic members, or increased measured prevalence. Because the overall population is almost constant, the increase in chronic membership is matched by a decrease in the Non-chronic pool. Some more-recently introduced savings methodologies attempt to adjust for duration since chronic diagnosis, but this method is hampered by the availability of data, making it difficult to apply methods that introduce a true duration adjustment.

11.4.2 Decomposition by Service Sector

To further study the gap between Chronic and Non-chronic trends, we explored whether this divergence could be due to differences in service mix between the populations. Certain applications of the actuarially adjusted methodology apply a single trend to baseline costs. As actuaries are aware, trend is particularly susceptible to factors such as leveraging of plan design, change in mix of services, and covered population. If this is a concern, a refinement to the simple single composite trend approach may be applied that decomposes the calculation into service categories and further decomposes trend into its utilization and unit cost components. An example of such service category decomposition is shown in Figure 11.1.

Service Categories for Decomposition of Savings Calculation

- Inpatient Hospital (including. ICU, SNF)
- Emergency Room
- Outpatient Surgery
- Professional Charges
- Outpatient Office Visits
- Rehabilitation Facility
- Professional Office Visits
- X-ray/lab
- Prescription Drugs (non-inpatient)
- Other medical

Figure 11.1

An advantage of this decomposition is the ability to calculate a weighted average of the individual service line trends (derived from the non-chronic population) using weights appropriate for the chronic population.

Table 11.4 compares the composition of overall (Total) PMPM claims of each of the Chronic, Non-chronic and all member populations by major service category. For example, over the three-year period, Inpatient Hospital claims amount to $67.32 PMPM for the Non-chronic population, compared with $294.02 for the Chronic population, and $81.84 for the population as a whole. Data are annualized averages over the 4-year period 1999-2002. As one would expect, the composition of the claims dollar is different for each population, with Non-chronic members using relatively fewer inpatient hospitalization services (29.5% of their total expense) and relatively more physician office services (17.9%) than Chronic members (36.2% and 12.2%, respectively). The differences in service sector trends (hospital expenses growing relatively more slowly than certain outpatient expenses) when combined with these utilization differentials could result in different overall trends in each sub-population. While some trends were discernible within each service category (inpatient services generally fell over the 4-year period, while outpatient services generally increased) there was relatively little variation in the service category percentages over time.

TABLE 11.4

Comparison of Chronic and Non-Chronic Service Cost PMPM and Service Mix

	ALL YEARS	Claims PMPM								ALL SERVICES
	Mem Mons	Inpatient	Outpatient	Presc Drug	Emerg Rm	Laboratory	Phys Ofc	Rehab	Other	TOTAL
NON-CHRONIC	10,964,214	$67.32	$68.53	$33.47	$5.24	$4.46	$40.90	$0.91	$7.58	$228.40
CHRONIC	750,281	$294.02	$197.69	$158.37	$9.69	$10.64	$99.34	$6.29	$35.10	$811.15
ALL	11,714,495	$81.84	$76.80	$41.47	$5.52	$4.86	$44.64	$1.25	$9.34	$265.72
	ALL YEARS	Service Category Weights								ALL SERVICES
	Mem Mons	Inpatient	Outpatient	Presc Drug	Emerg Rm	Laboratory	Phys Ofc	Rehab	Other	TOTAL
NON-CHRONIC	10,964,214	29.5%	30.0%	14.7%	2.3%	2.0%	17.9%	0.4%	3.3%	100.0%
CHRONIC	750,281	36.2%	24.4%	19.5%	1.2%	1.3%	12.2%	0.8%	4.3%	100.0%
ALL	11,714,495	30.8%	28.9%	15.6%	2.1%	1.8%	16.8%	0.5%	3.5%	100.0%

Table 11.4 above shows that the PMPM cost and relative service category utilization of Chronic and Non-chronic members is different, with chronic members being heavier utilizers of inpatient hospital, prescription drug, and rehabilitation services. These are all service categories that, for chronic members, have relatively low trends.

Table 11.5 compares the trends in Chronic and Non-chronic populations, by major service category. Trends are 3-year average annualized rates, calculated over the 4-year period. Different trends by service are observed in each sub-population and in the population as a whole, with non-chronic member trends generally higher than those of chronic members.

TABLE 11.5

Comparison of Chronic and Non-Chronic Trends by Service Category

	3-Yr annualized	Service Category Trends								ALL SERVICES
	Mem Mons	Inpatient	Outpatient	Presc Drug	Emerg Rm	Laboratory	Phys Ofc	Rehab	Other	TOTAL
NON-CHRONIC	10,964,214	12.3%	15.4%	11.0%	19.4%	10.8%	16.5%	12.8%	9.0%	13.8%
CHRONIC	750,281	6.6%	8.3%	1.1%	12.1%	0.6%	8.9%	– 9.5%	– 1.7%	5.7%
ALL	11,714,495	15.8%	17.2%	13.7%	20.0%	11.4%	17.7%	12.6%	11.3%	16.0%

To test the effect of service category mix on trend, we applied the Chronic service category utilization percentages to the Non-chronic service category trends. Table 11.6 shows unadjusted Non-chronic trend, compared with Non-chronic trend adjusted for the Chronic population service distribution. The difference in service utilization accounts for relatively little of the difference in trends between sub-populations (between 0.3% and 0.8%, depending on the year, and 0.6% on average over the three-year period).

TABLE 11.6

Effect of Chronic Service Mix on Non-Chronic Trends

Year	Non-Chronic Trend	Adjusted Non-Chronic Trend	Difference
2000	13.5%	12.7%	0.8%
2001	14.9%	14.6%	0.3%
2002	13.0%	12.4%	0.6%
Three-Year Average	13.8%	13.2%	0.6%

11.4.3 Effect of Exclusions on Trend

In Disease Management applications, exclusions (both from the measured population and from the claims associated with the population) are often made to reduce potential confounding. Examples of exclusions of members are those with HIV/AIDS, and members who have a diagnosis of End-stage renal disease. Examples of exclusions of claims are those above a catastrophic limit (outliers) or claims for certain diagnoses (such as maternity or mental health).

We tested the effect of applying both member and claim exclusions on the Chronic and Non-chronic trends. Sample results are provided in Table 11.7.

.

TABLE 11.7

Effect of Excluding High-Cost Outliers on Trend

Year	Non-Chronic Cost PMPM	Non-Chronic Trend	Chronic Cost PMPM	Chronic Trend	Total Cost PMPM	Total Trend
1999	$148.08	–	$650.87	–	$168.47	–
2000	162.89	10.0%	625.12	– 4.0%	190.44	13.0%
2001	192.47	18.2%	706.81	13.1%	228.46	20.0%
2002	218.61	13.6%	751.95	6.4%	264.23	15.7%
3-Yr Annualized		13.9%		4.9%		16.2%

Excluding members and claims does not change the average 3-year trend for the Non-chronic or total population (16.2% vs. 16.0%; 13.9% vs. 13.8%). The Chronic trend is reduced (5.6% vs. 4.9%), and at the same time is more subject to variation year-to-year. This result suggests that the large claims in the Chronic population have been growing at a faster rate than corresponding large claims in the Non-chronic population. One important objective in commercial DM evaluations is to avoid incorrect conclusions due to random variation. This analysis suggests that including the full amount of high dollar claims makes the PMPM claims and trend of the Chronic population more variable. If the objective of a study is to avoid potential confounding due to variability, exclusion of large claims in excess of a stop-loss limit (also called "top-coding") appears to be justified.

11.4.4 Effect of Migration between Chronic and Non-Chronic Populations

Migration from the Non-chronic to the Chronic population causes divergence between the trends of each group. We tested this effect by assigning members to a group (Chronic or Non-chronic) retrospectively to the beginning of the first measurement period, irrespective of the period in which they met the chronic condition identification criteria. Thus, for example, in the results reported in Table 11.2, a member who is Non-chronic in 1999 and 2000, but meets the chronic test at January 1, 2001 will be classified in the Non-chronic group in 1999 and 2000 and re-classified to the Chronic group in 2001 and 2002. For the comparison below, this same member will be classified as Chronic for all 4 years of analysis.

TABLE 11.8

Effect Of Applying Retrospective ("Ever/Never Chronic") Identification Methodology

Retrospective Identification						
Year	3-Yr Annualized Non-Chronic Cost PMPM	Chronic Trend	Non-Chronic Member Months	Non-Chronic Trend	Total Cost Member Months	Total Trend
1999	1,410,116	00.0%	10,009,859	00.0%	11,419,975	00.0%
2000	1,440,371	15.5%	10,328,301	17.8%	11,768,672	16.7%
2001	1,437,872	17.2%	10,649,644	17.0%	12,087,516	16.2%
2002	1,317,536	16.3%	10,264,279	16.8%	11,581,815	15.3%
3-Year	Annualized	16.3%	Annualized	17.2%	Annualized	16.0%
Prospective Identification						
3-Year	Annualized	5.6%	Annualized	13.8%	Annualized	16.0%

When trend is measured on members assigned retrospectively from the beginning of the period, Chronic, Non-chronic and total trends are much closer: the Non-chronic group trend is at a slightly higher rate using the retrospective method (17.2%) vs. prospective (13.8%). The chronic trend is 16.3% using the retrospective method, considerably higher than the trend using the prospective method (5.6%). More important for commercial applications, either the Non-chronic or Total trend appears to be useable as a proxy for the Chronic trend measured on the retrospective basis.

The fact that both Chronic and Non-chronic trends are higher than overall trend in the case of the retrospectively identified population may appear to be anomalous. However, the lower trend in the overall population results from the relative growth rates of non-chronic members (0.8% per year) and chronic members (–2.2% per year) over the 4 years. During the four-year period, Non-chronic members increase from 63.0% of the total population to 65.6% of the total population. The lower PMPM cost of the Non-chronic population, combined with their relatively faster growth, depresses the overall trend in the population.

11.4.5 Effect of Canges in the Population Risk Profiles

One possible source of difference between Chronic and Non-chronic trends is differential changes in population risk over time. One commonly-used method for estimating member (and population) risk is the use of groupers or predictive models, which provide a single numerical value, at the individual member level. Each member is assigned a numerical "score" (which may also be aggregated to assess the risk of a population) based on factors in the individual member's risk profile. We applied a commonly-used and commercially-available grouper[7] to the Chronic and Non-chronic populations defined above. The DxCG model was applied prospectively that is, a risk score was predicted, based on the prior year's claims history, for each individual member for the following year. Results are shown in Table 11.9 for the Chronic and Non-chronic populations identified by the "once Chronic/always Chronic" methodology.

TABLE 11.9

Effect on Trend of Applying Risk Adjustment to the Prospective Methodology

Prospective Chronic Identification									
	CHRONIC				NON-CHRONIC				
Year	Risk-Score	Risk-Score Trend	PMPM Trend	Risk-Adjusted PMPM Trend	Risk-Score	Risk-Score Trend	PMPM Trend	Risk-Adjusted PMPM Trend
1999	3.162				0.878			
2000	2.814	– 11.0%	0.1%	12.5%	0.870	– 0.9%	13.5%	14.6%
2001	2.686	– 04.5%	9.9%	15.1%	0.894	2.8%	14.9%	11.7%
2002	2.622	– 02.4%	7.2%	09.9%	0.922	3.1%	13.0%	09.6%
3-yr Annualized		– 06.1%	5.6%	12.5%		1.7%	13.8%	11.9%

A risk score of 1.0 is the prediction that an individual or group will have the same PMPM cost as the mean of the entire insured population used for validating the risk adjustment model.

The trend in risk score indicates that the Chronic population becomes less risky over time. Conversely, the Non-chronic population becomes slightly more risky over time. Making a simple adjustment to the PMPM Trend observed in each population, (by dividing PMPM trend by the effect of population risk-score change), the Adjusted Trends become closer and are not significantly different.

The implication of this analysis may not be immediately obvious, so we remind the reader that unadjusted Non-chronic trend is often used as an estimator for Chronic trend, in the absence of a program. This analysis indicates that the lower trend in the Chronic population

[7] The DxCG grouper, used with permission of DxCG Inc., Boston. More information about groupers and alternative products may be found in Cumming et al., [35] and Winkelman & Mehmud [220].

(when compared with the Non-chronic population) is associated with a differential change in risk score. The practical application of this technique is illustrated in Table 11.10.

Table 11.10 contains some basic (hypothetical) data and a typical Disease Management program savings estimate. The baseline cost PMPM represents the average cost during a period prior to the initiation of a program for all included services for members who meet the inclusion criteria. As is the case in many calculations, the baseline cost PMPM is trended forward using the Non-chronic population experience as an estimate of that which would have been experienced by the Chronic population, absent the intervention program. The difference between the projected baseline cost and actual cost of the Chronic population is our estimate of program savings PMPM. The remainder of the calculation applies a Risk-adjuster to these numbers to determine a more accurate estimate of both Non-chronic trend, and the effect of change in the Chronic population risk-profile, allowing the (adjusted) Non-Chronic trend to be used as a potentially unbiased estimate.

TABLE 11.10

Application of a Risk-Adjusted Trend Model

Basic Data

The standard adjusted historical control savings calculation uses the unadjusted trends and cost PMPM, as follows:

Baseline Chronic Cost	$300
Trend (Non-chronic)	1.10
Trended Baseline Chronic Cost	$330
Actual Cost	$305

Population	Baseline Period	Intervention Period	Trend
Non-Chronic Cost PMPM	$100	$110	10.0%
Non-Chronic Risk Score	1.0	1.02	2.0%
Non-Chronic Cost PMPM, Adjusted for Risk Trend		$\frac{\$110}{1.02} = \$107.84$	
Risk-Adjusted Non-Chronic Cost Trend, PMPM	$100	$107.84	7.84%
Chronic Cost PMPM	$300	$305	1.67%
Chronic Risk Score	3.0	2.90	(3.33%)
Estimated Savings	$24 PMPM		

The Risk Adjusted historical control savings calculation uses the adjusted trends and cost PMPM, as follows:

Baseline Chronic Cost PMPM	$300
Risk-Adjusted Trend (non-chronic)	1.0784
Trended Baseline Chronic Cost	$323.52
Actual Cost	$305
Risk-Adjusted Actual Cost	$305/.967 = $315.41
Estimated Savings	$8.11 PMPM

Using the risk-adjusted trend as our estimate of Chronic trend gives a lower but more credible estimate of savings.

11.4.6 Effect of Re-Qualification on Chronic Population and Trend

It has been suggested that applying an annual re-qualification requirement will eliminate those ("false positive") members who satisfy the Chronic identification algorithms in the initial year but not the subsequent years. These members contribute to the "prevalence creep" observed earlier, as well as reducing the PMPM costs and trend in the Chronic population. (Since these members by definition do not qualify as Chronic in later years, their claims are lower than those members who continue to be Chronic and experience chronic costs.)

We applied a requirement that a member be included in the next year Chronic population only if the member experiences qualifying Chronic claims in the prior year. This is a different requirement to that in the base case, in which members are added continuously throughout the year when they meet Chronic identification criteria. We applied this algorithm for computational ease. Chronic prevalence is reduced, compared with the base case. Chronic prevalence in the case of re-qualification is calculated based on the beginning of the year population and is shown in Table 11.11.

TABLE 11.11

Year	Chronic Prevalence Original	Chronic Prevalence with Requalification
1999	4.1%	4.2%
2000	6.0%	4.6%
2001	7.0%	4.7%
2002	8.0%	5.3%

As expected, the application of re-qualification reduces the prevalence creep.

Table 11.12 compares Chronic and Non-chronic trends under the original assumptions and with re-qualification. Chronic trends with re-qualification are closer to Non-chronic (and overall) trends, although differences remain. As the ratio column shows, the three-year average ratio of Chronic to Non-chronic trend with re-qualification is 75.7%. This number varies between 57.8% and 90.9%, making it difficult to implement a "standard" adjustment to the Non-chronic trend to account for the observed difference. One factor that appears to be driving some of the difference is changes in observed Chronic prevalence: when there is a large year-on-year change in Chronic prevalence (as in 2000 and 2002) the ratio of Chronic to Non-chronic trend is relatively low. When the change in Chronic prevalence is large (as in 2001) the Chronic and Non-chronic trends are closer.

TABLE 11.12

	BASE TREND			REQUALIFICATION TREND		
Year	Chronic	Non-Chronic	TOTAL	Chronic	Non-Chronic	Ratio Chronic/ Non-Chronic
1999	–	–	–	–	–	–
2000	0.1%	13.5%	16.4%	9.4%	12.2%	77.1%
2001	9.9%	14.9%	16.4%	14.6%	16.0%	90.9%
2002	7.2%	13.0%	15.2%	8.1%	14.1%	57.8%
3-Yr Average	5.6%	13.8%	16.0%	10.7%	14.1%	75.7%

11.5. DISCUSSION

Those who pay for Disease Management programs want to understand whether they are receiving value for their money. Answering the value question means comparing the actual results to what would have been predicted absent the intervention. Apart from a randomized controlled clinical trial (in which it can be assumed that the control or comparison group's actual costs would answer the "in the absence of" question), the healthcare cost for the intervened group must be predicted from its cost in the "pre" year adjusted by a suitable trend. While it is commonly assumed that the cost trend for the Chronic group (who receive the intervention) would be identical to the Non-chronic trend in the absence of intervention, this assumption has not been proven.

This study showed that at least if Chronics are identified using a "once Chronic/always Chronic" methodology, this assumption may not be true. We found that in a large commercially insured population over a four year period the Chronic trend was far lower than the Non-chronic trend. This conclusion was unaffected by readjusting the Non-chronic trend to the Chronic population's service mix. Because this divergence in trends may be due to the prospective method of classifying Chronics, we applied a second (retrospective) methodology, which assumed that over the four-year span all members were either Chronic or Non-Chronic. While this methodology resulted in convergence of the trends, it may not be clinically defensible because people are first identified with chronic diseases at a specific point in time, when either qualifying tests (or the claims proxy used in DM analyses) are satisfied. The "once Chronic/always Chronic" methodology has greater clinical appeal—people do not become cured of their Chronic diseases.

Because migration of members from the Non-chronic to the Chronic pool may change the case (risk) mix in the pools, we applied a commonly-used and validated risk adjustment methodology. This resulted in the trends becoming almost identical.

11.6 LIMITATIONS

Because we used a commercially-available data-set, we had no information about the specific medical interventions, if any, present in the population. We expect that DM programs were limited during the time-period represented by the data, given the relative recent development of large-scale DM programs.

The results that we reproduce represent a single specific sample and may not be reproduced in other data. We encourage actuaries to follow our methods, however, and to publish detailed trend analyses in other populations.

11.7 CONCLUSIONS AND IMPLICATIONS FOR DISEASE MANAGEMENT PURCHASERS

1. When Chronics are identified using a prospective "once Chronic/always Chronic" algorithm, unadjusted Non-chronic (or total population) trend is a poor proxy for Chronic trend in DM evaluations.

2. Using trends calculated in this way introduces a bias into estimates of savings outcomes. Based on our analysis, the bias is upward (i.e. savings are over-stated as a result of the bias). This effect, which has not previously been described or discussed in the literature, may be called a "migration bias."

3. As an example of the effect of "migration bias", consider a DM evaluation in which the baseline cost of the Chronic population is $100 PMPM. Projecting this cost to the next period using the non-chronic trend we calculated (13.8%) would result in a projected cost of $113.80 PMPM. Savings would be estimated as the difference between the observed cost PMPM and the actual cost PMPM. Our results show that the actual Chronic trend that should have been used in this example is 5.6%, giving a projected cost PMPM of $105.60. The difference in projected baseline costs PMPM ($8.20) would be included in savings by a study that uses the trend projection and prospective Chronic identification methodology.

4. While using Chronic population identification algorithms that retrospectively classify members as never or always Chronic (or Non-chronic), the Chronic and Non-chronic trends are closer to convergence. This methodology is difficult to justify on clinical grounds.

5. Adjusting the Non-chronic trend for service mix has little effect on trend.

6. Adjusting both the Non-chronic and Chronic populations for the effect of change in population risk results in an adjusted Non-chronic trend that closely approximates adjusted Chronic trend.

7. When using a prospective "once Chronic/always Chronic" selection algorithm, the bias in trends can be corrected by using a risk adjuster to account for risk-change in each population over time.

8. The above conclusions about trend relativities hold when several years of trend are averaged. The results for individual years are less consistent, because trend (particularly within the Chronic population) is volatile. In a particular savings calculation, Non-chronic trend may be more or less close to the true underlying Chronic trend.

Operationally, the Non-chronic trend as estimated using a retrospective (ever/never Chronic) method may be used to assess the effect of DM interventions without adjustment. The methodology may be rejected by some analysts on clinical grounds. As an alternative, a risk-adjustment methodology may be applied to a prospective analysis. To do so, the Non-chronic trend would first be adjusted by dividing the Non-chronic PMPM trend by the trend in Non-chronic risk-score trend. An estimate would have to be made of the trend in Chronic risk-score, which will require sufficient data series to estimate the risk-score. There is also a potential for confounding because the risk-score post-implementation of DM will be affected (reduced) by the intervention. This effect is expected to be relatively small in a Chronic population, which is permanently subject to its conditions, making this a potentially practical method for trend correction in applications.

APPENDIX 11.1 RELATIONSHIP BETWEEN OVERALL TRENDS AND TRENDS OF SUB-GROUPS

A question frequently asked is why trends observed in sub-groups can be higher than the trend observed in the overall group? This effect is due to migration between populations.

The following is a typical example:

Non-chronic trend:	10%
Chronic trend:	8%
Overall trend:	7%

TABLE 11.A

	Baseline PMPM	Trend	Trended PMPM	Population Baseline	Population Time 1
Non-Chronic	$100.00	10%	$110.00	95%	96%
Chronic	$500.00	8%	$540.00	5%	4%
Total	$120.00		$131.50	100%	100%
Trend 0			10%		
			$128.06		
Trend 1			7%		

To illustrate the effect of migration we show two scenarios in Table 11.A:

Scenario 1: the population composition does not change from Baseline to Time 1. In this case, the overall trend, Trend 0, is 10% (the weighted average of the Non-chronic and Chronic population trends).

Scenario 2: in this example, the population shifts slightly in favor of the Non-chronic population which has a higher trend. In this case, the population shift (migration) affects the measured trend. Although the Non-chronic population has a higher underlying trend, the migration from high-cost chronic to low-cost non-chronic reduces the overall measured trend. Thus the overall trend is 7% in this example.

12 TESTING ACTUARIAL METHODS FOR EVALUATING DISEASE MANAGEMENT SAVINGS OUTCOMES

12.1 INTRODUCTION

This chapter applies the principles and methodologies discussed in earlier chapters to measure cost savings from a 2-year Disease Management program for the 200,000 Medicare members of a regional managed care plan. We then study how savings estimates change when we allow for four variations in key assumptions:

- Methods for identifying or excluding plan members;
- Requirements for eligibility in the health plan;
- Methods for calculating healthcare trend; and
- Study design.

Finally, we also examine the sensitivity of these results to product type by comparing the Medicare results to those of the Commercial HMO/POS product.

12.2 BACKGROUND

Highmark, Inc. is a large regional managed care plan headquartered in Pennsylvania, with more than 4 million members, most of whom reside in and around Pittsburgh. During the period of this study, approximately 2-1/2 million members were eligible for the Disease Management program. Eligible members were distributed in two main product groupings:

- Medicare Plus Choice (now Medicare Advantage): 200,000. Throughout this chapter we refer to these members as "Medicare" because of the change of designation.
- HMO and Point of Service: 1.1 million

Highmark has been a leader in applying innovative managed care approaches to improving health and reducing cost of its coverage. For several years, Highmark operated a number of medical management and Disease Management programs, both internally staffed and using outside vendors. In 2002, Highmark implemented new Disease Management programs operated by Health Dialog Inc., a Boston-based care management company. The DM programs were first offered to the Medicare and HMO/POS populations.

Highmark and Health Dialog wished to estimate cost savings from the DM programs. After considering several different methods, they ultimately decided to use the actuarial methodology described in Chapter 8 which estimated the savings results that we term the **"base-case savings."**

Highmark's management is aware of the complexity associated with calculation methods used to determine the cost effectiveness of DM programs. As a national leader in the evolution and understanding of effective delivery of healthcare to members, Highmark's management supported the Society of Actuaries study aimed at quantifying the sensitivity of estimated savings results due to variations in the specific components and key assumptions of the actuarial methodology.

12.3 METHODS

We compare the effect on estimated program savings of changes in different assumptions. All variations are compared with the "base-case savings". "Base-case savings" are calculated by applying the actuarial methodology described in Chapter 8. We report here on the impact on cost savings of four variations on the base-case results from the actuarial methodology, applying each variation to the same underlying dataset (with the exception of the Commercial HMO/POS results, which are obtained from the HMO/POS dataset, applying the base-case assumptions).

12.3.1 Base Case Assumptions

The base case consisted of a number of assumptions, as follows;

1. The base case is a "population" study, in which a "baseline" population measure is compared with the same population measure, calculated in the "intervention period". As discussed elsewhere in this book, the population methodology is used to overcome many of the potential objections that arise from "regression to the mean" that is observed in a cohort of selected, high-risk members.
2. "Chronic" patients are identified from diagnoses contained in medical claims or prescriptions. More detail of the specific identification criteria used to classify chronic members is found in Appendix 12.1. Not all claims were included in the study. Those claims that are subject to volatility (catastrophic claims for example) or are not manageable by the program (for example, maternity claims) are excluded. Details of all categories of excluded claims are found in Appendix 12.2.
3. A minimum of six-months of continuous health plan eligibility is required to be included in the study.
4. No "re-qualification" (as a Chronic member) is required: once a patient is identified as a "Chronic" member, he is always considered to be a Chronic member (this definition is consistent with the clinical view of Chronic disease).
5. The reference cost is estimated by applying a medical trend factor to the baseline cost of the Chronic population.

6. The medical trend that is applied to the Chronic population is that derived from the Non-chronic population. The assumption underlying the use of the Non-chronic trend as an adjustment is that the factors that cause increases in Chronic population costs (changes in provider contracts and practice patterns, introduction of new technology, for example) apply equally in the Non-chronic population, and can therefore be estimated from them. Trend is defined as the increase in per member per month cost in a "measured" population. All exclusions that apply to the Chronic population (for example, for catastrophic cases, or members who do not have six months of continuous eligibility) are applied to the Non-chronic population when calculating this trend (as discussed in Appendix 8.2).
7. Cost levels used in the study are set at the allowed charge level. While plan design may have some impact on results through its effect on utilization, for the most part the potential for confounding of the effect of changes in plan design is neutralized by the use of allowed charges[1].

12.3.2 Limitations

Our study is a leading example of research in which changes in various methodological approaches and assumptions are tested to gauge the sensitivity of Disease Management cost savings estimates. Further research is needed in this area. For example, in our analysis a series of single alternative assumptions is considered and compared to the base-case cost savings. A multivariate approach might be useful in which the impact of different assumption alternatives would be combined to replicate a particular study and assess the effect on base-case savings.

Due to limited resources, we restricted the analysis of the impact of the different alternatives to Highmark's Medicare plan. We did have access to the HMO/POS plan data and determined base-case savings for these plans to compare to the Medicare results. We have reported the base-case savings for both Medicare and Commercial products, which (on a Per Member Per Month basis) are similar. The similarity between Medicare and Commercial baseline savings suggests that the sensitivity analysis for Commercial populations may be similar to that of the Medicare population.

We have studied different ways of identifying Chronic patients. We have not studied the risk profile of patients who leave managed care organizations, patients who refuse to participate in DM programs or those who terminate from them. It was beyond the scope of this particular study and the data to track such measures as the number of enrolled members, the length of time in the program for each member and the rate of termination from the program was not available.

In this DM program, Health Dialog intervened in a variety of Chronic diseases. Health Dialog's program serves multiple conditions, as do those of an increasing number of DM vendors. Indeed, Health Dialog refers to their program as a "whole person" model and makes little or no distinction in terms of services provided to Chronic members based on conditions

[1] Highmark has recently seen increasing sales of consumer-directed health care plans in which the effect of plan design on utilization is expected to be more significant than in traditional plans. During the period of this study, consumer-directed health plans were not a significant component of Highmark's business.

and co-morbidities. Purchasers of DM programs and researchers are often interested in the cost savings associated with each disease, however, and it is reasonable to expect that savings from DM would vary by and within disease type. This level of analysis was also beyond our scope.

Finally, this chapter estimates the sensitivity of calculated claims savings under a number of reasonable assumptions. Purchasers of disease management programs usually require an estimate of a program's Return on Investment (ROI). Estimates of ROI would require information on program costs and costs of administration which were not available to us, and which therefore make the calculation of an ROI impossible.

12.3.3 Alternative Scenario Assumptions

In testing the sensitivity of results to changes in assumptions, all base-case assumptions are held constant and only the specific changes noted below are made. Specific variations analyzed are as follows:

1. Cohort analysis: Savings are calculated based on a before-and-after analysis of a cohort of plan members in a Disease Management program. This methodology (also called "pre-post") was once prevalent in the industry but following publication of methodology analyses[2] it is now less frequently encountered in the literature. We wished to test the difference in results that is observed by applying both population (base-case) and cohort (Alternative 1 below) methods to the same set of data.

2. Definitions/techniques to identify "Chronic" patients based on:
    a. Medical claims but not prescription drug claims;
    b. Primary diagnosis only, as identified from claims;
    c. Only claims submitted by hospitals (for inpatient or outpatient services);

3. Trend: we evaluate the use of a Non-chronic trend calculated using a retrospective Chronic identification algorithm. In the base case, "Non-chronic" member trend is used as a proxy for the (unmeasurable) chronic member trend, absent intervention. In this base case, Non-chronic member trend is calculated using a prospective classification of Chronic condition (that is, members are assigned to the Chronic population from the month that they first meet the Chronic identification criteria forward). Alternative approaches to calculating trend are discussed in Chapter 11, where we identify a bias (called "Migration Bias") due to the migration of members between groups. One way to mitigate this bias is the use of retrospective identification. In this case members identified as Chronic are classified in the Chronic group throughout the study beginning with the earlier of the date that the study begins or the date the member joins the plan (including the baseline period). While this technique avoids migration bias, it introduces other potential distortions (we measure the results for members who are not part of the managed population, for example). The extent and nature of this potential distortion remains to be analyzed.

---

[2] See Johns Hopkins[188], Fetterolf [59] and Fitzner et al. [62].

4. Continuous enrollment/eligibility definitions: to be included as a Chronic or a Non-chronic member in this analysis the member must have been continuously enrolled for a minimum of six months. Members with fewer than six months of continuous enrollment are included at the beginning of the month after completion of six months of enrollment. For this alternative, we studied the effect on the results of imposing no continuous enrollment requirement.

The base analysis is conducted using the Medicare product line. Finally, we apply the same assumptions to calculations made for the Commercial HMO/POS lines.

Enrollees and claims were tracked for a baseline year (pre-program initiation) and two subsequent intervention years. The alternative methods described above were then applied to recalculate the cost savings.

12.4 RESULTS

12.4.1 Base-Case Results

In Table 12.1 we apply the actuarially-adjusted measurement methodology as described in Chapter 8 to a baseline and two intervention periods in the Highmark Medicare population. The trend that is applied to the Chronic measured population is calculated from the experience of the Non-chronic, or Index, measured population. Note that we apply a 2-month non-measured period at the end of the baseline period to allow for the program to start and for enrollment to take place. Thus, the first period for which trend is calculated is actually 14 months (not 12). The initial Chronic measured prevalence is 21.3%, indicating that slightly more than one in five members has at least one Chronic condition and meet all the other requirements for inclusion in the study. The Chronic measured prevalence grows by 28% over the three-year study period, to 27.2%. It is worth noting that these Chronic measurements span a time period during which changes in CMS payments caused plans to begin to be more thorough in both the completeness and the coding accuracy of the diagnosis on claims submissions, which could have resulted in a small increase in the identification of Chronic members in the later periods.

As one might expect, the basic cost per member per month of the Chronic population is considerably higher than that of the Non-chronic population ($448.26 vs. $170.84). Estimated savings in Intervention Year 1 are 8.4% of the estimated Chronic cost PMPM, or 2.0% of all claims. Intervention Year 2 savings are estimated at 12.1% (3.0% of all claims). Estimated savings from the trend-adjusted method used here, increase considerably from the first to the second period. Non-chronic trends are 9.7% and 9.9%, respectively, in Intervention Years 1 and 2. Chronic trend is lower than the trend of the Non-chronic population. (For a more complete discussion of factors that influence Chronic trend measurement, see Chapter 11.)

TABLE 12.1

Highmark Medicare Base Savings Calculation			
Measure	Baseline 8/00 - 7/01	Intervention Year 1 10/01 - 9/02	Intervention Year 2 10/02 - 9/03
Ave no. Members	158,177	180,290	186,246
Ave. no. Chronic Measured Members	33,628	44,251	50,739
Chronic Measured Prevalence	21.3%	24.5%	27.2%
Trend (PMPM, Allowed Cost)			
Chronic Measured Population		0.5%	5.5%
Index Measured Population		9.7%	9.9%
Claims per member per month, Index Measured Population	$170.84	$187.46	$206.01
Claims per member per month, Chronic Measured Population			
Projected	$448.26	$491.88	$540.55
Actual	$448.26	$450.34	$475.27
Total Cost Savings, PMPM		$41.54	$65.28
Total Savings ($ millions)		$22.1	$39.7
Savings as % of total claims for the Line-of-business		2.0%	3.0%

12.4.2 Alternative 1: Cohort (Pre-Post) Analysis

Many earlier studies of DM savings outcomes were performed comparing the historical and current experience of a cohort ("Pre-post"). This methodology has come under increasing criticism in the literature and from consultants, who have pointed out the potential for "regression to the mean" to be observed (and counted as savings) when the cohort is identified at the point of claim (that is, at the peak of the members' resource utilization cycle). As a result of this criticism, the pre-post cohort method has tended to be replaced in industry studies by a population methodology in which newly identified members who meet the conditions for Chronic identification are allowed to enter the measured population. This is the base-case method used for this study. We wished to test, however, how the results of a cohort study would have differed for Highmark.

In Table 12.2, the identification of "Chronic" patients is exactly the same as the base-case in the Baseline period. Beyond the baseline year, no new entrants to the cohort are allowed. By Intervention Year 2, the number of Chronic members falls by 43% relative to the Base Case, because new entrants are not allowed. Thus, we follow a closed cohort forward in years 1 and 2. We use the same trend assumptions as in the base-case, because the Index population excludes members who are Chronic (and not part of the closed cohort), thus representing a truly Non-chronic population.

TABLE 12.2

Alternative 1 - Cohort (Pre-Post) Analysis			
Measure	Baseline 8/00 - 7/01	Intervention Year 1 10/01 - 9/02	Intervention Year 2 10/02 - 9/03
Ave. no. Chronic Measured Members (Base Case)	33,628	44,251	50,739
Ave. no. Chronic Measured Members	33,628	34,957	29,252
Chronic Measured Prevalence	21.3%	19.4%	15.7%
Trend (PMPM, Allowed Cost)			
Chronic Measured Population		0.9%	6.7%
Index Measured Population		9.7%	9.9%
Claims per member per month, Chronic Measured Population			
Projected	$448.26	$491.88	$540.55
Actual	$448.26	$452.29	$482.62
Total Cost Savings, PMPM		$39.59	$57.93
Total Cost Savings, PMPM (Base Case)		$41.54	$65.28
Total Savings ($ millions)		$16.6	$20.3
Savings as % of total claims for the Line-of-business		1.5%	1.5%

Note that the average number of Chronic measured members in the cohort is lower in Intervention Years 1 and 2 than that in the base-case. The average number of members in Intervention Year 1 is slightly higher than that in the Baseline Year, which appears to be counter-intuitive in a cohort. It should be remembered that members included in the baseline year may not contribute a full year to that year's exposure (because they become eligible for measurement during the year) whereas they will contribute a full year in Intervention Year 1 (unless the member terminates).

Our hypothesis for this alternative was that the cohort methodology would produce higher savings than the base-case. The savings in this alternative are lower, both on a PMPM and total basis (by 4.7% in Intervention Year 1, and 11.3% in Year 2). This outcome could be the result of two possible effects: our identification algorithm for the Chronic population, particularly the 3 month claims-free requirement for newly-identified members, is effective at minimizing regression to the mean, while the effect of including newly-identified members in the Chronic measured population effectively creates some bias because these members tend to be lower-cost than the rest of the cohort. We did not have an opportunity to explore these effects in this study, but recommend this as part of any follow-up work.

12.4.3 Alternative 2: Chronic Identification Criteria

a. Based on medical claims but *not* prescription drug claims;
b. Based on primary diagnosis only, as identified from claims;
c. Based only on claims submitted by hospitals (for inpatient or outpatient services);

In Table 12.3, only medical claims (no pharmacy claims) are used to identify Chronic patients. In this alternative, the number of identified Chronic members is lower in the baseline year by 6.1%. The number of identified members becomes closer to the original base-case number over time, as other criteria identify Chronic members.

TABLE 12.3

Alternative 2a - Chronic Patients Identified Using Only Medical Claims

Measure	Baseline 8/00 - 7/01	Intervention Year 1 10/01 - 9/02	Intervention Year 2 10/02 - 9/03
Ave. no. Chronic Measured Members (Base Case)	33,628	44,251	50,739
Ave. no. Chronic Measured Members	31,586	42,724	49,968
Chronic Measured Prevalence	20.0%	23.7%	26.8%
Trend (PMPM, Allowed Cost)			
Chronic Measured Population		(1.6%)	4.0%
Index Measured Population		9.0%	8.9%
Claims per member month Index Measured Population	$176.92	$192.92	$210.03
Claims per member per month,			
Chronic Measured Population			
Projected	$471.19	$513.80	$559.36
Actual	$471.19	$463.84	$482.20
Total Cost Savings, PMPM		$49.96	$77.16
Total Cost Savings, PMPM (Base Case)		$41.54	$65.28
Total Savings ($ millions)		$25.6	$46.3
Savings as % of total claims for the Line-of-business		1.5%	3.5%

Several things are noteworthy in this alternative: the average cost per Chronic measured member is higher than in the Base Case, which is to be expected, given the use of hospital and medical claims for identification. The Index measured population cost is higher in the baseline year (reflecting the fact that some patients with Chronic claims, who would qualify as Chronic under a different set of rules, remain in the Non-chronic population). The Non-chronic population trends at a slightly lower rate than in the Base Case. The higher Chronic measured population cost, however, results in higher savings per Chronic measured member and higher overall savings (the higher PMPM savings more than offset the lower number of Chronic members).

Using only primary diagnosis finds fewer, but sicker Chronic members with higher PMPM than in other scenarios. The number of identified Chronic members in Table 12.4 is lower than either the Base-case or Alternative 2a (13% fewer than the number of Chronic members in the baseline period in the base-case). Once again, the number of identified Chronic members becomes closer to the base-case over time.

TABLE 12.4

Alternative 2b - The Effect of using Only the Primary Diagnosis on Medical Claims to Identify Chronic Members.

Measure	Baseline 8/00 - 7/01	Intervention Year 1 10/01 - 9/02	Intervention Year 2 10/02 - 9/03
Ave. no. Chronic Measured Members (Base Case)	33,628	44,251	50,739
Ave. no. Chronic Measured Members	29,190	42,724	49,968
Chronic Measured Prevalence	18.5%	23.7%	26.8%
Trend (PMPM, Allowed Cost)			
Chronic Measured Population		(1.6%)	4.0%
Index Measured Population		9.0%	8.9%
Claims per member month Index Measured Population	$179.81	$192.92	$210.03
Claims per member per month, Chronic Measured Population			
Projected	$484.58	$528.66	$568.63
Actual	$484.58	$476.44	$483.31
Total Cost Savings, PMPM		$52.22	$85.32
Total Cost Savings, PMPM (Base Case)		$41.54	$65.28
Total Savings ($ millions)		$24.8	$50.5
Savings as % of total claims for the Line-of-business		2.2%	3.8%

Savings per Chronic member per month are 26% higher in year 1 and 31% higher in year 2, compared to the base-case savings. Despite the smaller number of Chronic members, the higher PMPM savings results in total savings that are higher than the base-case, by 12.2% and 27.2% in years 1 and 2, respectively.

If enrollees are identified as "Chronic" from diagnoses obtained only from hospital-based claims, the number of Chronic members is lower than in any other scenario (15% lower than in the base-case). Again, the number of identified Chronic members converges to those in the base-case over time.

TABLE 12.5

Alternative 2c - Identifying Chronic Members using Hospital Claims Only			
Measure	Baseline 8/00 - 7/01	Intervention Year 1 10/01 - 9/02	Intervention Year 2 10/02 - 9/03
Ave. no. Chronic Measured Members (Base Case)	33,628	44,251	50,739
Ave. no. Chronic Measured Members	28,710	40,902	49,402
Chronic Measured Prevalence	18.2%	22.7%	26.5%
Trend (PMPM, Allowed Cost)			
Chronic Measured Population		(2.0%)	6.3%
Index Measured Population		7.6%	6.8%
Claims per member month Index Measured Population	$186.75	$200.85	$214.59
Claims per member per month, Chronic Measured Population			
Projected	$463.32	$498.32	$532.39
Actual	$463.32	$454.18	$474.72
Total Cost Savings, PMPM		$44.14	$57.67
Total Cost Savings, PMPM (Base Case)		$41.54	$65.28
Total Savings ($ millions)		$21.7	$34.2
Savings as % of total claims for the Line-of-business		2.0%	2.6%

The inclusion of members in the Non-chronic population who otherwise would qualify as Chronic has the effect of raising the initial PMPM claims of the Non-chronic group, while at the same time reducing this population's trend. Because of the reduced Non-chronic trend the savings per Chronic member per month are 6% higher in Year 1, but 12% lower in Year 2, relative to the base-case. Total savings in intervention Year 1 are close to those of the base-case, but Year 2 savings are considerably lower (-14%) due to the combination of lower per member per month savings and lower measured member months. The point at which a Chronic member is identified and re-classified from the Index to the Chronic population appears to affect the measured trend for both the Index and Chronic groups, and thereby to affect the savings calculation. This analysis suggests that a commercial purchaser of Disease Management services comparing results of different programs needs to know not only how the Chronic population is identified, but also what has been done with the claims of the "suspect" Chronic population – those that would qualify as Chronic under different criteria.

12.4.4 Alternative 3 – Retrospective Chronic Identification

In the actuarial method, as used in the base-case, a single trend factor is calculated from the Index Population for Year 1 and Year 2 and applied to estimate base-case cost savings. Alternative 3 (Table 12.6) applies a different Chronic identification algorithm, in which members are classified as Chronic at the beginning of the baseline period, irrespective of when the Chronic member first meets the identification criteria. Similarly, the Index population is identified as the complement of the Chronic population. This approach to identification results in a Non-chronic population trend that is not affected by the migration that potentially affects the base case trend calculation. This approach results in average claims PMPM that are lower for both the Chronic and the Non-chronic populations. Consistent with the lack of migration from Non-chronic to Chronic population over time, Non-chronic trend is higher than in the base-case. Chronic trend is also higher because newly-identified Chronic members are not added to the population over time.

TABLE 12.6

Alternative 3 - Retrospective Chronic Identification

Measure	Baseline 8/00 - 7/01	Intervention Year 1 10/01 - 9/02	Intervention Year 2 10/02 - 9/03
Ave. no. Chronic Measured Members (Base Case)	33,628	44,251	50,739
Ave. no. Chronic Measured Members	50,699	54,278	57,575
Chronic Measured Prevalence	32.1%	30.1%	29.3%
Trend (PMPM, Allowed Cost)			
Chronic Measured Population		11.9%	11.7%
Index Measured Population		11.7%	12.5%
Claims per member month Index Measured Population	$158.58	$177.17	$199.37
Claims per member per month, Chronic Measured Population			
Projected	$375.92	$420.01	$472.63
Actual	$375.92	$420.48	$469.62
Total Cost Savings, PMPM		($0.47)	$3.01
Total Cost Savings, PMPM (Base Case)		$41.54	$65.28
Total Savings ($ millions)		($0.3)	$2.0

In the case of the Retrospective Chronic Identification method, we first note that the number of Chronic measured members is relatively constant over the three years of the study, rising slightly from the baseline period to Year 1, and remaining relatively flat in Year 2, as members who are identified as Chronic in subsequent periods are assigned to Chronic status in earlier periods. The number of Chronic measured members in the final year (Intervention

Year 2) is higher than in the corresponding base-case scenario because members who are identified in later periods are not required to meet the same timing requirements for measurement in this methodology, and are thus counted as Chronic for the entire period for which they are eligible. The Chronic measured population numbers, which are higher than in the base case in the last year, may appear anomalous. In the base-case, newly-identified members are counted as Chronic only after they satisfy all claims-based criteria, and only after a 3-month waiting period. On average, therefore, assuming continuous identification, newly-identified members contribute slightly less than ½ year to total Chronic member years in the year of first qualification. Under the retroactive identification method, these members contribute immediately on identification, and contribute 12 months for each measurement year for all years in which they were a plan member.

The average PMPM cost for the Chronic members is lower than that of Chronic measured members in the base-case (by 16%), which is consistent with our expectations given the number of Non-Chronic members assigned to this group in the early years. The Index population trend is higher than the base-case (11.7% vs. 9.7% in Year 1 and 12.5% vs. 9.9% in Year 2). In the base-case, the Measured group experienced very little trend (0.5% in Year 1 and 5.5% in Year 2). In the Retrospective Chronic Identification method, the Chronic Measured population experiences a very similar trend to the Index population. The lack of significant differential in the Chronic and Non-chronic trends results in small savings with this method (in Year 1, savings are actually negative, although this result is not statistically significant).

12.4.5 Alternative 4 – Continuous Eligibility

In the actuarial method, as used in the base-case, members were included in the study at the later of their attainment of six months of continuous eligibility or the beginning of the baseline period. In order to test the sensitivity of the results to the continuous eligibility criterion, we analyzed the results with no such requirement. In order to make this alternative operational, we also removed the requirement that members be at least 3 months post-chronic identification before they are included in the measurement population. Results were as follows:

TABLE 12.7

Alternative 4 - Continuous Eligibility Criteria			
	Baseline	Intervention Year 1	Intervention Year 2
Measure	8/00 - 7/01	10/01 - 9/02	10/02 - 9/03
Ave. no. Chronic Measured Members (Base Case)	33,628	44,251	50,739
Ave. no. Chronic Measured Members	39,811	50,394	56,063
Chronic Measured Prevalence	25.2%	28.0%	30.1%
Trend (PMPM, Allowed Cost)			
Chronic Measured Population			
Index Measured Population		9.8%	10.7%
Claims per member month Index Measured Population	$169.99	$186.66	$206.77
Claims per member per month,			
Chronic Measured Population			
Projected	$548.59	$603.05	$667.33
Actual	$548.59	$544.67	$561.501
Total Cost Savings, PMPM		$58.36	$105.83
Total Cost Savings, PMPM (Base Case)		$41.54	$65.28
Total Savings ($ millions)		$35.3	$71.2
Savings as % of total claims for the Line-of-business		3.2%	5.5%

In this alternative, a number of members who are clearly high cost (primarily those initially identified through a hospital claim, for example) are now included in the measurement population for the study. This raises the average PMPM cost from $448.26 to $548.59 (a 22% increase). This increase in the base cost, coupled with a slightly higher trend in the Index population, increases the estimated savings PMPM by 41% (first year) and 62% (second year). The change also increases the number of measured members, and thus the total savings. One of the objections often raised to the base case methodology by purchasers is that the use of claims truncation increases the savings. Our analysis suggests that the opposite may be true. The inclusion of large claims increases the base PMPM and therefore the overall savings.

This study has focused on Highmark's Medicare population. The program was also implemented within the Commercial (HMO/POS and PPO) populations. We also performed an assessment of the DM program in the commercial HMO/POS population; we did not pursue the PPO because the product was in transition and the program was judged too immature to permit the DM program results to be analyzed.

12.5 COMMERCIAL HMO/POS SAVINGS CALCULATION

The initial Chronic measured prevalence is 3.7%, indicating that relatively few members were initially identified with one or more Chronic condition, and met all the other requirements for inclusion in the study. The Chronic prevalence grew by 51% over the three-year study period, to 5.6%.

TABLE 12.8

Alternative 5 - Results in Commercial Products

Measure	Baseline 8/00 - 7/01	Intervention Year 1 10/01 - 9/02	Intervention Year 2 10/02 - 9/03
Ave. no. Chronic Measured Members (Base Case)	1,030,204	1,107,120	1,027,539
Ave. no. Chronic Measured Members	38,126	53,799	57,444
Chronic Measured Prevalence	3.7%	4.9%	5.6%
Trend (PMPM, Allowed Cost)			
Chronic Measured Population		5.5%	8.4%
Index Measured Population		20.3%	12.5%
Claims per member month Index Measured Population	$56.89	$68.435	$77.00
Claims per member per month, Chronic Measured Population			
Projected	$273.94	$286.19	$532.39
Actual	$273.94	$251.07	$474.72
Total Cost Savings, PMPM		$35.12	$49.88
Total Savings ($ millions)		$22.7	$34.4
Savings as % of total claims for the Line-of-business		1.1%	1.6%

Estimated savings for the HMO/POS population are similar in magnitude to those for the Medicare population, both on a PMPM and total basis. The mechanism by which the savings are derived differs significantly: the Medicare population consists of far more Chronic members with a cost PMPM that is approximately twice that of the HMO/POS population. Conversely, the trend assumption used to project the baseline cost to the intervention period is higher in the HMO/POS population than the Medicare population[3]. At the line-of-business level, the lower prevalence and costs result in savings that are lower than in the Medicare population (although still significant).

[3] The trend assumptions used in the baseline calculations, although they appear high in the first intervention year, have been reconciled with Highmark's overall population trends for the relevant periods.

12.6 DISCUSSION

At present, there is no consensus among actuaries, health economists, accountants, or health services researchers on how DM program cost savings estimates *should* be made. Our results demonstrate that, even within the same general methodology, the estimates of cost savings can vary substantially, depending on how Chronic patients are identified, how patients are included based on continuous enrollment criteria, the treatment of Non-chronic members who are "suspect" Chronic patients and who may later be added to the Chronic population, and how trend is handled. The following table summarizes all comparative PMPM savings results:

TABLE 12.9

Savings PMPM Under Different Scenarios						
Table No.	**Scenario No.**	**Scenario**	**Intervention Year 1 10/01 – 9/02**	**% Change Compared with Base-case**	**Intervention Year 2 10/02 – 9/03**	**% Change Compared with Base-case**
1	0	Base-case	$41.54	-	$65.28	-
2	1	Cohort	$39.59	(4.7%)	$57.93	(11.3%)
3	2a	Medical claims only identification	$49.96	20.3%	$77.16	18.2%
4	2b	Primary diagnosis only identification	$52.22	25.7%	$85.32	30.7%
5	2c	Hospital claims only identification	$44.14	6.3%	$57.67	(11.7%)
6	3	Retrospective identification	($0.47)	(100.0%)	$3.01	(95.4%)
7	4	Continuous eligibility criteria	$58.36	40.5%	$105.83	62.1%
8	5	Commercial HMO Product	$35.12	n/a	$49.88	n/a

Many of the methodology choices and assumptions are subtle and difficult to identify in published studies and vendor reporting. It is thus critical for DM companies and purchasers to increase their disclosure in this area. Our results show that in a large population study, whether results are estimated using a cohort or population methodology has relatively little effect on savings. This result appears to contradict some of the current thinking in the industry, which has largely moved away from cohort studies. Our result may be influenced by the fact that we used the initial Chronic cohort, which was identified from a mix of hospital, drug and medical claims. Our identification criteria find members in all stages of disease, while cohort studies that identify high-risk, hospitalized (or recently hospitalized) members are more likely to be subject to the effect of regression to the mean at the individual member level. The retrospective identification method generates trends that are similar in the Chronic and Non-chronic populations, and therefore appears to generate little or no savings. This method, while it has a certain intuitive and statistical appeal, runs counter to clinical perceptions of disease (members are classified as Chronic, even though they have no Chronic condition and are not managed as such). As Table 12.6 shows, the PMPM costs of both the Chronic and the Non-chronic populations are lower, initially, than in any other methodology, reflecting the mix of Chronic and "future chronic" members assigned to the Chronic population. Whether this is a true claim cost PMPM or whether some adjustment should be made to it requires more analysis. Much more work needs to be done in the area of understanding and applying appropriate trends at the population level before these results can be accepted into the mainstream.

Finally, the Commercial HMO/POS results are presented for completeness, even though they are not truly comparable with the Medicare results. Purchasers of DM programs will be encouraged that the Commercial results are as close to those of the Medicare population as they are. Given the similarity of the underlying results to the Medicare base-case, we expect that similar sensitivity will be found in the Commercial population to that observed in the Medicare population.

12.7 CONCLUSIONS

The calculation of cost savings of Disease Management programs by actuaries is still an inexact science. This study demonstrates that estimates of cost savings can vary substantially, depending on the methods used to identify and exclude patients. Our research in these chapters, however, supports the actuarial approach to the analysis using:

- Rigorous identification of members who meet defined criteria and their inclusion in the study population at appropriate times;
- Control of study eligibility over time, linkage of members and their claims; and
- Careful development of an appropriate adjustment trend assumption.

Purchasers of programs should take equal care about the assumptions and data decisions that are taken "behind the scenes" in the calculation of program savings. Purchasers will increasingly look to their trusted healthcare financial advisors, their actuaries, for guidance on assumptions, methodology, calculations and to benchmark results. As this chapter shows, the results of a particular program can vary widely, based on these assumptions. Purchasers may wish to become involved more directly with the setting of assumptions in studies, and be willing to accept a range of outcomes, rather than a 'point' estimate of savings.

At the same time, actuaries should avoid the simplistic conclusion of dismissing Disease Management savings calculations as unreliable because of "regression to the mean". As our analysis throughout has shown, regression to the mean, which may occur at the individual member level, may not be observed in a large population with offsetting changes in member utilization. There are a number of potential biases in a population study of DM outcomes; regression to the mean may be one of them, depending on how the population is selected, but it may not be the greatest source of distortion. For the actuary who is approaching a new study or the review of a vendor's results, we provide a check-list of issues/assumptions that should be considered in Appendix 12.2.

Our review of the literature of Disease Management financial outcomes studies shows that there are very few published, peer-reviewed studies of populations. Much more data analysis and publication is needed for us to understand and to begin to develop the necessary tools (risk-adjustment; durational adjustment, and so on) and data that may assist us to correct for known biases.

More research of evaluation methods is also needed, which will require funding from DM companies, managed care organizations and the federal government. Clinical researchers and epidemiologists have striven to improve methods to conduct clinical trials and have considered and critiqued alternative research designs to evaluate new drugs, and medical and surgical procedures. Healthcare actuaries have an opportunity to make a substantial contribution to an exciting, evolving field of academic and practical importance. Further efforts in this field are warranted to validate financial models proposed by managed care organizations or disease management companies. Purchasers and actuaries who "validate savings" should be aware of the implications of different approaches that are commonly used.

APPENDIX 12.1: CHRONIC IDENTIFICATION CRITERIA

For the DM program, Chronic members are identified by Highmark using the criteria below. In addition, some members may be referred by physicians or health plan staff. These members are included in the management program, but excluded from the evaluation (both the intervention and reference (Index) groups). Newly-identified members were included in the Chronic measurement population after a 3-month waiting period (to allow for any effect of regression to the mean). During this period, these members were excluded from both the Chronic and index measured populations.

Diabetes Mellitus

At least one admission or ER visit with a primary diagnosis of diabetes (ICD-9 codes 250, 357.2, 362.0, 366.41, 648.0);

OR two professional visits in a twelve month period with a primary or secondary diagnosis of diabetes; (in range of 99 series E & M codes) and (92 series for eye visits);

OR one or more dispensed insulin, hypoglycemic, or anti-hyperglycemic (therapeutic class 172,173, or 174).
EXCLUDE 648.8x gestational diabetes.

Chronic Obstructive Pulmonary Disease (COPD)

At least one admission or ER visit with a primary diagnosis of COPD (491.xx, 492.xx, 494.xx, 496.xx) or primary diagnosis =466.xx with secondary diagnosis = (491.xx or 492.xx or 496.xx);

OR at least 4 primary diagnoses or secondary diagnoses (4 encounters in range of 99 series E & M codes)

OR 2 primary diagnoses or secondary diagnoses (2 encounters) for COPD (in range of 99 series E & M codes) AND 2 medication dispensing events for beta agonists, cortico-steroids, atrovent, serevent, theophylline or O2.

Congestive Heart Failure (CHF)

At least one admission with primary diagnosis of CHF (402.01, 402.11, 402.91, 404.01, 404.11, 404.91, 428.xx);

OR three or more physician encounters (in range of 99 series E & M codes) with a dx1 or dx2 for CHF (in 12 month time frame).

Coronary Artery Disease (CAD)

At least one admission with ICD-9 procedure code for CABG (36.1x, 36.2x); or ICD-9 procedure code for PTCA (36.01, 36.02, 36.05, 36.09) or any primary diagnosis of acute coronary ischemia (410.xx-414.xx).

OR four or more physician encounters (in range of 99 series E & M codes) with Dx1 for acute coronary ischemia.

Asthma

At least 1 ER visit primary diagnosis with icd-9 code = 493.x,

OR at least 1 inpatient discharge with code 493.x,

OR at least 4 outpatient visits primary or secondary diagnosis, icd-9 = 493.x (in range of 99 series E & M codes)

OR 2 outpatient visits primary or secondary diagnosis icd-9 = 493.x (in range of 99 series E & M codes) AND at least two asthma medication dispensing events.

APPENDIX 12.2: CHECK LIST OF ISSUES/ASSUMPTIONS FOR CONDUCTING OR EVALUATING A STUDY

No.	Issue	Discussion
	STUDY DESIGN	
1	Study design	What is the specific methodology used for the study? (For evaluation of study designs see Chapter 5.)
2	Study design: Population study	Does the study use a Population Methodology? (Population studies are preferred to cohort studies in order to minimize regression to the mean.) It may not always be possible to conduct a valid population study: for example for smaller employer groups. How is this addressed?
3	Study design: Reference Population	A reference population is defined to compare to the intervention population (e.g., historical; geographical, product, etc.)
4	Study design: method for overcoming small populations	For example, is there some form of credibility weighting employed in adjusting the results?
5	Study design: intervention time period	What is the study time-period (preferably 12 months post-beginning of intervention program). Where program is not in place for 12 months, how is this to be handled? Where launch is "staggered" or members are continuously invited, how is this handled?
6	Study design: baseline time period	What is the baseline time-period, when the study is an historical adjusted methodology?
	POPULATION DEFINITIONS	
7	Population definitions: chronic population	Objective claims criteria used for identifying eligible chronic population. Is methodology hospital claims only; hospital + medical; hospital + medical + prescription drugs? How will issue of false positive be handled as wider criteria are employed?
8	Population definitions: excluded population	Objective claims criteria used for identifying excluded population (e.g. AIDS, Transplants, etc.)
9	Population definition: excluded population	Are there any excluded members who are excluded based on subjective criteria (for example members in Case Management)? How will these members be evaluated?
10	Identification criteria: multiple years	Does the study require that members be re-qualified through claims each year in the study or do members accumulate in their groups as long as they are benefits-eligible?
11	Population definitions: newly-identified chronic and excluded population	How are the newly-identified members of the population handled? Are they included in the study immediately on identification? Are they included at the next anniversary? Is the treatment symmetrical in all years?
12	Eligibility criteria	Is there a requirement for continuous eligibility in order to be included in the study?
13	Eligibility criteria	How are terminating members (from health plan) handled? How are terminating members (from program) handled? Do they contribute to the study up to month of termination? Are they retroactively removed?
	DATA	
14	Data exclusions in dataset provided	Are there any data that will not be provided for analysis (for example certain states have privacy restrictions that pre-empt HIPAA)?
15	Data specifications	What dataset will be used for the study?
16	Data validation/ Reconciliation	What data validation process has been (will be) performed in order to ensure that data are complete, reliable and balance back to audited financial statements of the client?

No.	Issue	Discussion
17	Data exclusions in study	Define any excluded conditions (for example, maternity or cancer claims, where these are not the responsibility of the DM vendor).
18	Claims run-out	The same run-out months are included in each year of data used in the study (i.e., additional run-out does not continue to accumulate on earlier years).
	POTENTIAL SOURCES OF BIAS	
18	Prevalence creep	Are members re-qualified over time?
19	Trend bias	How is the potential bias in trend due to the effect of migration between Non-chronic and Chronic groups handled?
20	Geographic and product controls	Are the starting claims costs adjusted to place all members on the same actuarial basis? Is the control group sufficiently representative that its trend is a valid proxy for the intervention group?
21	Selection bias	How were members included in the study? Is the effect of selection bias overcome by performing a population study or is the study limited to enrolled members only?
	TESTS OF EQUIVALENCE	
22	Test the Intervention and Control populations for equivalence	Test the intervention and control populations (baseline and measurement populations, for example) for equivalence with respect to risk factors: - DRG distributions - Provider distributions - Age/sex distributions - In/out of network services
	TREND	
23	Method for calculating trend	Where there is a trend adjustment, what trend is used for a proxy? How is this adjuster calculated? How representative of the non-managed Chronic group expected trend is the adjuster? How stable is this measure over time? Has the measure been tested *prior* to the beginning of the program in order to evaluate its suitability as a proxy?
24	Validate the calculated trend	Is the vendor's choice of a trend assumption reasonable in relation to the plan's recent trend experience?
	REPORTING	
25	Reports are auditable	Reports are provided that support simple checking of the calculation at the aggregate level, while also supporting drill-down audits of selected cells and calculation components.
	CALCULATIONS	
26	Audit the calculated savings numbers	Have the savings numbers been calculated (mathematically) correctly? Are the numbers reasonable based on other experience of the actuary? Of the industry? Is there independent support for the savings (e.g., observed trend moderation)?
27	Audit the components of the calculated savings numbers	Are the components that make up the calculation reasonable (for example, the PMPM numbers for services categories; utilization numbers; unit cost numbers)?
28	Are the calculated savings plausible?	Validate the savings by decomposing into utilization reductions. Do the implied utilization reductions seem reasonable? A reduction of $100 PMPM in a Chronic population translates into a reduction of X in inpatient admissions. Is there support for this level of reduction in inpatient admissions?

PART 4

WELLNESS, INTEGRATED PROGRAMS, AND OTHER NEW DEVELOPMENTS IN CARE MANAGEMENT PROGRAMS

13 INTRODUCTION TO WELLNESS AND INTEGRATED PROGRAMS

13.1 HEALTHCARE EXPENDITURES

The emphasis in the U.S. healthcare system has been on the treatment of short-term acute health problems rather than early intervention and prevention. Physician and clinical services accounted for more than one-fifth of the health expenditure in the U.S. in 2006. Less than 5% of the health care budget is directed towards prevention activities and less than 1% of each research dollar is spent on behavioral-oriented prevention research Whitmer et al. [214]. According to the U.S. Centers for Disease Control and Prevention, chronic disease accounts for 75% of annual healthcare costs and is the cause of 70% of all U.S. deaths [194]. The traditional chronic diseases that are the target of DM programs (heart disease, chronic obstructive pulmonary disease, diabetes and nephritis) accounted for 38% of all deaths in the U.S. in 2005. Malignant neoplasms and stroke add another 29%.

It is generally held that a significant proportion of diseases and health conditions are preventable. Epidemiological research confirms that lifestyle factors play a major role in the acquisition of modifiable health risks that can lead to illness, morbidity and mortality. For example, McGinnis & Foege [135] suggest that diet/activity patterns, tobacco and alcohol use caused a 'substantial proportion of preventable deaths' and that these were the top three causes of death in the U.S. in 2000.

The World Health Organization [167] reported that death rates for all chronic diseases rise with increasing age but almost 45% of chronic disease deaths occur prematurely, under the age of 70 years. The number of DALY's (disability adjusted life years) caused by chronic disease is greatest in working age adults aged 30–59 years. In the U.S., chronic diseases cause major limitations in daily living for more than 1 of every 10 Americans (Centers for Disease Control and Prevention, op. cit.).

A Commonwealth Fund study, Davis et al. [37] estimated that health-related problems are responsible for approximately $260 billion in lost economic output each year in the United States. The study found that in 2003, 12% of working-age adults in the U.S. did not work because of health reasons or a disability and that 72% of those in work had taken sick days due to personal illness or that of a family member, or were distracted at work due to health concerns.

According to a recent survey, American employers are focusing upon disease management programs so that their employees maintain healthy outcomes for chronic conditions and to encourage employees to focus on lifestyle choices and their health care purchasing decisions

(Deloitte Consulting and Deloitte Center for Health Solutions [1]) The CDC believes that 'many Americans could enjoy 5-7 additional years of healthy life and avoid the costs associated with chronic disease if we improve access to quality health care services, emphasize healthy behavior, and focus on broad policies and strategies that offer the greatest good for the greatest number of people at the lowest cost' (Centers for Disease Control and Prevention, op. cit.).

Increases in healthcare spending over the past decade have placed steady pressure on the corporate 'bottom-line,' and the high cost of healthcare coverage of employees has led corporations to seek ways to better manage growth in healthcare costs. One trend of importance to actuaries is that attention is turning to illness prevention and the maintenance of health rather than managing illness and the cost of its treatment. This calls for a set of research and analytical skills complementary to those that actuaries use in assessing the outcomes of DM programs.

Changing healthcare expectations such as a greater concern for achieving healthier lifestyles and an improved quality of working life have driven a change of focus from illness management towards the prevention of ill health and disease. Corporate attention has centered on securing gains in health status as well as the ROI, alignment with business objectives and human capital management strategies.

13.2 WELLNESS, HEALTH PROMOTION, AND DISEASE PREVENTION

Wellness, health promotion, and disease prevention have been defined as 'a set of organized activities and systematic interventions, offered through corporations/worksites, managed care organizations, and governmental/community agencies, whose primary purposes are to provide health education, identify modifiable health risks, and influence health behavior changes' Mulvihill [141].

The workplace has become an important focus of the drive for behavioral changes necessary for a healthier lifestyle that brings benefits to the individual, the employer and the wider community. Workplace wellness programs primarily focus upon common modifiable health risks that have been shown to increase health expenditures such as obesity, consumption of tobacco and alcohol, stress, a sedentary lifestyle, depression, high blood pressure, high blood glucose levels, risky sexual behavior and the failure to use seat belts in vehicles. The current generation of worksite programs, characterized as 'health and productivity management (Goetzel &Ozminkowski [83]) are multi-faceted, integrating health promotion and disease prevention with demand and disease management programs.

The nature of work-related injuries and illnesses has altered due to:

- changes in work and the workplace environment shifting from manufacturing to services;
- the development of a knowledge economy;
- the extensive use of technology; and
- evolving human-resource and management practices.

Workplace healthcare has moved beyond the management of catastrophic incidents such as acute traumatic injuries to the longer-term management of work-related and non-work-related chronic conditions including those arising from lifestyle factors such as smoking, lack of exercise and poor nutrition.

The association between modifiable health risks and increased health care expenditures has been well established and workplace health promotion, illness prevention and disease management programs have been shown to be effective in modifying health risk. Interest is growing in the relationship between health status, productivity as measured by absence from work, presenteeism (sub-optimal work performance due to working while unwell or distracted by a family member's illness) and disability-related absences and the consequent economic implications for the employer.

Observers have noted that within organizations, programs designed to manage work related illness and injuries tend not to be integrated with those of a non-occupational focus such as health promotion (Ramsay [169] and Goetzel [75]). This has been attributed to historical reasons arising from a narrow organizational focus or 'silo' management of group health benefits, the fact that different benefits are regulated by different authorities and managed by different employer functional areas, and a tradition of different compensation mechanisms[1]. Goetzel et al. [78] believe that the aggregate costs of providing health and productivity programs to workers have not been adequately assessed. Noting that employers tend to examine and report upon program costs such as group health, disability, or workers' compensation as independent and unrelated units, the authors conclude that managers are unaware of other program costs and thus are unable to estimate total health and lost productivity costs for the organization.

Increasing recognition of the multi-determinants of workplace health has led to attempts to develop an integrated system that better coordinates the management of both medical care and health related workplace absences and that delivers economic benefit to the organization. Villagra [203] notes the trend towards 'integrating multiple chronic disease management programs onto a single platform' and Lewis [118] argues that an integrated system not only manages chronic diseases but incorporates wellness, advisory services, complex case management and care coordination in a 'one-stop shop' that makes an impact upon the entire healthcare budget. Edington [56] discusses so called 'Next Generation Programs' that incorporate diverse elements integrating health promotion and disease prevention, disease management, medical benefits, occupational health, employee assistance programs, work/life balance, workers' compensation, short and long-term disability, and productivity management.

13.3 WORKPLACE HEALTH

Worksite wellness programs evolved in the 1970s when some of the larger U.S. corporations sought ways to promote healthier lifestyles among their employees with attendant economic benefits. In the ensuing decades, U.S. employers have increasingly adopted worksite wellness programs as a key strategy to maintain or improve worker health risk status.

At first, the main focus was on improving the health of high-risk individuals at the Executive level. 'Second generation' programs in the 1980s expanded the offerings of workplace well-

[1] See Parry et al. [158], Sorensen & Barbeau [187], Seabury, et al. [182].

ness to address goals of improved employee health, reducing healthcare expenditures and demonstrating organizational commitment to employees' wellbeing.

Edington [56] characterizes the achievements of these programs as 'marginal,' pointing out that there was little success in achieving obviously lower levels of modifiable health risks such as obesity and a lower incidence of disease. He observes that the take-up rate of programs was slow until rapidly rising healthcare costs attracted corporate attention. Goetzel [73] notes a shift in corporate sentiment from a purely cost savings perspective to one focused on value for funds spent, the quality of care provided and in particular, the relationship between health and productivity. Occupational health and safety or the reduction and management of occupationally related illness and injury and also workers compensation obligations appears to be secondary in the workplace health literature, which to date has focused upon wellness and personal health risk reduction programs delivered at the workplace.

Most wellness programs target back care and injury prevention, physical exercise, stress management, tobacco use and substance abuse prevention. Additional health risks included in the majority of worksite wellness programs are weight management, medical self-care, consumer health education, cholesterol reduction, nutritional interventions, selected biometrics testing, and hypertension management (Chapman [26], [27]).

13.4 PREVALENCE OF WORKPLACE WELLNESS PROGRAMS

A number of studies report that over 90% of all workplaces with fifty or more workers in the U.S. have health promotion programs in place[2]. Organizations with over 750 employees 'almost universally offer resources aimed at improving worker health Riedel et al. [173].

The nature of workplace wellness programs offered varies significantly, ranging from information-only to annual health risk assessments and regular health screening through to comprehensive services including individual risk reduction counseling. Whitmer et al. [214] report that in a survey of 700 employers, 93% of employers provided some sort of employee health promotion program. There was great variability within these programs with only a small proportion making what the authors called 'serious health enhancement efforts'. Only 28% of employers offered health risk assessments (HRA) with 40% of these being offered annually; 75% of employers offered blood pressure and cholesterol screenings; 72% offered programs such as seminars and behavioral counseling; and 42% used financial incentives and disincentives to motivate employees. Incentives such as cash, discounts, rebates and merchandise are used by employers to encourage participation or to reward achieving specified healthcare goals.

Whitmer et al. (op.cit.) observe that a 'relatively small' group of employers provide comprehensive workplace health promotion programs and that expenditure per employee on these programs averaged about $60 per year which was less than the average $4,300 per person employer contribution for medical care across all forms of coverage in 2002.

---

[2] See Aldana [2] and Deloitte Consulting and Deloitte Center for Health Solutions 2005 [1].

13.5 HEALTH RISK AND RISK STATUS

Whereas Disease Management, Case Management and other utilization management techniques discussed in Chapter 2 aim to address health conditions (either chronic or acute) once they have occurred, the focus of wellness programs is on identification of conditions that are otherwise undiagnosed or untreated, and prevention of these condition(s) *before* they occur. This is done through the identification and management of "health risks." For example, obesity and lifestyle are often pre-cursors to diabetes; high cholesterol is a precursor to more serious heart conditions, and the association between smoking and various conditions has been known for many years. Thus, health risks are a significant problem. Risk has been shown to be modifiable and the capability of worksite wellness programs to modify risk has been demonstrated. Risk modification has been shown to translate into cost savings, better health outcomes and corporate benefit with respect to improved productivity. The worksite offers certain advantages over other settings for risk modification:

- The employer clearly has an interest in employee health because of its link to productivity;
- Employees spend a part of every day at the worksite, allowing the delivery of programs cost-effectively to a large number of individuals at one time;
- Employees may be more likely to participate as a way of "taking a break" from the work-day.

Worksite programs will always have one drawback over other types of delivery (for example, nurse telephonic outreach) because only the *employee* is present at the worksite, and employees rarely represent more than 50% of the entire employer covered population.

Risk is a key concept in worksite wellness and programs are premised on the assumption that as risk is modifiable, an individual's risk profile can be changed and that transition is possible between different levels of risk status.

The literature clearly shows that health risk drives costs and costs follow risk and that certain conditions are more expensive than others. There is 'strong and convincing evidence, (Reidel et al. [173]) about a direct relationship between personal health risk factors such as smoking, lack of exercise and poor diet and an increased incidence of related illnesses; that health status influences health-related costs; and that disease prevention and health promotion interventions improve personal health status. Disagreement exists as to the best use of limited resources available for health promotion and disease prevention, with some arguing that maintaining the greater population as low-risk is more cost-effective than focusing resources on diminishing the smaller but more expensive high-risk population. The literature has yet to address how the long-term lifestyle and behavior changes necessary to reduce risk can be sustained.

Most workplace wellness programs determine health risk status by using a combination of self-reported health behaviors and physiological measures (Heaney & Geotzel [91]). Data concerning health behaviors is gathered through a Health Risk Assessment (HRA) – a multiple choice questionnaire covering factors such as fitness, alcohol consumption, nutrition, tobacco use, stress and depression. Data is also gathered from biometric screening of factors including height, weight, blood pressure, cholesterol and blood glucose levels.

HRAs are described as being a core technology for health and wellness programs. HRA's focus on health education, longevity, or a more comprehensive approach including quality of life, medical and pharmacy utilization, disability absences, and presenteeism. Individuals receive a customized individual profile. At the organizational level, aggregated reports summarize individual health risk profiles and results are modeled with outcome data to create a population health-status scorecard.

Overall health risk is characterized as low, medium or high and determined by parameters that establish high-risk based upon work undertaken by the Health Enhancement Research Organization (HERO) and published in Goetzel et al. [76]. Low-risk is considered to be the presence of between zero and two risk factors, medium-risk is three to four risk factors, and high-risk is considered to be five or more risk factors (Edington [55]).

Values that define a high-risk status are summarized in Table 13.1.

TABLE 13.1

	Health Measure Risk	High Risk Criteria[3]	High Risk Criteria[4]
Self reported measures	Fitness	No vigorous exercise during a typical week	Less than one exercise session/wk
	Alcohol Consumption	Consumes five or more drinks two or more days each week	More than 14 drinks/wk
	Nutrition	Composite score based on total fat and saturated fat intake, consumption of fruit, vegetables, salt intake, use of low-fat dairy products, consumption of lean meat	
	Current tobacco use	Pipe, cigar, snuff or smokeless tobacco & cigarettes: high volume use (1+ pack cigarettes/day)	Current smoker
	Former tobacco use	Pipe, cigar, snuff or smokeless tobacco & cigarettes	
	Stress	Rated life as "quite or extremely stressful" and indicated not being effective in dealing with stress	Job satisfaction = partly or not satisfied. Life satisfaction = partly or not satisfied
	Depression	Answered 'most of the time' to the following question: "How often do you feel depressed?"	
	Perception of health		Fair or poor
	Safety belt use		Using safety belt less than 90% of time
	Use of drugs for relaxation		Few times a month or more
	Sexual health	Use of protection; safe sex; HPV immunization	Use of protection; safe sex; HPV immunization.
	Illness days		> 5 days last year
Biometric measures			
	Weight	30% or more above or 20% or more below the midpoint of the frame-adjusted desirable weight range for height	Body Mass Index –27.8 (men) 27.3 (women)
	Blood glucose	115 mg/dL or higher	
	Cholesterol	240 mg/dL or higher	> 239 mg/dL HDL cholesterol < 35 mg/dL
	Blood Pressure	systolic equal to or greater than 160 mm Hg and/or diastolic equal to or greater than 100 mm Hg	Systolic > 139mm Hg or Diastolic > 89 mm Hg

[3] See Anderson [6]
[4] See Edington [55]

13.6 SUCCESSFUL WELLNESS PROGRAMS

It has been suggested that there are six or seven critical components necessary for successful wellness programs. Chapman [26] considers these to be

- gaining senior and mid-level management support;
- sophisticated programming;
- a positive and upbeat image;
- implementing well-designed, balanced and well paced programming, and the
- effective use of incentives.

The Wellness Council of America [184] recommends seven benchmarks of success for implementing workplace wellness programs which include

- capturing senior level support;
- creating a cohesive wellness team;
- collecting data to drive health efforts;
- crafting an operating plan;
- choosing appropriate interventions;
- creating a supportive environment; and
- consistently evaluating outcomes.

Edington [56] covers most of the above points but includes policy level criteria such as alignment of corporate environmental policies and procedures; regular use of HRAs; stratification of individuals according to risk and triage into appropriate programs; provision of population based programs to all employees; use of incentives to motivate employees and enhance participation and use of evaluation to inform program developments.

13.7 CORE COMPONENTS OF A WORKPLACE WELLNESS PROGRAM

In general, the core components of a workplace wellness program include informational materials such as newsletters and health education materials. As discussed previously, Health Risk Assessments form the central part of all programs and cover areas such as exercise, activity levels, alcohol use, back care, demographic details, driving, eating habits, height, weight, mental health, biometric screening of metrics such as blood pressure and cholesterol levels, tobacco use, family history of chronic disease and readiness to undertake behavioral change. Follow-up interventions may include focused activities delivered through telephone, internet or onsite methods. These generally cover related programs such as weight management, nutrition, exercise, stress management, smoking cessation, cholesterol management, diabetes management, management of such things as hypertension, chronic heart failure, coronary artery disease, back care and ergonomics. Some onsite programs provide fitness facilities and intensive individual and group counseling sessions.

A corporate wellness program typically includes:

- Assessment of individuals status through HRAs;
- A program of risk modification tailored to the workforce needs such as specific health problems (e.g., as obesity, diabetes, chronic conditions);
- Activities ranging from specific disease management, weight control, nutrition advice and support, substance use management (tobacco, alcohol, controlled substances), to mental health issues, immunization, general informational activities on health and wellbeing;
- Level of intervention – ranging from information only (posters in cafeteria, brochures and pamphlets) through to specific individualized interventions;
- Location of programs – either onsite or offsite through negotiated vendors;
- Communication channels such as electronic, direct, paper based and incentives/ disincentives used;
- Evaluation strategy set up to study results of the program (both healthcare and financial);
- Integration within corporate framework such as profile within organization, priority given to supporting participation by line managers.

Chapman [28] distinguishes between three types of wellness programs. The first type is characterized as **Quality of Work Life**. The emphasis is on fun and development of workplace cohesion with little application of clinical health risk factor information and low expectations of economic return or cost savings. Activities undertaken in this style of health promotion include health fairs, 'lunch and learn' sessions, celebrity events and some biometric testing.

The second type is the **'Traditional Program'** of broad-based population wide programs that employees choose to attend. Clinical health risk is emphasized and biometric testing is used to direct individuals towards programs that might focus on such subjects as tobacco use, nutrition, exercise, weight management and stress management. These types of risk modification programs may be provided by the program vendor (often by nurse-telephonic coaching) or by an outside vendor. As a result of the screenings, members may be referred to other external programs, such as Disease Management or Case Management. Since Disease Management programs often include an element of risk factor modification, there is overlap between programs and the need for clear rules and prioritization with regard to patient management. The overlapping programs and responsibilities also pose challenges for program evaluation. Disease prevention through early detection may arise from clinical preventive screening activities. Some modest expectation of economic return is inherent in this style of program particularly in areas such as reducing sick leave and workers compensation costs, achieving health plan savings and improving absenteeism and presenteeism. Chapman states that the typical ROI investment of this style of program ranges between 1.5:1.0 to 3.5:1.0. Activities found in this style of program include health risk assessment, biometric testing, fitness clubs, web-based information, healthy cafeterias, self-care literature and newsletters.

The final type of program is typically called the **'Health and Productivity Management Program.'** A structured program with a high-risk focus, this format targets the majority of the employee population and often includes spouses. A systemic approach is taken which links health promotion activities with employer policies, employee benefits, referral opportunities and information services. It is an expensive model to deliver with a program budget in the range of $151 to $450 per employee per year. Significant behavioral change is expected as are savings in healthcare costs including sick leave, disability and workers compensation costs. The typical level of ROI has been documented from 3.6:1.0 to 7.0:1.0. Examples of activities include regular HRAs, risk stratification and interventions, telephonic coaching, medical self-care and consumer workshops, injury prevention, benefit linked incentives and wellness achievement incentives.

Evidence suggests that workplace wellness programs have been successful in achieving positive clinical outcomes and in moderating healthcare expenditures. Workplace health promotion that is of a comprehensive and multi-faceted nature can lead to improved population health, savings in healthcare costs to employers and to higher levels of employee productivity. Programs that offer specific, intense counseling to high-risk individuals in an environment that encourages all employees to participate in worksite wellness have been found to effectively reduce risk. Programs using newer web-based technologies appear to be particularly effective. Successful programs need to be of adequate breadth and duration, offer intensive services and to have sustained participation levels.

Contributing to the cost of these types of wellness programs is the increasing prevalence of employer incentives aimed at encouraging employee participation in the assessment process (completion of the HRA). Legally, the employer is unable to provide focused or differential incentives, and must make the same incentive available to all employees. An incentive that is provided to a large percentage of the workforce (and their dependents) can be costly for an employer. This in turn makes the economics of such programs more marginal.

13.8 Absenteeism, Presenteeism, and Productivity

Productivity is defined as the value of an output in terms of goods produced or services rendered for a given unit of input. While conceptually straightforward, it is an elusive concept to measure and work related illness research studies have primarily resorted to the use of subjective self-report methods that estimate the impact of ill health upon personal performance (Burton [18]). Riedel et al. [173] note the difficulties of accurately assessing work production due to considerable variance in productivity measurements according to job type and industry sector, with little in common.

Recent research has identified that medical care costs are only a proportion of health and productivity costs faced by employers (Goetzel [79]). Productivity losses such as absenteeism and presenteeism as the result of employee ill health are infrequently measured (Burton [19]). Interest is growing in determining workplace productivity losses related to common health conditions (Goetzel op. cit.). Absenteeism includes personal illness days, short-term and long-term disability and workers compensation days and is commonly used to measure productivity (Edington [55]). An emerging concept is that of presenteeism or on-the-job productivity losses due to illness. Presenteeism is considered to be a hidden cost of illness. A 1999 study calculated the costs of lost productivity due to presenteeism as 7.5 times greater than absenteeism costs. Presenteeism costs due to chronic conditions such as migraine, allergies and back pain were estimated to be between 15 and 30 times the costs of absenteeism[5].

13.9 INTEGRATED PROGRAMS

The wellness industry has grown up in parallel with other types of programs that focus on employee productivity and well-being. These programs range from efforts to maintain a healthy and safe workplace (OSHA compliance) through programs aimed at reducing on-the-job injuries and illness (often managed by the corporate risk-management function or a workers' compensation manager), non-occupational illness and injury (managed by a disability carrier and the human resource function) and Employee Assistance Programs (managed by a specialist Behavioral Health vendor). These programs are in addition to any of the traditional medical management programs that an employer may have in place with its Third-party Administrator or insurer to manage its medical claims. Clearly, opportunities should exist to rationalize and integrate the programs. Such efforts, however, need to address not only competing providers of services but also the diverse departmental responsibilities within a company (often in response to divergent regulatory authorities).

A trend towards integrating health and productivity solutions is apparent with a number of examples from the field illustrating this concept. As yet to be rigorously examined by the academic literature, anecdotal case studies have been used to illustrate integrated systems in practice. Concerned by high short-term disability costs that were translating into long-term disability claims, a multinational publishing company (Devine [41]) identified that the underlying causes of illness-related absenteeism would be best addressed by a system integrating disease management with disability management. Following a two year implementation period, the flow through rate from short-term to long-term disability had reduced by 30% and long-term disability claims were reduced by 25%, medical costs were $4.8m lower than previously projected and benefit plan cost increases were reduced from double digit to single digit growth. In another case, a longitudinal study of the 'Live for Life' program at Johnson & Johnson evaluated the outcomes of an integrated health promotion, occupational health and safety, employee assistance, disability management and benefits management with a financial impact study finding cost savings on employee health care and administrative costs of around $8.6 million per year (Goetzel [75]).

Believed to be superior to individual stand-alone program management, the benefits of integrated programs include the assumption of benefit arising from a holistic approach integrating interventions across the continuum of care from wellness and risk management through to disease management of chronic conditions, complex case management and predictive modeling. Goetzel (op. cit.) describes integrated programs as those that align human resources benefits management with employee healthcare programs with the intention of enhancing morale, improving organizational safety, reducing turnover and increasing productivity. Programs include health insurance, disability and workers' compensation, employee assistance, paid sick leave, and occupational safety programs and those focused on work/life issues. Van den Eynde [201] suggests that the integration of offers provides a new opportunity for consumer and provider engagement by providing a 'new data stream that im-

---

[5] See Onsite Healthcare webpage [153].

proves their understanding and accountability to act.' Loeppke [124] noted a new focus in workplace healthcare management on health and productivity and total cost management with integration and coordination being key drivers of that approach as opposed to the fragmentation experienced previously.

Integrated programs use a population health management focus and have arisen from the need to streamline and better coordinate services, and from changes in medical processes including pay-for-performance of physicians and migration to the use of electronic health records, clinical risk being equated with financial risk and the introduction of human performance management systems. Villagra [203] cautions that a consistent framework for evaluating clinical and financial outcomes of disease management and integrated programs is necessary to improve the reliability and comparability of studies.

13.10 CONCLUSION

Employer interest in the outcomes of their investment in employee health is high. In recognition of the multi-determinants of employer purchased healthcare, organizations are beginning to look for strategies or programs that achieve a hitherto elusive goal — improving quality of care while yielding an acceptable return for the organization's investment. There is interest in developing integrated systems that better coordinate the management of medical care and health related (both occupational and non-occupational) workplace absences and diminished on-the-job performance. An integrated medical management system that draws together all elements of an organization's worksite health program into the one structure is believed to potentially confer benefits in terms of better coordinated service delivery, greater utility for consumers and service providers and efficiencies of operation and scale as well as better information for management decision making.

Health risk has been shown to be clearly related to medical care costs, and certain health care conditions have been demonstrated to be linked to workplace absences or diminished performance at work. The literature shows that health risk drives costs and costs follow risk and that certain conditions are more expensive than others. Research has effectively shown the value of undertaking workplace wellness initiatives in the reduction of health risks and the impact of these programs on reducing medical care costs. Research interest is beginning to address the cost of absenteeism and presenteeism to business but has yet to comprehensively investigate strategies to actively manage these factors. One significant inhibiting factor is the difficulty of obtaining valid data (or even, in the case of presenteeism, developing a workable definition that allows the phenomenon to be tracked). The increasing use of flexible work arrangements, telecommuting and paid-time-off arrangements have reduced the frequency of structured time and attendance-keeping within the workplace, making it difficult to obtain the necessary data for analysis. Given the prevalence and total costs of chronic conditions, significant opportunity exists to examine the relationship between improved worker health and productivity management.

The emphasis in worksite wellness programming has changed from the traditional health promotion and concern for the ROI achieved, to that of health and productivity management. This linking of human capital management with employee well-being and the strategic imperatives of the employing organization effectively argues the business case for employer sponsored worksite wellness programs.

14 EVALUATION OF WORKSITE WELLNESS PROGRAMS: SELECTIVE REVIEW OF THE LITERATURE

14.1 INTRODUCTION

Comprehensive, multi-component workplace wellness programs confer benefits to both the individual and to the sponsoring organization in terms of the potential for healthier lifestyles to mitigate and address some sources of future healthcare costs. The inclusion of workplace wellness programs into corporate strategy rests in part upon an economic argument that a clear positive relationship exists between modifiable health risk and healthcare expenditure.

A significant body of literature has evolved over the past thirty years examining the impact of workplace wellness programs. The literature primarily reports on clinical effectiveness and the cost-effectiveness of mitigating risk. There has recently been considerable discussion of the 'business case' for health promotion and disease prevention including cost-benefit or ROI and there is a growing interest in examining the relationship between health risk and productivity.

In this chapter we first review the literature on workplace wellness programs and their associated health- and cost-improvement. We then turn to the literature that addresses health-related productivity improvement. Finally we briefly discuss some of the measurement problems inherent in this area.

14.2 WORKPLACE WELLNESS PROGRAMS – THE LITERATURE

The workplace wellness literature is seen as falling into two key areas of investigation (Goetzel [72]). The first examines whether participation in wellness programs has an impact upon specific risk reduction such as smoking cessation and whether the transition of individuals between risk 255 (high-risk to low-risk or vice versa) has any impact upon healthcare costs. The second key area of investigation takes a broader viewpoint and investigates the overall economic impact of health promotion and disease management programs.

Several comprehensive literature reviews and meta-analyses have been published in the past ten years that cover the impact of health promotion programs with respect to health outcomes achieved, cost-effectiveness or the ROI of programs. Literature reviews considered to be seminal works in the health promotion and disease prevention field include those by Heaney and Goetzel [91], Riedel et al. [173], Aldana [2], Pelletier [162], and Chapman [26].

Case studies investigating outcomes of health promotion and disease prevention programs are a feature of the workplace wellness literature. Many studies have been published and thoroughly reviewed. Studies often cited with the strongest research designs and large numbers of subjects include those of Johnson & Johnson, Citibank, Dupont, the Bank of America, Tenneco, Duke University, the California Public Retirees System, Procter and Gamble, and Chevron Corporation (Goetzel & Ozminkowski [82]). According to these authors, when methodological variances are taken into account, most of these worksite programs studied achieved positive cost outcomes. In addition to case-specific reports, comprehensive discussion and summaries of case studies are widely available and for example, can be found in Golaszewski [84] and Riedel et al. [173] who provide brief summaries of case methodologies and outcomes. The National Business Group on Health [89] summarizes worksite evaluations by the type of program and ROI achieved.

Workplace health promotion and disease prevention programs have been shown to be effective in modifying health risk. Several comprehensive reviews have examined the evidence that supports the health and cost benefits of worksite wellness programs.

In their analysis of forty-seven studies that described thirty-five multi-component worksite wellness programs, Heaney and Goetzel [91] (p.305), found that there was 'cautious optimism' about the effectiveness of these programs. While noting that the most effective strategies for 'engaging employees in successful behavioral change…have not yet been adequately identified' they concluded that worksite wellness programs effectively reduced health risk if certain conditions were present. Specifically, the authors suggested that a comprehensive program that included individual risk reduction counseling for high-risk employees in a work environment that offered risk reduction to all employees was more likely to result in overall decreased health risks among employees.

The clinical effectiveness and cost-effectiveness outcomes of comprehensive worksite health promotion and disease management programs have been regularly reviewed by Pelletier. In the fifth report in his series, Pelletier [162] reviewed 15 U.S. studies of clinical-effectiveness and cost-effectiveness published between 1998 and 2000. His review found that although none of the programs reduced all indicators of risk, the majority of programs that were of adequate intensity, breadth and duration did decrease the number of risks sufficiently to result in overall risk reduction. Pelletier expressed 'cautious optimism' that comprehensive, multi-factorial risk and disease management interventions were both clinically and cost-effective.

Ozminkowski et al. [157] in their study of the Citibank Health Management Program sought to estimate change in health risk attributable to participation in either an intensive program or a less intensive program. Using a pre-post test methodology, the study found in the intensive program that small but statistically significant improvements for all participants were found in eight of ten risk categories including risk related to seatbelt use, exercise habits, stress levels, fiber intake, diet, cigarette use, and blood pressure. The researchers concluded that participation in the intensive program was associated with significant reductions in health risk and a positive affect on the bottom line occurred even with small changes in risk.

Riedel et al. [173] provide a comprehensive overview of the literature on the relationships between workplace disease prevention and health promotion and productivity. This review found that evidence for performance-based cost-benefit is limited and primarily drawn from absenteeism data. The evidence for medical cost-benefit of disease prevention and health promotion interventions was found to be moderate. Comprehensive, multi-factor programs were found to be effective whereas there was limited evidence for the efficacy of single-focus interventions. The authors concluded that there is 'strong and convincing evidence' about a direct relationship between personal health risk factors such as smoking, tobacco use, sedentary lifestyle and diet and increased incidence of related illnesses; that health status influences health related costs; and that disease prevention and health promotion interventions improve personal health status.

14.3 HEALTH RISK AND ASSOCIATED MEDICAL CARE EXPENDITURE

The association between modifiable health risks and increased health care expenditures has been well established. Anderson et al. [6] examined the relationship between modifiable health risks and group-level health care expenditures and found that 25% of total health care expenditures were attributable to ten modifiable health risks. A direct relationship between the level of risk and subsequent healthcare cost was found. In this study, stress was found to be the most costly factor. Other high cost risks included tobacco use, being overweight and a sedentary lifestyle. They determined that these high-risk factors could be reduced through lifestyle modification, behavior change or pharmacological intervention.

Goetzel et al. [76] measured the impact of ten modifiable health risk behaviors on healthcare expenditure. The study found that high-risk employees had significantly higher expenditures in seven of the ten risk categories than did those classified as low-risk. The most costly health risk was depression which was found to have 70% higher health care costs. Stress was associated with 46% higher health care costs, elevated blood sugar was 35% higher, obesity 21%, smoking 20%, blood pressure 12%, and lack of exercise 10% higher health care costs. These risk factors were also found to have a higher likelihood of having extremely high outlier expenditures. Employees with multiple risk profiles had higher expenditures than those without these profiles. For example, higher expenditures were experienced in those with heart disease (228% higher), psychosocial problems (147% higher) and stroke (85% higher).

After years of large-scale, longitudinal research investigating the relationship between employee health status and healthcare costs, Edington [57] concluded that an association exists between high-risk individuals and high medical costs. Moreover, his research demonstrated that costs followed changes in risk. Edington observed that significant changes in personal health practices were associated with significant changes in medical claims costs so that 'when individuals changed cost categories, their risks changed accordingly'. In other words, increases or decreases in overall health risk have a corresponding increase or decrease in medical claims costs. The nature of risk was found to change over time and no single variable changed only in one direction. The evaluation of risk change over time is seen in terms of the "net" gain, or the result of the changes in risk in both directions. Edington's research has also found that the cost associated with each increased risk factor is greater than the cost associated with each decreased risk factor. In one study (Edington [55]), the mean cost increase per risk increased was found to be $350 per year compared with the mean cost decrease per risk decreased of $150 per year. Edington suggests that programs that focus on maintaining employees in the low-risk category may be a more effective use of resources rather than focusing upon high-risk populations only.

Chapman [28] summarizes data from six studies that examined the actuarial relationship between selected health risks and health cost. The relationship between high-risk and high costs was established by a weighted average of the difference in per capita annual health costs between the low-risk group and the high-risk group. This relationship between risk and cost was found to be stress 38.9%, smoking 22.4%, eating habits 16.2%, obesity 11.0%, seat belts 7.7%, blood pressure 7.6%, alcohol use 7.5%, cholesterol 7.3%, exercise 6.3%, and drugs & medications 1.1%.

One study (Wright et al. [221]), examined the relationship of health risk level to charged medical costs to determine the excess cost of higher risk individuals as compared to low-risk persons. Two years of medical claims from six corporations were used to determine costs of health risk assessment (HRA) participants and non-participants. The study found that excess medical costs due to excess risk ranged from 15% to 31% for HRA participants and 24% to 38% if non-participants were included. Behavioral health risk factors were found to be associated with approximately 25% of total healthcare expenditures.

Yen et al. [222] examined excess health risks of employees and various excess cost measures such as time away from work, medical claims and pharmacy claims. Excess costs were considered cost per risk factor as well as total excess costs by risk status. The study found that excess health risks were significantly associated with excess costs. Of the total healthcare related costs of the organization studied, medical claims accounted for 50%, time away from work for 40%, and pharmacy claims were responsible for 10% of the total costs in both overall and excess cost measures. The authors concluded that there was significant financial benefit attached to improved employee health if medical claims and time away from work were addressed.

14.4 FINANCIAL IMPACT OF WELLNESS PROGRAMS

Reviewing twenty years of literature Golaszewski [84] found evidence to support the economic merit of health promotion. Health promotion interventions were found to provide positive financial returns, especially with respect to health care costs and absenteeism reduction.

In a comprehensive literature review of 72 peer-reviewed articles examining the financial impact of health promotion programs, Aldana [2] concluded that healthcare costs and illness-related absenteeism were strongly related to high stress levels, excess body weight and multiple risk factors.

Increased health care costs due to changes in risk were found to occur within a short time period. Chapman [27] suggests that, as a considerable proportion of medical claims are related to about a dozen modifiable risk factors, between 30% and 60% of health plan costs could either be modified or avoided. Pronk et al. [168] investigated weight management, smoking and low levels of physical activity and found that adverse health risks translate into higher healthcare charges in a relatively short period of time of around 18 months. Edington [55] also found that changes in medical costs associated with changes in health risk could occur within one year.

Chapman [26] undertook a meta-analysis of forty-two studies evaluating the economic impact and return of worksite health promotion programs. He updated this review in 2005 with an additional 14 articles that met the inclusion criteria for a total of 56 studies. He concluded that worksite health promotion was a significant strategy available to organizations to enhance productivity. Chapman noted that strong evidence existed for average reductions of around 25% in sick leave, health plan costs and workers' compensation and disability costs. He also observed that the more recent studies covered programs using newer prevention technologies such as internet based information and high-risk intervention telephone counseling. These technologies were associated with a higher level of economic impact with approximately double the average cost-benefit ratio reported in studies of programs using traditional health promotion and disease management models.

Small changes in risk level can result in significant economic benefit. Leutzinger et al. [116] applied a predictive model with four different risk scenarios using data from Union Pacific Railroad to estimate future medical care expenditures over a ten year period. The projected future medical care expenditure was developed from employee demographics, health risk profiles and ten health risk measures with the additional effects of medical cost inflation being excluded. The baseline scenario assumed preservation of underlying risk trends and projected that healthcare costs would increase by 26.1% over the ten year period. The second scenario assumed a static risk factor prevalence rate and projected increases of 23.2% over the duration. The third scenario modeled a very small decrease in each risk category of 0.1% per year. This resulted in a 20.7% projected increase in costs over the decade. Finally, it was found that an aggressive health promotion program that achieved a 1% annual reduction (i.e.: 10% over 10 years) of individuals in each risk category would result in a 5.8% increase in healthcare expenditures over the ten year period. The cost-benefit ratio for the fourth scenario was 1:4.07. For the Union Pacific Railroad worksite wellness program to pay for itself it was estimated that health risks must be reduced by at least 0.09% per year.

Goetzel et al. [81] used a similar prospective ROI model to estimate the impact of corporate health-management and risk-reduction programs at the Dow Chemical Company. A baseline case was established using demographic, health risk and medical expenditure information and three scenarios of risk adjustment were modeled over 10 years. The results indicated that even small reductions in health risks would yield health care costs savings. In the base case, expenditure was projected to increase by 35.5% over the 10 years. The midpoint scenario (0.1% annual risk reduction) estimated healthcare cost increases of 29.7% over 10 years. Costs of this program were estimated to slightly exceed expenses and the ROI was 0.76 cents per dollar invested. In contrast, healthcare costs in the greatest impact scenario (risk reduced by 1% annually or 10% over the 10 years) were estimated to increase 13.7% compared to the base year with an ROI of 1:3.21.

In an effort to build a business case for investing in workplace wellness programs, evaluative attention has focused upon investigating the potential ROI in addition to the achievement of clinical outcomes. ROI is commonly used to estimate cost-benefit of wellness programs, measuring the costs of the program against the expected financial return of the program. Ozminkowski & Goetzel [156] discuss the limitations of using of ROI and suggests that a Net Present Value[1] figure is to be preferred, arguing that it is more useful as it 'offers an answer in simple dollar terms and can always be calculated.' Limitations with ROI analysis over a multi-year period include the need to make adjustments for both inflation and discounting

[1] Net Present Value = the difference between the total discounted inflation-adjusted benefits and the costs of the program over its useful life.

and the fact that many future benefits and costs in wellness programs are often deferred and are difficult to quantify.

Nevertheless, many studies have determined the ROIs of various wellness programs. Goetzel et al. [80] reviewed ROI studies of health, demand and disease management programs and found ROI estimates between $1.40 in benefits per dollar spent to $13 per dollar spent. Goetzel [73] stated that "the return from well-designed comprehensive programs may be at least $3 to $8 per dollar invested, within 5 years following program initiation." Aldana [2] concluded that the average ROI for studies reporting healthcare costs alone was $3.48 per dollar spent. If absenteeism was included then the ROI was $5.82. Serxner et al. [183] reviewed workplace wellness ROI literature and found that health promotion and disease prevention programs achieved ROIs of between 1.5:1.0 to 3.0:1.0 and disease management programs achieved ROI of between 1.2:1.0 to 1.8:1.0. Different programs produced different returns. Goetzel et al. (in Anderson et al. [5]) found that the median benefit of health management programs was $3.14 per dollar invested, the median benefit for demand management programs was $4.50 and the median benefit of disease management programs was $8.88.

14.5 Risk Transition

Worksite wellness programs aim to maintain or improve an individual's risk and to prevent an individual from moving to a higher risk status. Research indicates that participation in a comprehensive program produces improvements in population health outcomes (Edington et al. [57]; Ozminkowski et al. [157]). High-risk individuals have been shown to benefit from programs that provide risk-reduction counseling as part of a comprehensive health promotion program Heaney & Goetzel [91]; Pelletier [162].

Opinion is divided as to whether programs should concentrate resource allocation on managing high-risk individuals or on the maintenance of low-risk status among healthy individuals. Some argue that it is more cost-effective to invest resources in the highest risk/highest cost population rather than dilute the effectiveness of limited resources by spreading them over a wider population (Heaney & Goetzel and Pelletier). Musich et al. [143] note that few studies focus on low-risk maintenance.

Risk is not considered to be static, but rather subject to a natural flow or fluctuation between high and low Edington [55]. Within any fixed population health risks and medical care costs fluctuate continuously both increasing and decreasing independently of a health promotion program. Edington [56] contends that the natural flow of health risks within a population is towards high-risk in the absence of programs targeted at maintaining the population at low-risk. Therefore, Edington argues, low-risk maintenance is an 'important contributor to the net change of risk levels within a population.' A successful health promotion strategy should move individuals from high-risk to low-risk and prevent transitions in the reverse Edington et al. [57]. With regards to where organizations should direct available resources in health promotion programs, Edington [55] suggests that the maximum cost-benefit is gained from focusing on low and medium-risk populations. He believes that focusing on high-risk populations is only viable if program resources of more than $300 per person are available.

Burton et al. [18] use 'churn' to describe fluctuations in an individuals risk status – adding risk as well as reducing risk over time. In a study of health risk and presenteeism, these researchers found that the least amount of churn occurred in health risks that were relatively stable over short periods of time such as smoking, alcohol use and safety belt use. Risk factors such as physical activity, life dissatisfaction, stress and weight management showed the greatest amount of change. The authors concluded that corporations should focus on low-risk maintenance rather than attempting to move people from high-risk to low-risk, 'an outcome which has eluded many worksite health promotion programs.'

Musich et al. [143] examined the effectiveness of a comprehensive workplace health promotion program in influencing risk status transitions in the short-term and long-term at General Motors Corporation. Employees completed two HRAs and participated in appropriate workplace wellness programs. Net risk transition was measured in the short-term (from Year 1 to Year 2) and in the long-term (from Year 1 to Year 5). Significant increases were found in the numbers of individuals who transitioned to lower risk status with around 48% of the net risk reduction occurring in the first year of the program and the remaining 52% spread over the remaining four years. A net gain of 5.0 percentage points of low-risk individuals was achieved in the first year of the program and this gain of low-risk individuals was 10.4 percentage points at the end of the five years. The authors observed that net gains in low-risk individuals were not the result of static changes, but rather, individuals moved between categories of risk with some improving their health status in the short-term but returning to high-risk status in the longer-term. Furthermore, the net gain was the result of some individuals remaining at low-risk, others improving their health status and transitioning to low-risk and others increasing their risk status or maintaining high-risk status. In this study, most individual health risks showed improvements. In both the short-term and the long-term, significant improvements were found in blood pressure, stress, safety belt use, physical activity, life satisfaction, smoking, and alcohol use. Significant increases in risk for weight were found in both the short-term and long-term periods. The average age of participants was just under 50 years at commencement of the study and the population aged five years over the duration. The study found that over 84% of those who were originally at low-risk remained so and attribute this in part to the success of the program, particularly for an age group in which chronic diseases begin to become evident.

The authors found the General Motors program to have been successful in achieving risk reduction among participants by increasing the numbers moving from higher risk to lower risk categories. Most of the risk reduction took place early in the program. No evidence was found to show that the program slowed the transition towards high-risk. They concluded that as population risk reduces, the focus of workplace programs should change from targeting risk reduction to maintaining low-risk in the long-term.

14.6 HEALTH RISK AND PRODUCTIVITY

It has been noted that until recently, productivity losses such as absenteeism and presenteeism as the result of employee ill health have been infrequently measured (Burton [19]). However, research interest is growing in determining workplace productivity losses related to common health conditions (Goetzel et al. [79]) Absenteeism includes personal illness days, short-term and long-term disability and workers' compensation days and is commonly used to estimate lost productivity due to illness (Edington [55]). It is generally agreed that using absenteeism as the sole indicator of the indirect cost of illness may significantly underestimate productivity losses from workplace ill-health (Goetzel et al. [78]; Collins [30]). Research attention is turning towards the concept of presenteeism or on-the-job productivity losses due to illness, understood as either diminished performance due to personal illness or incapacity or to concerns about illnesses of family members and significant others. A wide variety of instruments for assessing presenteeism were recently reviewed in Mattke et al. [132].

Medical care costs are only a proportion of health and productivity costs faced by employers (Goetzel et al. [79]). Several studies suggest that the cost of absenteeism and presenteeism are considerably greater than the direct medical costs and that the costs of presenteeism are greater than those of absenteeism (Goetzel et al. [78]; Collins et al. [30]; Nicholson et al [147]). For example, in a broad-ranging literature review, Mattke et al. quote the average presenteeism loss per employee per year as being 12% of full productivity with a range of between 5.7% and 17.9% whereas the average cost of absenteeism was 4.3% of full productivity with a low of 0.8% and a high of 10.8%. Variance in the losses was related to the measurement instruments used as well as to condition related differences.

In a study seeking to estimate the relationship between condition-related prevalence, associated costs and presenteeism, Goetzel et al. analyzed the total cost of health, absence, short-term disability, and productivity loss data for ten health conditions. Conditions with the greatest impact on presenteeism were arthritis, hypertension, depression/sadness/mental illness, allergy, migraine/headache, and diabetes. Several chronic conditions were found to have a high proportion of total costs attributable to presenteeism including migraine/headache (89% of total costs), allergies (82%) and arthritis (77%). The study found that presenteeism costs were higher than medical costs in most conditions making up between 18% and 60% of overall total costs and thus is a significant factor to be managed by employers. The study concluded that from 'one fifth to approximately three fifths of the total dollars attributable to common health conditions faced by employers could be a result of on-the job productivity losses.'

Burton et al.[19] investigated the influence of health risk on self-reported productivity and found that ten of twelve health risk factors studied were significantly associated with self-reported work limitations. Presenteeism was found to be strongly associated with the 'perception-related' risk factors of life dissatisfaction, job dissatisfaction, poor health, and stress. The study found that productivity fell as the numbers of risk factors rose. Compared with low-risk individuals, employees who were categorized as medium-risk were found to be 6.2% less productive and workers who were high-risk were 12.2% less productive.

Burton et al. [18] explored the relationship between changes in risk and productivity a little further. Analyzing the results of two HRAs administered two years apart they found that changes in health risks were associated with changes in presenteeism. Risk reduction was associated with improved productivity whereas those who increased their number of risks or remained of high-risk status lost productivity. Employees who moved from high-risk status to low-risk status over the duration of the study made the highest productivity gains. The study estimated that the addition of any one risk factor would result in a 2% decrease in work-related productivity and this was estimated to be $950 per year per risk changed.

In a study of the Dow Chemical Company's implementation of an integrated health management system to minimize health-related costs and maximize health-related productivity, Collins et al. [30] estimated that the total cost of chronic conditions was 10% of the total labor costs in the U.S. company with 6.8% of those costs attributable to presenteeism, 2.3% from medical care and 1.0% from absenteeism. Goetzel et al. [78] analyzed health and productivity management data from 43 organizations and found that costs were distributed between group health (47%), staff turnover (37%), unscheduled absences (8%), non-occupational disability (5%) and worker's compensation programs (3%). A 2006 study of unscheduled absences showed that only 35% were due to personal illness with 65% caused by other reasons including family issues (24%), personal need (18%), stress (12%) and an entitlement mentality (11%) (CCH [199]).

Presenteeism is difficult to quantify (Burton et al. [17]). Many studies focus on the impact of various chronic conditions such as migraine, seasonal allergies and depression on worker productivity (Burton et al. [18]) and it has been suggested that the presence of a chronic condition is the 'most important determinant of reported levels of work impairment and absence' (Collins [30]). Stewart et al. [189] used a self-report retrospective methodology to examine the impact of common pain conditions on productivity. An estimated productivity loss attributable to these conditions was $61.2 billion annually with the majority of lost time (76.6%) due to reduced performance at work rather than to absences from work.

Correlations between productivity studies and medical claims and absence data bases identified that presenteeism costs were higher than medical costs and comprised 18% to 60% of the total direct and indirect costs (Burton et al. [18]). One organization estimated that its direct medical costs (medical and pharmaceutical) were 24 %, with indirect costs being divided between presenteeism (63%), absenteeism (6%), short-term disability (6%) and long-term disability (1%). Workers' compensation was found to be less than 1% (Hemp [95]). Other estimates also suggest that presenteeism may account for up to 60% of total direct and indirect costs of employee ill health whereas medical, pharmacy, absenteeism, and disability costs account for the remaining 40% (Burton et al. [18]). A 2001 study found that "productivity loss potential dwarfs direct benefits program costs" with estimated productivity losses to be 76%, disability costs 6% and medical costs 24% (Parry & Auerbach [159]).

Some limited research has examined the importance of linking data from medical care, disability and lost productivity to understand how medical care delivery affects short-term disability costs (Parry & Auerbach; Parry et al. [160]). One analysis (Parry et al.) of a database of 183 employers over an eighteen month period found that medical care accounted for 80% of total medical and disability expenditure. On average, each disability case in this study involved 3.4 medical conditions and each claimant filed 1.1 disability claims. It was found that disability costs increased with the number of medical episodes and also with longer disability durations suggesting that medical complexity drove disability costs. A small group of claimants were responsible for a disproportionate level of claims with 10% of those filing disability claims accounting for more than half the total medical and disability costs. Predictive modeling was suggested as a way of anticipating and managing the likely impact of this high-cost group. In terms of lost productivity associated with disability absences, it was estimated that this cost an average of $22,800 per disability claim compared with $13,600 in medical costs and $3,800 in disability costs with musculoskeletal, neoplasm and circulatory conditions being the most significant causes of lost productivity. The study concluded that there was value in integrating medical and disability as 'meaningfully related' databases to manage healthcare and disability costs, productivity losses and develop measures for judging the outcomes of health care interventions.

With regard to occupational health and safety, it is believed that the direct costs of work-related injuries and illnesses that fall under the worker's compensation category such as indemnity payments, insurance administration expenses and medical services substantially underestimate the true cost of productivity losses attributable to work-related injuries and illnesses (Tompa [198]). Indirect costs such as return to work and retraining programs, recruitment and training of replacement workers and lost production are not accounted for, nor are the social costs of injury such as pain and suffering and time lost or unpaid home-based care provided by family members.

14.7 HEALTH RELATED PRODUCTIVITY - ESTIMATING FINANCIAL IMPACT

Presenteeism and absenteeism are significant factors in the cost of health related productivity loss to the employer. Methodological and data issues make accurate clinical and financial measurement difficult (Levin-Scherz [117]). One of the major issues when investigating productivity lost due to ill-health or lifestyle problems is the difficulty in attributing observed changes directly to interventions. Several different types of research protocols discussed in earlier chapters have been utilized in an attempt to overcome methodological shortcomings.

As discussed earlier in this book, the use of random controlled trials (RCTs) to compare and contrast results of an experimental program group with a control group that is not part of the program is the preferred methodology but RCTs are difficult to achieve in an operational setting and ethical issues arise regarding the withholding of treatment or information from individuals. Alternative strategies include quasi-experimental methods such as a 'services-avoided' methodology which compares the costs of requested services to approved and ultimately utilized services; 'pre-post' studies that compare before and after results achieved by a particular population; population level analyses comparing achievements against agreed benchmarks, and the use of statistical methods such as equivalence adjustments for patient health status mix, demographic characteristics, inflation or selection biases.

Issues that contribute to measurement difficulties include changes in group composition over the measurement period (such as changes in health plan enrollments), disease progression (resulting in higher costs despite program interventions), changes in external variables such as new clinical developments or legislative changes, and data management, methodological design and statistical issues, as discussed elsewhere in this book.

Attribution of a monetary value to lost productivity has been one of the greatest difficulties encountered to date due to the lack of an established and validated method to derive monetary estimates of the cost of lost productivity (Mattke et al. [131]). The use of the wage rate, compensation costs or salary conversion methods have been most commonly used to quantify the impact of lost time but this has been primarily applied to absenteeism and is more difficult to estimate with respect to presenteeism (Pauly et al. [161]). Tompa [198] notes that in many empirical studies, the cost of sickness absence and the cost-effectiveness of health promotion programs are based upon the direct cost of wages paid to absent workers. Berger et al. [11] include a self-reported estimation of percent of productive time lost in a day rather than just days absent as a means of calculating the impact of underperformance and Burton et al. [18] also used self-reported percentages of time at work estimated to be lost due to physical or emotional ill health. Salary-based data is considered to give the lower-bound estimate of lost productivity as losses from a day's work could be greater than the day's wage (Pauly et al. [161]).

Berger et al. [11] detail two methods in use for the valuation of indirect costs, namely the 'lost wages' or the 'human capital' method and the 'friction cost' method. In the lost wages method, with full employment assumed, wage rates equal the value of marginal revenue generated by an additional worker, forgone earnings indicate indirect costs, an individual's gross compensation is used to measure lost productivity and absenteeism is deduced through days lost by estimated average daily earnings. Problems identified with this method include failure to incorporate other dimensions such as loss of leisure time and the utility of any health consumption and variations in the use of wage rates for the calculations such as using industry average wage rates or those of specific occupational groups.

The friction cost method is suggested by some as an alternative to the human-capital method which was felt to over-estimate absence-related productivity whereas the friction cost method enables the calculation of a 'more realistic' estimate of productivity costs (Olsen & Richardson [152]; Brouwer & Koopmanschap [14]). The friction period is the period of time and associated transaction costs needed to replace a sick worker and this time will differ according to short-term and medium-term effects of illness on production output. The length of the friction period and subsequent indirect costs is dependent upon the state of the labor market. This method adopts a high-level perspective that the opportunity cost to society of replacing a sick worker is zero as the replacement worker is assumed to have otherwise been unemployed – this is despite the payment of sick leave benefits to the absent worker. Indirect costs in this case are the value of lost production plus any other costs of maintaining production, filling the vacancy and training the substitute worker. Studies using the friction cost method use national data rather than firm level data. Berger et al. [11] are critical of this method believing it to be useful at a national labor market level but not at a firm level and that it fails to consider certain indirect costs such as well-being, the value of lost leisure to the incoming worker and quality of life.

Pauly et al. [161] identify that the average wage per day can be a reasonably accurate measure of lost productivity for some firms whereas for others it will 'substantially underestimate the cost of lost work time.' Their research identified three key factors that determined the magnitude of loss of productivity. An accurate estimation of the true cost of lost productivity was found to be dependent upon the degree to which production relies upon a team rather than an individual worker, the cost (both in terms of wages and knowledge capital) of replacing an absent worker and the penalties associated with lost production particularly if the output is time sensitive.

This 'team production model' is further extended by the work of Nicholson et al. [147], [148] who have found that the cost associated with missed work varies across job types and is related to ease of replacement of the absent worker, the extent to which the job role is part of a team and the time sensitivity of the outputs. Nicholson et al., developed a set of multipliers to determine the true cost of an absence in the job for thirty-five occupational categories based on these three dimensions. Jobs that were more complex or had a higher impact on outcomes were allocated higher multipliers. The multipliers were developed from a survey of over 800 managers covering fifty-seven jobs in twelve industries that covered a broad range of the three job characteristics that were under investigation. The managers estimated the ease of worker replacement, the consequences of an absence, and estimated the costs of absence including factors such as overtime, lost sales and recruitment expenses. Different multipliers were developed to account for short term absences (three days) and longer term absences (two weeks). A multiplier of 1.00 meant that the costs of absence in that position equated with the daily wage for that position. For example, it was estimated that the replacement costs of a waiter or fast food restaurant cook attracted a multiplier of 1.00 as the cost of absence was close to the daily wage whereas a truck driver attracted a multiplier of 1.28, a registered nurse 1.40 and an aerospace engineer 1.70, these being replacement costs of 28%, 40% and 70% greater than the daily wage for that position.

The study concluded that some jobs were considered to be of more consequence to a firm than others and that greater productivity loss was incurred through absences in jobs that were hard to replace, were important components of a team and worked on time sensitive outputs. It was felt that the capability to determine the level of these three characteristics may be useful to organizations in seeking to manage their costs of absence. Furthermore, the study supported the hypothesis that the cost of absence of work can be greater than just the wage cost and suggested that developing an absenteeism multiplier might prove to be useful. Interestingly, Collins et al. [30] reported being in the process of applying the thirty-five indicators to the Dow Chemical Company data base and expected to find that by applying these multipliers, the total costs of lost productivity at Dow would be significantly higher than previously estimated using self-report survey methods.

14.8 DISCUSSION OF THE EVIDENCE

The literature discusses the difficulties in establishing a direct relationship between health promotion, disease prevention programs, absence management and clinical effectiveness and economic benefit.

Concern is expressed about variety of evidence standards and varying research designs that have been used in attempts to establish a causal relationship between health risk behaviors, healthcare costs, interventions and changes in health risk (Anderson et al. [5]). Confounding factors that cloud the research picture include population aging and technological developments. Variability of program design and in evaluation methodologies makes comparisons of program achievements difficult (Heaney & Geotzel [91]). Randomized control trials are the preferred research method (Aldana [2]; Ozminkowski & Goetzel [156]). Others point out the difficulties of achieving a truly random experimental design in the workplace. Concerns include privacy and the expense of conducting such trials. So called quasi-experimental or well-designed controlled trials without randomization and cohort or case-control studies are considered to be methodologically acceptable (Aldana).

Study limitations raised concerning many evaluations of worksite health promotion and disease prevention programs include the self-selection of subjects, a high attrition rate, short duration of evaluations (generally 1 to 3 years), the subjectivity of measures, use of self-report tools such as HRAs, diffusion of information, statistical instrumentation issues and a 'investigator bias,' or the influence of investigator's expectations on the results and interpretation (Goetzel [74]).

Absenteeism is generally measured either through payroll data or through self-report. Both methods have methodological problems regarding accuracy of record keeping or of recall and are reliant upon whether a company collects such data (Mattke et al. [132]). Presenteeism data is usually gathered through short-term recall surveys (Burton et al. [19]; Mattke et al. [132]). Such surveys ask for self-perceived levels of impairment, comparisons of factors such as efficiency, performance and productivity and an estimation of unproductive time at work. Difficulties with these methods include differences in perception of what is considered to be 'unproductive time' and norms of this factor within particular workplaces or within employee groupings. Survey instruments regularly used include the Health and Performance Questionnaire (HPQ), the Work Limitations Questionnaire (WLQ), the Work Productivity and Activity Impairment Questionnaire (WPAI), and the Stanford Presenteeism Scale (SPS) (Burton et al. [18]; Mattke et al. [132]).

Strategies undertaken by organizations to fill vacancies have considerable bearing upon the quantification of loss from absenteeism. These include the availability of 'perfect' replacements, whether a talent pool of replacement workers exists, the capacity to redeploy existing staff or to use temporary staff, or whether the organization must forgo revenue due to staff absence. Presumably organizations use some combination of the above in an effort to maximize profitability or at least to minimize loss. Other costs such as management attention needed to fill the vacancy also need to be considered.

14.9 CONCLUSION

Extensive research spanning thirty years provides growing evidence that workplace health and wellness programs for the most part, secure improved health outcomes for employees and reductions in employer healthcare costs. Awareness is increasing of the economic impact of illness related productivity losses and attention is being directed towards the quantification of this impact. The full costs of absence appear to be not well understood in most organizations. The literature points out that there are hidden costs of illness which are not just restricted to medical costs but include the loss of productivity as a result of short-term disability, long-term disability, workers compensation, absenteeism and presenteeism. Presenteeism has been clearly demonstrated to be considerably more costly to an organization than absenteeism, workers compensation and medical care. Methodological difficulties abound in relation to attributing a monetary value to lost productivity and in establishing a causal relationship between intervention and outcome. New directions are becoming apparent in the literature with research into the connections between workplace wellness and productivity including absenteeism and presenteeism. In identifying the hidden costs to business of illness-related absenteeism and presenteeism, recent research has improved the knowledge and awareness of the costs of ill health through new streams of inquiry.

15 THE RELATIONSHIP BETWEEN HEALTH RISK FACTORS AND HEALTH CARE CLAIMS COST IN PROGRAM DESIGN AND EVALUATION

15.1 INTRODUCTION

It is well established that lifestyle behavior is associated with higher cost illnesses such as obesity (and its attendant conditions, like diabetes), high blood pressure, and heart disease. In Chapter 13 we introduced wellness, a relatively new intervention program, and discussed some of its components, one of which is the health risk assessment, a questionnaire that is completed by participants at the start of the program to identify risk factors in the population, and provide a baseline for assessing progress during the intervention program. Chapter 14 is a review of the growing literature that has been published on wellness programs and their outcomes.

This chapter covers the practical outcomes from wellness programs, and their measurement. Traditionally, wellness programs are evaluated using either a variation of the adjusted historical control model as applied to DM programs, or a methodology that assigns a dollar value to the change between two points in time in each risk factor measured in the population. The first of these methods is difficult to apply in a population setting in which all members are potentially receiving some form of intervention (case management, disease management, or wellness) because there is no longer a "non-managed" population to use as a source of information about the trend in cost of the population, absent intervention. The alternative methodology, assigning dollar values to changes in risk, holds some promise but applicable data on risk values may be difficult to obtain. Information exists in the literature that may be useable for practical outcomes evaluations, but outcomes as reported in the literature may not always be applicable to other situations.

In order to answer the question about the value of risk-factor reduction empirically, we performed an analysis of the dollar value of risk factors, using a specific data set. The dollar values developed in this chapter may be used (with adjustment where appropriate) in evaluating risk factor changes in other populations as a component of wellness program outcomes evaluation.

Specifically, our objectives in this chapter are:

1. To understand the value of Health Risk Assessment data to explain Health Care claim costs;
2. To identify a method for prioritizing members for interventions; and
3. To quantify costs and changes in cost associated with health risk assessment attributes[1].

[1] The analysis that forms the basis for this chapter is of the *association* between risk factors and costs. We did not have data for, nor did we analyze, the reduction in costs due to risk factor reduction.

This chapter is in three parts. In Part 1, we develop a predictive model that relates health risk factors and claims costs. In Part 2, we illustrate how the model may be used to plan intervention programs and prioritize member interventions. In Part 3 we illustrate how the relationship between risk factors and claims costs developed in Part 1 may be used to estimate the savings from risk factor reduction due to an intervention program.

15.2 PART 1: MODEL DEVELOPMENT

15.2.1 Study Design

We developed multivariate regression models that predict member claims costs based on independent variables (risk factors).

15.2.2 Patients and Methods

The study population consists of members of a commercial health plan (HMO and PPO coverage), with 24 months of continuous enrollment from April 2005 through March 2007, who had completed self-reported Health Risk Assessment (HRA) surveys between May 2005 and March 2006. Self reported health care attributes were available for 18,610 members and include responses to more than 400 questions on lifestyle factors, family history, and conditions which are not identifiable through claims (e.g. obesity, smoking and other behavioral factors). The HRA covers the following factors:

- Personal Disease History: (presence of a diagnosis of Asthma, Cancer, Depression, Heart Disease, High Blood Pressure, Stroke and other selected high cost diseases);
- Family Disease History (Diagnosis of Cancer, Heart Disease, High Blood Pressure, Stroke etc.);
- Health Screenings and Immunizations: (Influenza, Pneumonia,..);
- Alcohol Consumption: (Ability to limit drink in various stressful situations.);
- Injury Prevention Behavior: (Gun safety, wearing seat belts etc.);
- Nutrition: (Consumption of grains, nuts, dairy, and portions thereof);
- Physical Activity: (low, medium, high intensity);
- Skin Protection (use in outdoor activities);
- Stress and Well-Being (ability to handle stressful situations);
- Tobacco use (cigar vs. pipe vs. cigarette, how many, how addicted);
- Weight Management (Body Mass Index); and
- Women's Health (pregnancy status, receiving hormone replacement therapy).

15.2.3 Method of Analysis

The independent variable used to develop the model is health care claims costs for the following year. Health care claims cost is defined as the sum of in-patient, out-patient, physician, pharmacy and other costs, measured at the allowed charge level. To reduce the impact of outliers, maximum cost was truncated at $100,000. The mean annual cost after truncation was $3,586. The distribution of costs is shown in Table 15.1.

TABLE 15.1

Distribution of Annual Claim Cost (April 2006-March 2007)	
Quantile	Estimate
95th percentile	$12,965
75% Q3	$3,659
50% Median	$1,269
25% Q1	$372
5%	$0

Since cost is highly positively skewed and cannot be negative, we attempted to model it using various approaches. Different models were considered, including log cost and a two-stage approach (first predicting members with positive cost using a logistic regression approach, coupled with a linear model to predict the amount of cost for those members who had claims). Comparing gaps between predicted cost and actual costs led us to retain the linear regression approach. Dunn et al. [54] comment: "It is our experience and that of Diehr et al. [42] and Kilian et al. [108] that, as a method of prediction (forecasting), a one-part model involving ordinary least squares on raw costs data consistently performs as well as, if not better than, ordinary least squares on logged costs or the more theoretically satisfying log-linear generalized linear model."

This approach is also relevant since we intend to use the estimates of the linear regression model to quantify the impact of Health Risk Assessment attributes on cost. Diehr et al. (op. cit.) comment: "When the goal is understanding the system, a two-part model seems best because it permits the investigator to distinguish factors that affect the propensity to use any services from factors that affect volume of utilization once the person has entered the system... . For understanding the effect of individual covariates on total costs, a one-part model is most useful because it generates a single regression coefficient for each variable and so can be interpreted easily."

We therefore use a linear regression model to predict Health Care claims costs from April 2006 to March 2007. We use the single variable, (DxCG prospective Med+Rx risk) and any HRA attributes prior to April 2006 that were identified by the regression as significant explanatory variables. A model development dataset containing half the members was constructed for development, and the model was validated on the other half of members (the model validation dataset)[2]. As expected, the presence of female-specific conditions, especially pregnancy, make the relationship of costs with age very different for females and males. We therefore ran the Chow test[3] to establish that separate models by gender were warranted and decided to develop separate male and female models.

---

[2] The model development and validation datasets were created by sorting the entire data first by cost and then placing every other member in the two different datasets. Thus, they are split randomly on cost.

[3] The Chow test is an econometric test of whether the coefficients in two linear regressions on different data are equal.

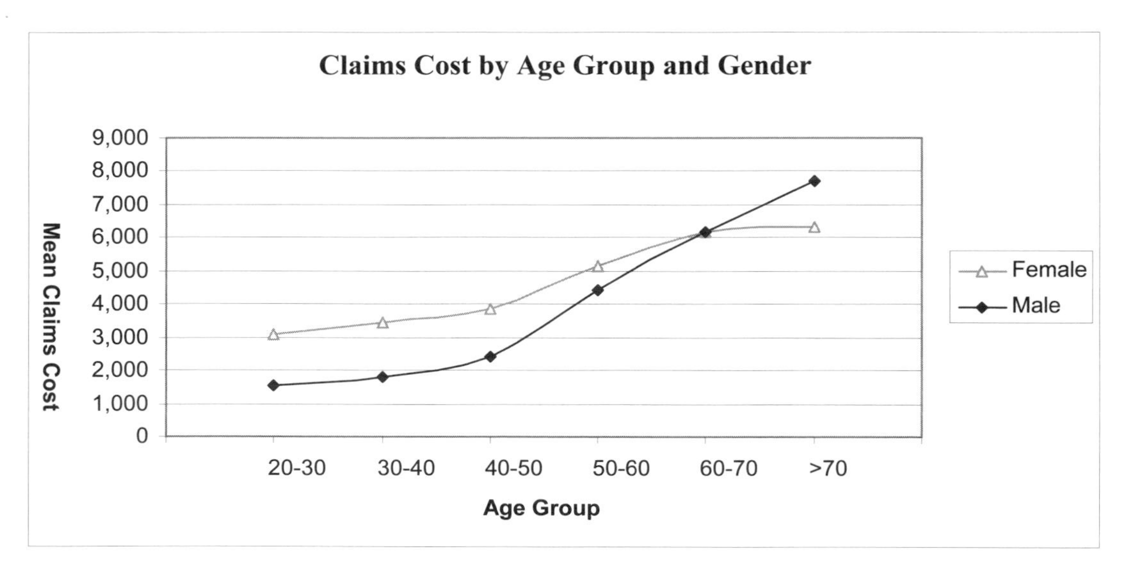

FIGURE 15.1

TABLE 15.2

Mean Claim Costs (April 2006-March 2007) by Gender			
	All	Males	Females
# Members	18,610	8,576	10,034
Mean Cost	$ 3,586	$ 2,974	$ 4,109

Three versions of models were developed with different explanatory variables:

1. DxCG prospective Med+Rx risk only;
2. DxCG prospective Med+Rx risk and HRA variables;
3. HRA variables only.

Appendix 15.1 contains a brief description of the DxCG model and the construction and use of DxCG prospective risk scores. Model 1 was used as a benchmark to compare performance of models 2 and 3 and thereby estimate the value of Health Risk Assessment attributes. Coefficients of the linear model explaining claim costs are used to quantify costs and changes in costs associated with HRA risk factor variables. We chose to exclude HRA variables showing general quality of health and work days missed due to health reasons in order to allow more specific HRA variables to enter the models.

For model development, each HRA variable was considered for inclusion. We first determined the range over which a meaningful relationship with claims cost exists. For variables for which the response was missing, we assigned a value. Many HRA variables take discrete values (e.g. 1-5 (less confident to more confident)). Numeric values were assigned to these variables in order to develop the model. A stepwise regression model approach (Hocking [96]) was used to first identify the subset of variables to consider for the model and then the best model was identified in an iterative process to reduce multi-collinearity among final variables in the model.

15.2.4 Results

Male Cost Models

The baseline cost model with DxCG prospective Med+Rx risk as the only explanatory variable had a squared correlation coefficient (R^2) of 0.1124. The R^2 for the model including Health Risk Attributes is 0.145 (29% improvement). As expected, the most important variable explaining cost is the DxCG prospective Med+Rx risk score. HRA variables at the 0.01 level of significance include a binary variable that flags the member's personal disease history for the high-cost conditions of Congestive Heart Failure (CHF), Osteoporosis, Angina, TIA (mini-stroke lasting less than 24 hours); and the body mass index (BMI) of the member. Care was taken to limit binary variables of existing conditions to those that were relatively uncorrelated with other HRA attributes. Other personal history variables such as high blood pressure, presence of diabetes and obesity were excluded. The personal history HRA variables that were kept are relatively rare (and are therefore determined to add incremental value over the DxCG risk score) and also relatively uncorrelated with other HRA variables such as exercise, stress, nutrition variables. Overall collinearity was reduced by keeping the Condition index below 30 and the variance inflation factor below 3.

Other variables at the less than 0.05 level of significance come from the health risk attributes of Immunizations and Health Screening, Stress and Well-Being, Tobacco Use, Physical Activity, Nutrition and Family Disease History. The model parameter estimates are shown in Table 15.4. All variables have signs (positive/negative) consistent with their expected impact on health care cost. The range of values that the variables can take, their mean values and the contribution of each variable to predicted cost at the mean value is also shown to aid in the interpretation of the model.

Interpretation of the Male Prospective Risk + HRA model (Table 15.3): the mean male cost is $2,974. The model intercept has a value of $4,297, implying that many members will experience reductions in cost due to the presence or absence of the risk factors. Each member's DxCG prospective risk score is multiplied by the parameter estimate, 1,865; presence of a personal or family history of the targeted diseases also raises cost. Costs are reduced by stress management, smoking cessation, physical activity and eating fruit. Somewhat counter-intuitively, the presence of a member health screening or immunization also indicates higher than average costs, possibly reflecting the fact that higher-risk members are more likely to undergo these services.

In the third male cost model using HRA variables only (Table 15.4), we excluded prospective risk in order to allow more HRA variables to enter the model. Here we create a model that can be applied by users who have access to HRA data but not risk-scores. As a result, additional variables, such as existing personal/family disease history, health screening and immunizations appear in the model. Interestingly, the value of the Personal Disease History variable in the HRA-only model is approximately equal to the sum of the DxCG Prospective Risk and Personal History variables in the Risk Score and HRA model (Table 15.3). The squared correlation coefficient (R^2) of this model is 0.079.

Some of the HRA model variables are similar to those in the Male Prospective Risk + HRA model. Variables reducing the member's cost are physical activity and the use of skin protection. The personal health history variable also reduces the cost, indicating the absence of any major disease.

TABLE 15.3

Male Cost Model Based on Prospective Risk and HRA Variables

Attribute	Variable	Coeffi-cient	*Pr* > | *t* |	Range of variable	Mean Variable	Contribution to predicted cost at mean value
	Intercept	4,297	0.001	1	1.00	4,297
Risk	DxCG prospective Med+Rx risk	1,865	<.0001	0.16-7	1.36	2,529
Personal Disease History 1	Congestive Heart Failure (CHF), Osteoporosis, Angina, TIA (mini-stroke lasting less than 24 hrs)	9,231	<.0001	0 (No), 1 (Yes)	0.02	157
Weight Manage-ment	BMI group	374	<.0001	1 (< 25), 2 (25-29.99), 3 (30-34.99), 4 (35-39.99), 7 (> 40, no value)	2.29	856
Immuni-zations	Pneumonia	973	0.0019	0 (No),1 (Yes)	0.18	174
Stress and Well-Being	Please rate how confident[4] you are that you can practice stress management techniques consistently.	(553)	0.0065	1-3. No value=3	2.66	(1,473)
Stress and Well-Being	In the last month, how often have you felt difficulties were piling up so high that you could not overcome them?	285	0.0157	1 (Never), 2 (Almost Never), 3 (Sometimes, No value), 4 (Fairly Often), 5 (Very Often)	2.12	604
Tobacco	Please rate how confident you are that you can keep from smoking cigarettes when you feel bored.	(447)	0.0176	1-5, No value=4.5	4.34	(1,937)
Physical Activity	Low-intensity physical activity – days per week	(293)	0.0245	5-7, No value=5	5.70	(1,668)
Nutrition	On a typical day, how many servings of fruit do you eat?	(373)	0.0353	1 (None, no value) 2 (one) 3 (two plus)	2.12	(790)
Family Disease History	Has anyone in your immediate family (father, mother, brother, sister) been diagnosed with Colorectal Cancer	1,134	0.0433	0 (No) 1 (Yes)	0.05	55
Health Screen-ings	Have you had a Clinical Skin Exam by a health care provider within the last 12 months?	545	0.0466	0 (No) 1 (Yes)	0.26	144

[4] All variables rating confidence have responses from 1-5 which denote less confidence to more confidence.

TABLE 15.4

Male Cost Model Based On HRA Variables Only

Attribute	Variable	Coefficient	$Pr > \|t\|$	Range of variable	Mean variable	Contribution to predicted cost at mean value
Intercept		2,579	0.0069	1	1.00	2,579
Personal Disease History 1	Have you ever been diagnosed with any of the following: Congestive Heart Failure (CHF), Osteoporosis, Angina, TIA (mini-stroke lasting less than 24 hrs)	11,945	<.0001	0 (No) 1 (Yes)	0.02	203
Weight Management	BMI group	529	<.0001	1 (< 25), 2 (25-29.99) 3 (30-34.99) 4 (35-39.99) 7 (> 40, no value)	2.29	1,210
Tests	Have you had a PSA Test (prostate specific antigen) within the last 12 months?	1,146	<.0001	0 (No) 1 (Yes)	0.32	370
Immunizations	Pneumonia	1,377	<.0001	0 (No) 1 (Yes)	0.18	247
Personal Disease History 2	Have you never been diagnosed with any of the following: list of 27 major conditions (included in above personal history variables as well)[5]	(1,108)	0.0003	0 (No) 1 (Yes)	0.22	(248)
Stress and Well-Being	In the last month, how often have you felt difficulties were piling up so high that you could not overcome them?	408	0.0007	1 (Never) 2 (Amost Never) 3 Sometimes, No value), 4 (Fairly Often), 5 (Very Often)	2.12	865
Physical Activity	Low-intensity physical activity - days per week	(392)	0.0038	5-7, No value=5	5.70	(2,232)
Health Screenings	Influenza (flu) within the last 12 months?	714	0.0079	0 (No) 1 (Yes)	0.35	249
Health Screenings	Have you had a Clinical Skin Exam by a health care provider within the last 12 months?	793	0.0074	0 (No) 1 (Yes)	0.26	210
Nutrition	Do you for any reason NOT eat foods from one or more of the following groups: Grains, Nuts, Dairy, Seeds, Eggs	795	0.0239	0 (No) 1 (Yes)	0.15	121
Personal Disease History 3	Have you ever been diagnosed with any of the following: Stroke, Peripheral Vascular Disease, Colorectal, Emphysema	2,588	0.0383	0 (No) 1 (Yes)	0.01	22
Family Disease History	Has anyone in your immediate family (father, mother, brother, sister) been diagnosed with Colorectal Cancer	1,185	0.0423	0 (No) 1 (Yes)	0.05	58
Skin Protection	Please rate how confident you are that you can consistently use sunscreen when exposed to the sun for more than 15 minutes?	(228)	0.0133	1-5,9 No value=9	2.92	(664)

[5] Angina, Asthma, Breast Cancer, Coronary Artery Disease, Congestive Heart Failure, Cervical Cancer, Chronic Bronchitis, Colorectal Cancer, Diabetes, Emphysema, Heart Attack, High Blood Pressure, Hepatitis B, High Blood Sugar, High Cholesterol, Other Heart Disease, Obesity, Osteoporosis, Peripheral Vascular Disease, Prostate Cancer, Sexually-transmitted disease, Skin Cancer, Stroke, TIA (mini-stroke lasting less than 24 hours), Back Pain, Chronic Obstructive Pulmonary Disease (COPD), Depression.

The precise impact on a member's cost depends on the values of the HRA variables as shown in Table 15.5. We use estimates from this model to quantify the impact of Health Risk Assessment variables on cost and show the cost associated with each value that the variable can take.

TABLE 15.5

Impact of HRA attributes on Male Health Care Cost

Attribute	Variable	Values	Cost Impact ($)
	Intercept	1	2,579
Personal Disease History 1	Have you ever been diagnosed with any of the following: Congestive Heart Failure (CHF), Osteoporosis, Angina, TIA (mini-stroke lasting less than 24 hrs)	0 (No) 1(Yes)	– 11,945
Weight Management	BMI group	1 (< 25) 2 (25-29.99) 3 (30-34.99) 4 (35-39.99) 5 (> 40, no value)	529 1,057 1,586 2,114 3,700
Immunizations	Have you had a PSA Test (prostate specific antigen) within the last 12 months?	0 (No) 1 (Yes)	– 1,146
Immunizations	Pneumonia	0 (No) 1 (Yes)	– 1,377
Personal Disease History 2	Have you never been diagnosed with any of the following: list of 27 major conditions (included in above personal history variables as well)	0 (No) 1 (Yes)	– (1,108)
Stress and Well-Being	In the last month, how often have you felt difficulties were piling up so high that you could not overcome them?	1 (Never) 2 (Almost Never) 3(Sometimes, 0 value) 4 (Fairly Often) 7 (Very Often)	408 816 1,225 1,633 2,858
Physical Activity	Low-intensity physical activity - days per week	< = 5 6 7	(1,958) (2,350) (2,741)
Health Screenings	Influenza (flu) within the last 12 months?	0 (No) 1 (Yes)	– 714
Health Screenings	Have you had a Clinical Skin Exam by a health care provider within the last 12 months?	0 (No) 1 (Yes)	– 793
Nutrition	Do you for any reason NOT eat foods from one or more of the following groups: Grains, Nuts, Dairy, Seeds, Eggs	0 (No) 1 (Yes)	– 795
Personal Disease History 3	Have you ever been diagnosed with any of the following: Stroke, Peripheral Vascular Disease, Colorectal, Emphysema	0 (No) 1 (Yes)	– 2,588
Family Disease History	Has anyone in your immediate family (father, mother, brother, sister) been diagnosed with Colorectal Cancer	0 (No) 1 (Yes)	– 1,185
Skin Protection	Please rate how confident you are that you can consistently use sunscreen when exposed to the sun for more than 15 minutes?	1 (Not at all confident) 2 (Not confident) 3 (Fairly confident) 4 (Confident) 5 (Very Confident) 9 (No Value)	(228) (455) (683) (910) (1,138) (2,048)

The predicted cost for a male can thus be obtained by aggregating the cost associated with that person's response for each of the above HRA attributes.

Female Cost Models

The baseline cost model with only DxCG prospective Med+Rx risk as the explanatory variable had a squared correlation coefficient (R^2) of 0.1491. The inclusion of Health Risk Attributes raises the squared correlation coefficient (R^2) to 0.173 (15.8% improvement). Here again, the most important variable explaining cost is the DxCG prospective Med+Rx risk score as would be expected. A binary variable that flagged the member's personal disease history of rare but high cost conditions of Chronic Obstructive Pulmonary Disease (COPD), Congestive Heart Failure (CHF), Coronary Heart Disease (CHD), Peripheral Vascular Disease (PVD) and Stroke is the next most important variable. Other variables include Immunizations and health screening, Stress and Well-Being and Physical Activity. Unlike the male model, the body mass index (BMI) of the member is not significant. Instead, an indicator showing the female's pregnancy status and intention (whether planning to become pregnant in the next six months) impacts prospective cost. The model parameter estimates are shown below in Table 15.6. All variables have signs (positive/negative) consistent with their expected impact on Health Care cost.

TABLE 15.6

Female Cost Model on Prospective Risk and HRA Variables

Attribute	Variable	Coefficient	$Pr > \|t\|$	Range of variable	Mean variable	Contrib. to predicted cost at mean value
Intercept		461	0.4202	1	1.00	461
Risk	DxCG prospective Med+Rx risk	2,001	<.0001	0.4-7	1.75	3,505
Personal Disease History	Chronic Obstructive Pulmonary Disease (COPD), Congestive Heart Failure (CHF), Coronary Heart Disease (CHD), Peripheral Vascular Disease (PVD) and Stroke	8,141	<.0001	0 (No),1 (Yes)	0.01	97
Health Screenings	Have you had a SIGMOIDOSCOPY within the last 5 years? (tube inserted in rectum to check for lower intestine problems)	966	0.0005	0 (No),1 (Yes)	0.18	176
Health Screenings	Influenza (flu) within the last 12 months?	737	0.0007	0 (No),1 (Yes)	0.39	284
Physical Activity	Moderate-intensity physical activity - days per week	(449)	0.0024	0 (0,no value), 1 (1-4), 2 (5-7)	0.93	(417)
Immunizations	Pneumonia	677	0.0192	0 (No),1 (Yes)	0.16	109
Stress and Well-Being	Please rate how confident you are that you can find support for the changes you are making.	(514)	0.022	-1 (no value), 1-2	1.88	(965)
Stress and Well-Being	In the last month, how often have you been angered because of things that happened that were outside your control?	1,042	0.0284	0 (Never, Almost Never, Sometimes, Fairly Often), 1 (Very Often, No Value)	0.05	56
Stress and Well-Being	Please rate how confident you are that if you decided to get help for depression you could find a caring professional to talk with.	104	0.0308	1-5, 10 (no value)	4.48	465

TABLE 15.6 (Continued)

Attribute	Variable	Coefficient	$Pr > \|t\|$	Range of variable	Mean variable	Contribution to predicted cost at mean value
Physical Activity	HIGH intensity activities (hours per week):	(268)	0.0356	0-3, no value=0	0.34	(92)
Women's Health	Select the appropriate answer regarding pregnancy status/plan	391	0.0627	1 (Not planning), 2 (No Value), 3 (Planning) 4 (Pregnant)	1.13	443

In the third female cost model, we excluded prospective risk in order to allow more HRA variables to enter the model. As a result, the model includes more existing personal/family disease history variables. Health screening and immunizations, body mass index, skin protection, nutrition and tobacco consumption are also significant in the model. The squared correlation coefficient (R^2) of this model is 0.089.

TABLE 15.7

Female Cost Model Based On HRA Variables Only

Attribute	Variable	Coefficient	$Pr > \|t\|$	Range of variable	Mean variable	Contrib. to predicted cost at mean value
	Intercept	190	0.83	1	1	190
Personal Disease History	Chronic Obstructive Pulmonary Disease (COPD), Congestive Heart Failure (CHF), Coronary Heart Disease (CHD), Peripheral Vascular Disease (PVD) and Stroke	10,553	<.0001	0 (No), 1 (Yes)	0.01	126
Health Screenings	Have you had a SIGMOIDOSCOPY within the last 5 years? (tube inserted in rectum to check for lower intestine problems)	2,045	<.0001	0 (No), 1 (Yes)	0.18	372
Weight Mgt	Body Mass Index	118	<.0001	26-45, no value=40	29.61	3,495
Health Screenings	Influenza (flu) within the last 12 months?	1,176	<.0001	0 (No), 1 (Yes)	0.39	453
Personal Disease History	Have you never been diagnosed with any of the following: list of 27 major conditions (included in above personal history variables as well)	(1,220)	<.0001	0 (No), 1 (Yes)	0.19	(230)
Personal Disease History	TIA (mini-stroke lasting less than 24 hrs), Heart Attack, Angina, Breast Cancer, Emphysema	2,589	<.0001	0 (No), 1 (Yes)	0.03	77
Immunizations	Pneumonia	1,118	0.00	0 (No), 1 (Yes)	0.16	180
Physical Activity	Moderate-intensity physical activity - minutes per day	(46)	0.00	0-20	13.49	(617)
Stress and Well-Being	In the last month, how often have you been angered because of things that happened that were outside your control?	1,632	0.00	0 (Never, Almost Never, Sometimes, Fairly Often), 1 (Very Often, No Value)	0.05	87
Skin Protection	Please rate how confident you are that you can have your skin checked by a doctor once a year?	224	0.00	1-5,7 No value=7	3.11	695

TABLE 15.7 (Continued)

Attribute	Variable	Coeffi-cient	*Pr* > |*t*|	Range of variable	Mean variable	Contrib. to predicted cost at mean value
Women's Health	Are you currently on hormone replacement therapy (Estrogen Therapy, Premarin) or planning to start?	999	0.00	0 (No),1 (Yes)	0.11	106
Women's Health	Select the appropriate answer regarding pregnancy status/plan	590	0.01	1 (Not planning), 2 (No Value), 3 (Planning) 4 (Pregnant)	1.13	668
Physical Activity	HIGH intensity activities? (hours per week)	(306)	0.02	0-3, No value=0	0.34	(104)
Nutrition	On a typical day, how many servings do you eat of whole grain or enriched bread, cereal, rice, and pasta?	(868)	0.03	0 (None, No Value) 1 (1, 3, 4, 5), 2 (6+)	0.99	(859)
Tobacco	Please rate how confident you are that you can keep from smoking cigarettes when you feel you need a lift.	(294)	0.06	1 (Not at all confident) 2 (Not confident), 3(Fairly confident), 4(Confident) 0 Value =1.5	1.74	(511)

We use estimates from the above model to quantify the impact of Health Risk Assessment variables on cost in Table 15.8. We show minimum and maximum ranges for continuous variables within which the change in cost due to a one-unit change in the variable is the parameter estimate. For discrete variables that take a limited set of values, we show the cost associated with each value that the variable can take.

TABLE 15.8

Impact of HRA Attributes on Female Health Care Cost			
Attribute	**Variable**	**Values**	**Cost Impact**
	Intercept	1	190
Personal Disease History 1	Chronic Obstructive Pulmonary Disease (COPD), Congestive Heart Failure (CHF), Coronary Heart Disease (CHD), Peripheral Vascular Disease (PVD) and Stroke	0 (No) 1 (Yes)	– 10,553
Health Screenings	Have you had a SIGMOIDOSCOPY within the last 5 years? (tube inserted in rectum to check for lower intestine problems)	0 (No) 1 (Yes)	– 2,045
Weight Management	Body Mass Index	26 (Min) 40 (No Value) 45 (Max)	3,069 4,722 5,312
Health Screenings	Influenza (flu) within the last 12 months?	0 (No) 1 (Yes)	– 1,176
Personal Disease History 2	Have you never been diagnosed with any of the following: list of 27 major conditions (included in above personal history variables as well)	0 (No) 1 (Yes)	– (1,220)
Personal Disease History 3	TIA (mini-stroke lasting less than 24 hrs), Heart Attack, Angina, Breast Cancer, Emphysema	0 (No) 1 (Yes)	– 2,589
Immunizations	Pneumonia	0 (No) 1 (Yes)	– 1,118

TABLE 15.7 (Continued)

Attribute	Variable	Values	Cost Impact
Physical Activity 1	Moderate-intensity physical activity - minutes per day	20 (Max) 0 (Min, No Value)	– (915)
Stress and Well-Being	In the last month, how often have you been angered because of things that happened that were outside your control?	0 (Never, Almost Never, Sometimes, Fairly Often) 1 (Very Often, No Value)	– 1,632
Skin Protection	Please rate how confident you are that you can have your skin checked by a doctor once a year?	1 (Not at all confident) 2 (Not confident) 3 (Fairly confident) 4 (Confident) 5 (Very Confident) 7 (No Value)	224 447 671 894 1,118 1,565
Women's Health 1	Are you currently on hormone replacement therapy (Estrogen Therapy, Premarin) or planning to start?	0 (No) 1 (Yes)	– 999
Women's Health 2	Select the appropriate answer regarding pregnancy status/plan	1 (Not Planning (I am not planning on becoming pregnant in the next 6 months.)) 2 (No Value) 3 (Planning (I am planning on becoming pregnant in the next 6 months.)) 4 (Pregnant (Currently pregnant))	590 1,181 1,771 2,361
Physical Activity 2	HIGH intensity activities? (hours per week)	0 (Min, No Value) 3 (Max)	– (917)
Nutrition	On a typical day, how many servings do you eat of whole grain or enriched bread, cereal, rice, and pasta?	0 (None, No Value) 1 (1, 3, 4, 5) 2 (6+)	– (868) (1,736)
Tobacco	Please rate how confident you are that you can keep from smoking cigarettes when you feel you need a lift.	1 (Not at all confident) 1.5 (No Value) 2 (Not confident) 3 (Fairly confident) 4 (Confident)	(294) (441) (588) (883) (1,177)

The predicted cost for a female can be obtained by aggregating the cost associated with that person's response for each of the above HRA attributes. Note that there is a large negative factor associated with not having any major diagnosis in the past which will impact the majority of females.

To summarize results, the ability to predict health care costs with reasonable accuracy, as measured by the squared correlation coefficients (R^2) of the linear models improves by at least 15% with the inclusion of HRA attributes.

TABLE 15.9

R^2 of Linear Models to Predict Claims Cost		
Model	Male	Female
1) DxG prospective risk only	0.112	0.149
2) DxG prospective risk & HRA	0.145	0.173
3) HRA risk factors only	0.079	0.089
Improvement of 1 over 3	43%	68%
Improvement of 2 over 1	29%	16%

Conclusions

Although HRA attributes on their own do not match the performance of the DxCG prospective Med+Rx risk-only model, including HRA attributes improves the ability to predict cost. We are able to identify the health risk attributes that impact cost over and above the DxCG prospective Med+Rx risk and estimate the cost associated with each of these attributes. The model can also be used to rank-order members by cost to target them for preventive care and use the drivers of cost to determine the strategy of treatment.

15.3 PART 2: USE OF THE MODEL FOR INTERVENTION PROGRAM PLANNING

Predicting costs associated with different risk factors allows for the assessment of patient opportunity as a first step in program design. We illustrate use of the female model's risk factors from Table 15.8, showing an example of two female members in Table 15.10. For each member, we show initial values of variables and predicted cost, followed by assumed values, predicted costs and resulting savings as a result of an intervention program. The model variables are listed below based on our ability to impact them positively by intervention. Personal and Family Disease history, Immunizations and Health Screenings reflect conditions and risk factors that are unlikely to change and are not, therefore, susceptible to management by a wellness programs. We therefore focus instead on variables that we can change with a management program. The initial predicted cost for both members A and B is approximately $8,000, relatively high compared with the median female cost. To estimate the potential savings, we are limited to considering improvement in only the manageable variables. While member A has higher-than-average predicted costs driven primarily by high BMI and stress levels, that of member B is high because of BMI, a skin condition, smoking habit and unbalanced diet (no grains). For member A, controlling anger (reducing stress), reducing BMI and increasing moderate exercise will potentially decrease predicted cost by $3,305 with potential savings indicated by values shown in the table. For member B, reducing BMI, improving nutrition and ceasing smoking will decrease predicted costs by less ($2,377) since her levels of other variables (moderate exercise and stress management) indicate a reasonable degree of management. Since "confidence" (in the patient's ability to navigate the healthcare system, direct her own care and to have skin checked by a doctor once a year) is likely to be higher for those with skin problems, we are unlikely to see a reduction in cost due to this variable in the short term (this variable captures the fact that those with skin problems are likely to be higher cost. We will see a reduction in the value for this variable (confidence to get skin checked annually) only in the long term when the skin treatments effect is realized.)

In both cases, the potential for savings if all the above changes are made is sufficiently high to justify extending a management program to these members, and continuing follow-up to ensure that improvement is made and sustained.

The principles of Chapter 5, the economics of care management programs, may be applied in wellness programs as well.

TABLE 15.10

Pre & Post Intervention Costs – Example of Two Female members

		Member A					Member B				
		Initial		Post-Intervention Predictions			Initial		Post-Intervention Predictions		
Variable	Coef-ficient	Values	Pre-dicted Cost	Values	Pre-dicted Cost	Savings	Values	Pre-dicted Cost	Values	Pre-dicted Cost	Savings
1 Intercept	190	1	190	1	190	–	1	190	1	190	–
2 COPD,CHF, CHD, PCD or Stroke	10,553	0 (No)	–	0 (No)	–	–	0 (No)	–	0 (No)	–	–
3 Sigmoidoscopy within the last 5 years?	2,045	1 (Yes)	2,045	1 (Yes)	2,045	–	1 (Yes)	2,045	1 (Yes)	2,045	–
4 Influenza in last 12 months?	1,176	1 (Yes)	1,176	1 (Yes)	1,176	–	1 (Yes)	1,176	1 (Yes)	1,176	–
5 Never diagnosed any of 27 major conditions?	(1,220)	0 (No)	–	0 (No)	–	–	0 (No)	–	0 (No)	–	–
6 TIA , HA, Angina, Breast Cancer, Emphysema	2,589	0 (No)	–	0 (No)	–	–	0 (No)	–	0 (No)	–	–
7 Pneumonia	1,118	0 (No)	–	0 (No)	–	–	0 (No)	–	0 (No)	–	–
8 Currently/planning hormone replacement therapy?	999	0 (No)	–	0 (No)	–	–	0 (No)	–	0 (No)	–	–
9 Pregnancy status/plan	590	1 (No plan)	590	1 (No plan)	590	–	1 (No plan)	590	1 (No plan)	590	–
10 Body Mass Index	118	35	4,132	26	3,069	(1,062)	35	4,132	26	3,069	(1,062)
11 Moderate intensity exercise-min. per day	(46)	0	–	10	(458)	(458)	20	(915)	20	(915)	–
12 In the last month, how often angered?	1,632	1 (V. Often)	1,632	0 (Fairly Often)	–	(1,632)	0 (Sometimes)	–	0 (Sometimes)	–	–
13 Rate confidence on annual skin check	224	1 (Not at all confid)	224	1 (Not at all confid)	224	–	5 (V. Confid)	1,118	5 (V. Confid)	1,118	–
14 High intensity activities? (hrs per week)	(306)	0	–	0.5	(153)	(153)	0	–	0.5	(153)	(153)
15 Servings of grain per day?	(868)	1 (1, 3)	(868)	1 (4, 5)	(868)	–	0 (None)	–	1 (1,3)	(868)	(868)
16 Rate confidence to not smoke when blue	(294)	4 (Confid)	(1,177)	4	(1,177)	–	1 (Not at all conf)	(294)	2 (Not Confid)	(588)	(294)
Prediction			$ 7,944		$ 4,639	$ (3,305)		$ 8,042		$ 5,665	$ (2,377)

15.4 PART 3: USING THE MODEL FOR SAVINGS ESTIMATION

As an example of the application of the methodology for savings estimation, we use the female HRA-only model to develop savings based on the model parameters. Part 2 showed how to identify the type of intervention likely to economically justify intervention programs at the individual member level. We show overall savings at a program level associated with improvement in variables through interventions that lead individuals to less risky behavior. Personal and Family Disease history, Immunizations and Health Screenings reflect conditions that are unlikely to change and cannot be impacted. We focus on variables that we can influence favorably and accordingly, model variables are listed based on our ability to impact them positively by intervention. In Table 15.11 we illustrate the use of the model coefficients to estimate savings based on measurable improvements in manageable variables. If intervention can influence members to reduce risky behavior (by shifting higher risk members to lower risk categories), and thereby change the mean variable value, the coefficient for the variable can be used to quantify the cost savings achieved due to the intervention. Assuming 100 female members in this program, the initial predicted cost is $412,821 (column f) total based on cost coefficient (column c) and initial mean values (column d) from Table 15.7. Improving mean values of variables (to levels in column e) will result in cost savings of $34,256, or a cost reduction of 8%.

TABLE 15.11

Savings Estimation Based on Female HRA only model

Attribute	Variable	Cost Coefficient (Table15.7)	Mean Variable (Baseline) (Table 15.7)	Mean Variable (Post Intervention)	Cost (Baseline)	Cost Improvement
(a)	**(b)**	**(c)**	**(d)**	**(e)**	**(f)**	**(g)**
Weight Management	Body Mass Index	$118	29.61	28.00	$349,521	$(18,981)
Physical Activity	Moderate-intensity physical activity - minutes per day	(46)	13.49	15.00	(61,736)	(6,905)
Stress and Well-Being	In the last month, how often have you been angered?	1,632	0.05	0.04	8,700	(2,196)
Physical Activity	High intensity activities? (hours per week)	(306)	0.34	0.50	(10,450)	(4,835)
Nutrition	Servings of grain per day?	(868)	0.99	1.00	(85,937)	(1,220)
Tobacco	Rate confidence to avoid smoking when blue	(294)	1.74	1.74	(51,089)	(120)
All other variables (in table 8)					263,812	-
TOTAL					$412,821	$(34,256)

15.5 APPLICATION TO OTHER PROGRAMS AND SITUATIONS

As with any other model, our estimates should be treated with caution because of the low correlation coefficients in the models.

While the data presented here are from a specific HRA applied to members of a particular commercial health plan, we believe that the results have some general applicability and can be used to design programs and evaluate program outcomes for a variety of situations. We have provided underlying population cost data in Table 15.1 that may be used to adjust the savings estimates, based on comparable costs for the population being assessed. Ultimately, the methods described here are practical and may be applied by anyone who wishes to design or evaluate wellness programs.

APPENDIX 15.1 RISK SCORES AND THEIR USE IN OUR MODELS[6]

The underlying model is built using DxCG's prospective risk scores. These scores are calculated by applying certain grouper rules to the diagnosis codes inherent in member claims data. The rules, created specifically for the particular model (in this case, DxCG) group together subsets of the 15,000 + diagnosis codes (ICD-9 codes) into clinically-similar categories, further detailed below. The clinically-similar groupings then become condition categories used as explanatory variables in a multiple regression model whose result is a set of coefficients, or weights, that reproduce the claims of the population.

DxCG's Clinical Classification System

Diagnosis codes are the basis for the clinical mapping and grouping of health conditions. DxCG's software processes all diagnoses for an individual in order to identify the presence of one or more of 784 DxGroups which group clinically related ICD-9-CM codes, and as such, are clinically homogeneous (e.g., cardiomyopathy/ myocarditis). These groups are then further collapsed into 184 higher-level clinical groupings called Condition Categories (CCs). CCs are groups of financially-related DxGroups that imply similar levels of resource use. Individuals may have multiple DxGroups or CCs. CCs are organized by body system or disease (e.g., Congestive Heart Failure). An example is shown below.

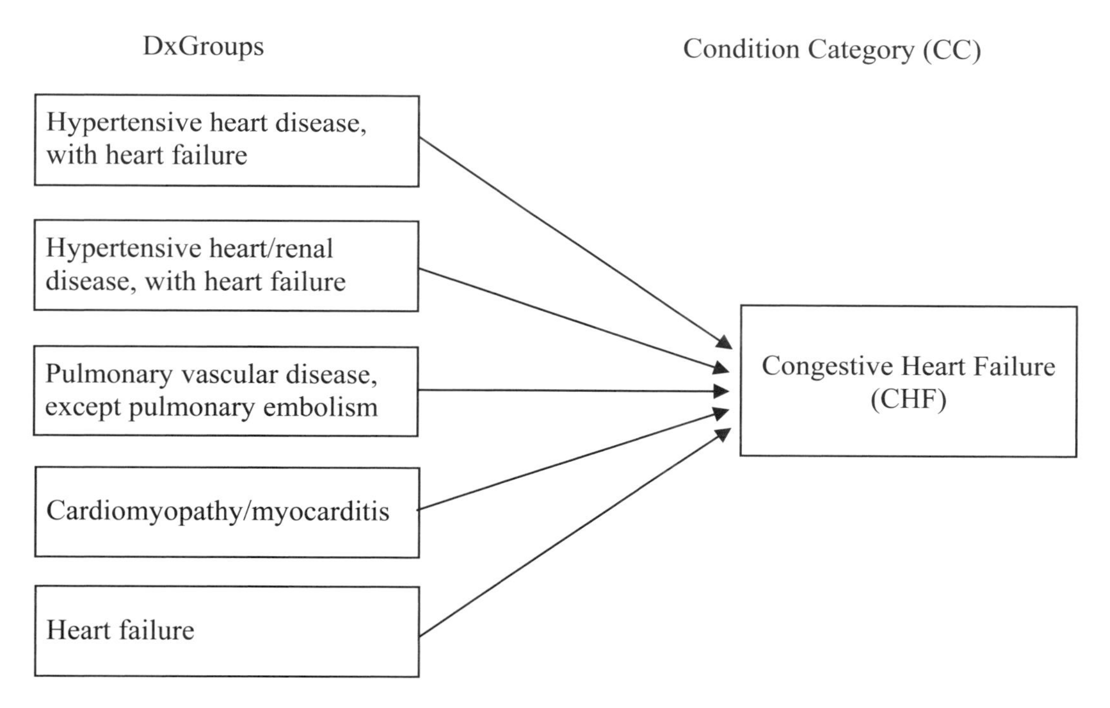

DxCG's system then imposes hierarchies on sets of related CCs to rank clinically similar CCs in order of severity. In a hierarchical scheme for a related set of CCs, lower severity conditions are less costly than more complex conditions. There are 31 sets of hierarchies in the

[6] Vincent Kane FSA, MAAA and Anju Joglekar PhD of DxCG Inc. contributed to this Appendix.

DxCG system, which create 184 Hierarchical Condition Categories (HCCs). An example of such a hierarchy follows.

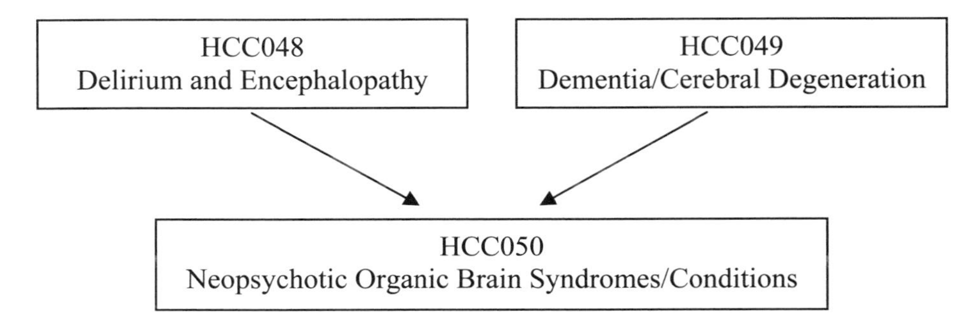

HCCs are the building blocks used in core models to make predictions. Imposing hierarchies improves the statistical precision of the estimated parameters within DxCG models. The imposition of clinical hierarchies also decreases the model's sensitivity to coding idiosyncrasies.

When more than one (related) condition category is present in a patient record, the hierarchy will assign a zero coefficient to the less-severe condition, if connected along the same hierarchical path. An example of a simple model is shown below.

TABLE 15.A

Condition Category	Risk Score Contribution	Notes
Diabetes with No or Unspecified Complications	0.0	Trumped by Diabetes with Renal Manifestation
Diabetes with Renal Manifestation	2.1	
Hypertension	0.0	Trumped by CHF
Congestive Heart Failure (CHF)	1.5	
Drug/Alcohol Dependence	0.6	
Age-Sex	0.4	
Total Risk Score	**4.6**	

In the example above, there are two areas where the patient is identified with two different Condition Categories within the same disease hierarchy: 1. Diabetes, and the more severe condition, Diabetes with renal manifestation, and 2. Hypertension, and the more severe form of heart disease, Congestive Heart Failure (CHF). The model assigns coefficients only to the higher-severity conditions, resulting in no double-counting when the overall patient risk is calculated as the sum of individual Condition Category coefficients.

The highest-level clinical grouping in the DxCG system is the Aggregated Condition Category (ACC). There are 30 ACCs which organize condition categories into body systems (e.g., ACC for Liver includes CCs for end stage liver disease, cirrhosis of liver, chronic hepatitis and other liver related conditions). ACCs are not used in DxCG's predictive models but are mainly useful for high level population profiling and reporting.

TABLE 15.B

Summary of DxCG Grouping Levels

DxCG Grouping Level	Number of Groups	Application
ACC	30	Population profiling, reporting
CC	184	Clinical screening, reporting
HCC	184	Making predictions, clinical screening, reporting
DxGroup	784	Clinical screening, reporting

Development of Relative Risk Scores

The coefficients in the regression model represent the marginal contribution of each condition category to overall cost. As in the example (Table 15.A), the model has the following form:

$$C = \alpha + \sum_i \beta_i K_i$$

where:

α is the intercept (independent of explanatory variables);

K_i is the set of independent explanatory variables (age/sex buckets and condition categories);

β_i is the set of coefficients, or weights, that apply to the explanatory variables.

C is the dependent variable, in the case of the DxCG model, usually a claims cost number.

The expected marginal dollar contribution for each condition category is then adjusted to a "relative risk score" component by dividing by the average claims for the entire population, including members with no claims during the year. A smoothing process occurs to ensure that relative risk score components are consistent with their clinical interpretation. The resulting model is additive by age/sex and condition category. Relative risk score weights are summed across all the member's conditions to arrive at the total relative risk score.

There are two major types of DxCG models: concurrent and prospective. The concurrent (also called retrospective) model is used to reproduce actual historical costs. For the purpose of the model discussed in this chapter, the prospective model is used because future costs are predicted. For prospective prediction, members with no claims receive a relative risk score component based on age/sex alone.

For our models, we use a relative risk score by individual plan member. The relative risk score is generated by applying the coefficients of the model to a claims database which has first been run through a grouper process to identify the condition categories present in the population. Prospective relative risk score values may range from close to 0.0 to over 200 times the average cost. In our applications, we observed risk scores in a range between 0.0 and 10.0, with a median value around 1.5.

Our single variable models are based on the single variable, risk score. Our models that combine HRA and risk score values include the risk score, together with the independent HRA variables.

PART 5

CONCLUSION

16 Post-Script

16.1 Introduction

The preceding chapters about care management interventions and their implications for actuaries are analytical, objective and based on research. This, the final chapter, gives me an opportunity to make some personal reflections on the state of care management evaluation.

16.2 Recent Developments in Care Management

16.2.1 Medicare Health Support

One important recent development in care management (although not directly in methodology) was the introduction in 2005 of the Medicare Health Support (MHS) program. This program applies to Medicare fee-for-service members with diabetes and/or heart failure. Section 721 of the Medicare Modernization Act of 2003 (MMA) (the same act that brought us Medicare Part D coverage for prescription drugs and expanded accessibility to health savings accounts) authorized development and testing of voluntary chronic care improvement programs, now called Medicare Health Support, to improve the quality of care and life for people living with multiple chronic illnesses. The Centers for Medicare and Medicaid Services (CMS) awarded eight different programs to disease managers in different regions. Three vendors have subsequently withdrawn from the program, and CMS has reduced the savings target from [Fees Plus 5% of Total Chronic Claims] to just fees (break-even). These developments, which imply that the enrollment and savings targets are not being met, are not particularly encouraging for the current models, and may lead to the development of new models in the future.

Assessment of the MHS program results involves a comparison of the managed population with a randomized control group. This program will finally provide the industry with the answers to two questions:

1. Does care management "work" (that is, produce a statistically-significant difference in financial and clinical results in the managed population)?

2. Potentially more important, how do the financial results measured by the randomized control methodology differ from results measured by a standard industry methodology (such as the actuarially-adjusted methodology described in Chapter 8)? While this comparative analysis is not part of the program, many researchers are anxiously awaiting the opportunity to perform just such a comparative analysis.

16.2.2 Plausibility of Results

Practitioners have also contributed to advances in outcomes measurement, although the techniques have not been published in the peer-reviewed literature. Al Lewis, president of the Disease Management Purchasing Consortium International, recommends the use of what he calls "Plausibility Factors". These factors are not a substitute for a calculation of savings, but rather, a method for testing for causality (See Chapter 7) that would make the calculated savings possible ("plausible"). Plausibility analysis requires the calculation of the following statistic (the plausibility factor) for the entire health plan:

$$\frac{\text{Disease-Specific Admissions/1000 (Program Year)}}{\text{Disease-Specific Admissions/1000 (Baseline Year)}}$$

The use and the limitations of utilization-based measures, however, need to be clearly understood. The methodology most-frequently encountered in DM evaluation is the adjusted historical control methodology. Work done by DMAA committees and other researchers in the industry has helped to codify the use of this methodology, and in particular, factors that need to be considered in order to ensure equivalence between the intervention and comparison populations.

Plausibility factors, being utilization-based, are a special case of the more general example of causality demonstration using changes in utilization. They deserve closer scrutiny, however, because they are being promoted, and are becoming accepted, as demonstrating validity. However, the factors themselves have never been subjected to the type of scrutiny that has been applied to calculation methodologies.

Use of Plausibility Factors

The theory of plausibility factor use is that they independently validate the measured financial results of a DM savings calculation, by demonstrating that utilization is reduced by the intervention, consistent with the financial measurement. Plausibility factors are generally utilization rates per 1,000 of the overall population for hospital admissions and emergency room visits for certain primary diagnoses. The primary diagnoses are: diabetes, coronary artery disease, chronic obstructive pulmonary disorder, heart failure and asthma. The proposed interpretation of the Plausibility measures is that if the savings calculation results in positive savings but the utilization-based measures do not, the savings are not validated. Rather than reconciling the two contradictory results, the Plausibility factors are so dispositive that their results always trump any other outcomes calculation.

How Valid is the Utilization-Based Calculation?

In order to be a valid test of the outcomes of a savings calculation, utilization-based measures must be calculated on the same basis as the savings. With Plausibility factors this is not the case. The Plausibility factors are a poor validator because:

1. In a DM evaluation, the measurement population is carefully constructed to consist of members with sufficient eligibility to be enrolled and managed by the program and to exclude members and conditions that may confound the calculation. As calculated the Plausibility factors bear only a tenuous relationship to the population being managed and measured. Their use implicitly assumes comparability between populations, but this comparability is not demonstrated.

2. Plausibility factors, because they apply to admissions and ER visits for primary diagnoses only, represent a very small percentage of all admissions and costs for chronic patients. For example, within a commercial population, these admissions and ER visits only account for 3% of the total claims costs for members with diabetes and the admissions only account for approximately 7 % of inpatient spend. Even a very successful program that avoided 25% of diabetes admissions could never demonstrate enough savings to warrant program costs under this methodology. Therefore, by definition, purchasers must be assuming that the program beneficially affects other utilization measures of the population. So failure to demonstrate reduction in the direct utilization measures does not necessarily imply lack of success with other types of utilization.

3. Plausibility factors do not take account of changes in population. Because the denominator is the entire population, a change in population size will change the measured rate of chronic admissions per 1000, independent of any impact of a DM program (positive or negative).

4. Plausibility factors do not take account of the risk profile of a population. It is entirely possible, for example, that a new group of relatively high-risk members may replace a relatively low-risk group, increasing the measured chronic admission rate per 1000.

5. The Plausibility factors take no account of volatility in admission rates.

6. The Plausibility factors, unlike the underlying adjusted historical control methodology, take no account of existing trends in the population. While admission trends are low (lower than overall trend) they are still non-zero. To understand this point, consider the following table which illustrates the actual trends in discharges per 1000 for selected chronic conditions for Medicare patients between 1998 and 2003. Over the 5-year period, the average trend in admissions for diabetes, heart conditions and COPD was low (but positive); syncope and renal failure experienced positive (and relatively large) trends, while the trend in bronchitis and asthma admissions was negative. Trends in individual years deviated from the average, indicating the volatility in admission rates per 1000.

TABLE 16.1

Medical Discharges per 1000 by Condition*

Year DRG	Diabetes 294	Renal Failure 316	Bronchitis & Asthma 096	COPD 088	Heart 132-144	Syncope 141-142
1998	2.214	2.455	1.597	10.254	17.954	3.283
1999	2.187	2.566	1.773	10.617	17.738	3.367
2000	2.280	2.768	1.470	9.925	18.744	3.608
2001	2.458	3.001	1.352	10.047	19.949	3.915
2002	2.516	3.174	1.428	10.275	19.682	4.089
2003	2.450	3.984	1.385	10.335	18.706	4.259
Annualized Trend	2.1%	10.2%	–2.8%	0.2%	0.8%	5.3%

*Actuarial Trend, i.e., per member per month

Towards a Unified Theory of Utilization Based Measurement

Tom Wilson [218] highlighted the importance of demonstrating a causal pathway for any savings calculation. The reduction in utilization is a powerful demonstration of causality. However, if we are going to use utilization measures to validate savings calculations we need to give them the same careful consideration that the industry has given the actual financial calculations in the past few years. Without it, the results of a utilization based demonstration could be at odds with a financial calculation, without a clear indication of which measure is correct.

16.2.3 Duration Adjustment

A technique that is promoted among some practitioners is the use of duration adjustment. This technique recognizes that utilization and cost of chronic patients changes over time, often increasing as the patient becomes older or acquires other conditions. In a typical DM evaluation (as we have noted in the course of this study) the chronic population "matures" between the baseline and intervention period simply because one more year passes. Maintaining the same mix of "duration" is thus difficult. In a typical DM evaluation, only three years of data are available, making it difficult to analyze duration since initial diagnosis. Nevertheless, it is possible to separate "select" (incident, or newly-diagnosed members) from "ultimate" members (those identified with the condition before the baseline period), analyze these members separately, and apply a weighting to the results of each group, when the mix changes significantly.

16.3 WHERE TO FROM HERE?

More work needs to be done to understand some of the areas we analyzed, and those discussed above. Other areas for future research include:

16.3.1 Chronic Identification

In Chapter 12 we consider the effect on the measured results of changes in the way chronic members are identified. In Chapter 11 we also demonstrated that *when* the member was identified as chronic, it can have a significant effect on trend, and thus, on the estimated savings from a program. Understanding the impact of these issues on a study is not just an actuarial task and will require involvement of clinical and actuarial researchers.

16.3.2 Transition States

I have discussed some of the implications of a transition state model earlier. If we understood chronic members' propensity to change states (particularly as their disease condition matures over time) we could perhaps do a better job of analyzing how and whether an intervention has changed that propensity.

16.3.3 What "Works" in Care Management?

Those of us who are practitioners in this area have been focused, because of the needs of our employers and clients, on assessing the impact of a program, particularly on financial outcomes. This focus has often been on program results at the expense of attempting to discern the impact of different types of intervention within sub-populations. For example, a typical disease management program may include different types of interventions delivered to many different member sub-populations (with different conditions; co-morbidities; level of severity and risk). Programs often co-exist within a health plan, with case management interventions that apply yet more intensive management to a member's problems. My prediction for care management in the future is that we will see fewer, more intensive interventions targeted at smaller chronic populations, within integrated programs that include both intensive case management and broader population management (or wellness), often delivered through a more cost-effective medium such as the internet. This trend will increase our need to know what works, with whom. It will also increase the need for more accurate predictive models to be able to identify those members who match the "target" profiles. The Value Chain approach, outlined briefly in Chapter 5, may provide a basis for understanding program components. But it will require the DM companies to be willing to share much more detailed data if we are to answer questions like "what works?"

16.3.4 A "Standard" Methodology

The DM industry has struggled and failed for a number of years to agree on a standard measurement methodology. By default, however, most evaluations tend to be performed using a variant of the Actuarially-adjusted Historical Control Methodology. Given that a large percentage of industry evaluations are performed using a similar methodology, with variation being in the details (chronic definitions; timing; exclusions and inclusions), I have suggested above that a more potentially useful expenditure of the industry's resources would be in understanding the impact on the measured results of these definitions, as a pre-cursor to developing a common set of definitions. The industry has for too long struggled to respond to the demand for an absolute result (how much was saved), a problem that may soon be answered by the Medicare Health Support program, rendering industry efforts redundant. Instead, the industry should borrow a leaf from the National Council for Quality Assessment (NCQA) book and develop a set of measures *together with standard definitions* that health plans and those performing interventions could produce that would allow comparisons to be performed. I do not think that any user of NCQA's HEDIS measures would necessarily believe that these are an *absolute* measure of health plan quality or, for that matter, that they are the only measures of health plan quality. But the measures, imperfect as they are, have the advantage of being standardized, produced by all health plans, and therefore comparable. The DM industry could perhaps learn from the experience of NCQA and develop similar measures (and definitions) that would allow valid comparisons between programs and vendors.

And in conclusion….

Thank you for your interest in this subject, and our study. I look forward to actuaries taking a prominent role in this, as in other aspects of managed care.

BIBLIOGRAPHY

1. "2005 Wellness Survey." Washington, D.C: Deloitte Consulting and Deloitte Center for Health Solutions. (2005).

2. Aldana, S.G. "Financial Impact of Health Promotion Programs: A Comprehensive Review of the Literature." *American Journal of Health Promotion.* 15(5) (2001): 296-320.

3. Allen J.K. et al., "Nurse Case Management of Hypercholesterolemia in Patients with Coronary Heart Disease: Results of a Randomized Clinical Trial." *American Heart Journal.* 144(4) (2002): 678-86.

4. "An Analysis of the Literature on Disease Management." Congressional Budget Office (CBO). Washington, D.C. October 13, 2004.

5. Anderson, D.R., et al., "Conceptual Framework, Critical Questions, and Practical Challenges in Conducting Research on the Financial Impact of Worksite Health Promotion." *American Journal of Health Promotion.* 15(5) (2001): 281-288.

6. ___. "The Relationship Between Modifiable Health Risks and Group-level Health Care Expenditures." *American Journal of Health Promotion.* 15(1) (2000): 45-52.

7. Aubert R.E., et al., "Nurse Case Management to Improve Glycemic Control in Diabetic Patients in a Health Maintenance Organization." *Annals of Internal Medicine.* 129(8) (1998): 605-12.

8. Bachler, R,I. Duncan and I. Juster. "A Comparative Analysis of Chronic and Non-Chronic Insured Commercial Member Cost Trends." *North American Actuarial Journal* 10(4) (2006):76-89.

9. Bailey, W.C., et al., "Asthma Self-Management: Do Patient Education Programs Always Have an Impact?" *Archives of Internal Medicine* 159(20) (1999): 2422-88.

10. Bailit, H.L., and C. Sennett. "Utilization Management as a Cost-containment Strategy." *Health Care Financial Review Annual Supplement.* (1991): 87-93.

11. Berger, M., "Alternative Valuations of Work Loss and Productivity." *Journal of Occupational and Environmental Medicine*. 43(1) (2001): 18-24.

12. Bodenheimer, T., E.H. Wagner, and K. Grumbach. "Improving Primary Care for Patients with Chronic Illness." *Journal of the American Medical Association.* 288(15) (2002): 1909-14.

13. Bratton, D.L., et al., "Impact of a Multidisciplinary Day Program on Disease and Healthcare Costs in Children and Adolescents with Severe Asthma: A Two-Year Follow-Up Study." *Pediatric Pulmonology.* 31(3) (2001): 177-89.

14. Brouwer, W. and M. Koopmanschap. "The Friction-cost Method: Replacement for Nothing and Leisure for Free?" *Pharmacoeconomics*. 23(2) (2005): 105-111.

15. Brown, M. "The National Economic Burden of Cancer: An Update." *Journal of the National Cancer Institute.* 82 (1990): 1811–1814.

16. Bruce, D. and J. Dickmeyer. "Don't Overlook Disease Management Programs for Low-Incidence, High-Cost Diseases to Improve your Bottom Line." *Journal of Health Care Finance.* 28(2) (2001): 45-49.

17. Burton, W. "The Role of Health Risk Factors and Disease on Worker Productivity." *Journal of Occupational and Environmental Medicine*. 41(10) (1999): 863-877.

18. Burton, W., et al., "The Association Between Health Risk Change and Presenteeism Change." *Journal of Occupational and Environmental Medicine.* 48(3) (2006): 252-263.

19. ___. "The Association of Health Risks with On-the-Job Productivity." *Journal of Occupational and Environmental Medicine.* 47(8) (2005): 769-777.

20. Calhoun J. and P. Casey. "Case Management Redesign in a Managed Care System: One Company's Experience." *Managed Care Quarterly.* 10(4) (2002): 8-12.

21. Canny, J. "Innovative Care for Chronic Conditions: Defining the Problem and Offering Effective Solutions." Presentation to the 20th Annual Academy Health Research Meeting, Nashville: June 2003.

22. Capomolla, S., et al., "Cost/Utility Ratio in Chronic Heart Failure: Comparison Between Heart Failure Management Program Delivered by Day Hospital and Usual Care." *Journal of the American College of Cardiology.* 40(7) (2002): 1289-66.

23. Celebi, D. "The Power of Predictive Modeling: Rules-based tools can forecast costs and health risk for an entire population or a single patient." *Healthcare Information.* 20 (8) (August 2003): 56.

24. "Chronic Disease Overview." Centers for Disease Control and Prevention. Accessed January 2, 2008 www.cdc.gov/nccdphp/ overview.htm#2.

25. "Cost-effectiveness of Intensive Glycemic Control, Intensified Hypertension Control, and Serum Cholesterol Level Reduction for Type 2 Diabetes." Centers for Disease Control (CDC). *Journal of the American Medical Association.* 287 (2002): 2542-51.

26. Chapman, L. "Meta-Evaluation of Worksite Health Promotion Economic Return Studies." *The Art of Health Promotion Newsletter.* Art of Health Promotion. (2003a): (6/6).

27. ___. "Proof Positive." Wellness Council of America Interview. (2003b): 1-6.

28. ___. "Planning Wellness. Getting Off to a Good Start. Part 1." *Absolute Advantage.* (2006): 5(4).

29. Cline, C.M., et al., "Cost Effective Management Program for Heart Failure Reduces Hospitalization." *Heart* 80(5) (1998): 442-46.

30. Collins, J., et al., "The Assessment of Chronic Health Conditions on Work Performance, Absence, and Total Economic Impact for Employers." *Journal of Occupational and Environmental Medicine* 47(6) (2005): 547-557.

31. Costantini, O., et al., "Impact Of A Guideline-Based Disease Management Team on Outcomes of Hospitalized Patients with Congestive Heart Failure." *Arch Internal Medical.* 161 (2001): 177-82.

32. Costich, T.D. and F.C. Lee. "Improving Cancer Care in a Kentucky Managed Care Plan: A Case Study of Cancer Disease Management." *Disease Management.* 6(1) (2003): 9-20.

33. Cousins, M. and Y. Liu. "Cost Savings for a PPO Population with Multi-condition Disease Management: Evaluating Program Impact Using Predictive Modeling with a Control Group," *Disease Management.* 6(4) (2003): 207-217.

34. "Crossing the Quality Chasm: The IOM Health Care Quality Initiative," Institute of Medicine. 2003.

35. Cumming, R.B., et al., "A Comparative Analysis of Claims-Based Methods of Health Risk Assessment for Commercial Populations." Society of Actuaries. 2002.

36. Davila, F. "Understanding Health and Healthcare Total costs: A Novel Perspective." *American Journal of Managed Care*. September (2002); Suppl:6-8

37. Davis, K. "Health and Productivity Among U.S. Workers." The Commonwealth Fund. New York: (2005): 1-10.
www.commonwealthfund.org/publications/publications_show.htm? doc_id=294176

38. DeBusk, R.F. et al., "A Case-Management System for Coronary Risk Factor Modification after Acute Myocardial Infarction." *Annals of Internal Medicine.* 120(9) (1994): 721-29.

39. DeCoster, C., et al., "Inappropriate Hospital Use by Patients Receiving Care for Medical Conditions: Targeting Utilization Review." *Canadian Medical Association Journal* 157(7) (1997): 889-96.

40. Delichatsios, H., M. Callahan, and M. Charlson. "Outcomes of Telephone Medical Care." *Journal of General Internal Medicine* 13(9) (1998): 579-85.

41. Devine, R., et al., "Crossing the Great Divide: How Integrated & Population-Focused Benefit Solutions Can Reduce Your Costs and Improve Employee Health." San Diego: IBI-NBGH Joint Forum on Health, Productivity & Absence Management. 2005

42. Diehr, P., et al "Methods for analyzing health care utilization and costs." *Annual Review of Public Health.* 20 (1999): 125-144.

43. "Disease Management Programs: What's the Cost?" American Academy of Actuaries. Washington, D.C. 2005.

44. "Disease Management Practice Note." American Academy of Actuaries. Washington, D.C. 2008.

45. "DMAA Definition of DM." Disease Management Association of America. Available at www.dmaa.org/definition.html. Accessed August, 2007.

46. Domurat, E.S. "Diabetes Managed Care and Clinical Outcomes: The Harbor City, California Kaiser Permanente Diabetes Care System." *American Journal of Managed Care.* 5(10) (1999): 1299-1307.

47. Dove, H., I.G. Duncan, and A.S. Robb. "A Prediction Model for Targeting Low-Cost, High-Risk Members of Managed Care Organizations." *American Journal of Managed Care*, 2003, 9 (5): 381-389.

48. Duncan, I.G. "Understanding the Economics of Disease Management" in *Health Section News.* Society of Actuaries Health Section. August 2003.

49. ___. "It's Time for the Industry to Move on from ROI." *Disease Management.* 7(3) (2004): 159-160.

50. ___. "An Introduction to Care Management Interventions and their Implications for Actuaries. Paper 6: An Actuarial Method for Evaluating Disease Management Outcomes." Society of Actuaries, 2005.

51. Duncan, I.G., ed. *Dictionary of Disease Management Terminology.* Washington, D.C: Disease Management Association of America. 2004.

52. ___. *Dictionary of Disease Management Terminology.* 2nd ed. Washington, D.C: Disease Management Association of America. Washington, D.C. 2006.

53. Duncan, I.G. and A.S Robb: "Population Risk Management: Reducing Costs and Managing Risk in Health Insurance" in L.C. Jain and A. Shapiro, eds. "Intelligent and other Computational Techniques for the Insurance Industry." *World Scientific*, December 2003.

54. Dunn, Graham, et al., "Describing, Explaining or Predicting Mental Health Care Costs: A Guide to Regression Models, Methodological Review." *British Journal of Psychiatry*, 183 (2003): 398-404.

55. Edington, D. "Emerging Research: A View from One Research Center." *American Journal of Health Promotion* 15(5) (2001): 341-349.

56. ___. "Who Are the Intended Beneficiaries (Targets) of Employee Health Promotion and Wellness Programs?" *North Carolina Medical Journal.* 67(6) (2006): 425-427.

57. Edington, D., et al., "The Financial Impact of Changes in Personal Health Practices." *Journal of Occupational and Environmental Medicine*. 39(11) (1997): 1037-1046.

58. Fetterolf D., D. Wennberg, and A. Devries, "Estimating the Return on Investment in Disease Management Programs using a Pre-post Analysis." *Disease Management.* 7(1)(2004): 5-23.

59. Fetterolf, D. "Notes from the Field: the Economic Value Chain in Disease Management Organizations." *Disease Management.* 9 (6) (2006): 316-327.

60. Fitzgerald, J.F., et al., A Case Manager Intervention to Reduce Readmissions. *Archives of Internal Medicine* 154(15) (1994): 1721-29.

61. Fitzner, Karen et al., "Principles for Assessing Disease Management Outcomes." *Disease Management.* 7(3), October 2004.

62. ___. "Disease Management Program Evaluation Guide." Disease Management Association of America. 2004.

63. ___. "Guide to Disease Management Outcomes Evaluation." Washington, D.C.: Disease Management Association of America. 2004.

64. Flynn, K.E., et al., "From Physician to Consumer: The Effectiveness of Strategies to Manage Health Care Utilization." *Medical Care Research and Review* 59(4) (2002): 455-81.

65. Fonarow, G.C., et al., "Impact of a Comprehensive Heart Failure Management Program in Hospital Readmission and Functional Status of Patients with Advanced Heart Failure." *Journal of American College of Cardiology.* 3(30) (1997): 725-32.

66. Forman, S.A., "Breakthroughs in High-Risk Population Health Management." San Francisco: Jossey-Bass Publishers, 2000.

67. Fries, J.F., et al., "Two-Year Results Of A Randomized Controlled Trial Of Health Promotion Program In A Retiree Population: The Bank Of America Study." *American Journal of Medicine* (94) (1993): 57-64.

67a. Galbreath, A.D., et al., "Long-Term Health Care and Cost Outcomes of Disease Management in a Large, Randomized, Community-Based Population with Heart Failure." *Circulation* (2004): 110; 1-9.

68. Garis R.I. and K.C. Farmer. "Examining Costs of Chronic Conditions in a Medicaid Population." *Managed Care.* 11(8) (August 2002): 43-50.

69. Gattis, W.A., et al., "Reduction in Heart Failure Events by the Addition of a Clinical Pharmacist to the Heart Failure Management Team." *Archives of Internal Medicine.* (1999): 1939-45.

70. Ghosh, C.S., et al., "Reductions in Hospital Use from Self Management Training for Chronic Asthmatics." *Social Science and Medicine* 46(8) (1998): 1087-93.

71. Gingrich, N., Ph.D. "Saving Lives and Saving Money." Washington, D.C.: The Alexis DeToqueville Institute, 2003.

72. Goetzel, R.Z. "The Role of Business in Improving the Health of Workers and the Community," National Institute of Medicine, 2001(a).

73. ___. "The Financial Impact Of Health Promotion And Disease Prevention Programs: Why is it So Hard to Prove Value?" *American Journal of Health Promotion* 15(5) (2001b): 277-280.

74. ___. "Better Outcomes Through Health and Productivity Management," Supplement to Managed Care. Las Vegas: 2005 Medical Director Colloquy, October 2005.

75. ___. "Examining the Value of Integrating Occupational Health and Safety and Health Promotion Programs in the Workplace." Washington, D.C.: National Institute of Occupational Safety and Health (NIOSH), 2005(a)

76. Goetzel, R.Z., et al., "The Relationship Between Modifiable Health Risks and Health Care Expenditures: An Analysis of the Multi-employer HERO Health Risk and Cost Database." *Journal of Occupational and Environmental Medicine.* 40(10) (1998): 843-854.

77. ___. "Return on Investment in Disease Management: A Review." *Health Care Financing Review*, 26(4) (Summer 2005): 1-19.

78. ___. "Health and Productivity Management: Establishing Key Performance Measures, Benchmarks, and Best Practices." *Journal of Occupational and Environmental Medicine.* 43(1) (2001): 10-17.

79. ___. "Health, Absence, Disability, and Presenteeism Cost Estimates of Certain Physical and Mental Health Conditions Affecting U.S. Employers." *Journal of Occupational and Environmental Medicine.* 46(4) (2004): 398-412.

80. ___ ."Evidence of a Return on Investment (ROI) from Selected Disease Management Programs: A Review of the Literature," 2003.

81. ___. "Estimating the Return-on-Investment from Changes in Employee Health Risks on The Dow Chemical Company's Health Care Costs." *Journal of Occupational and Environmental Medicine.* 47(8) (2005): 759-768.

82. Goetzel, R.Z. and R.J. Ozminkowski. "What's Holding You Back: Why Should (or Shouldn't) Employers Invest in Health Promotion Programs for Their Workers?" *North Carolina Medical Journal.* 67(6) (2006): 428-430.

83. Goetzel, R. and R. Ozminkowski. "Health and Productivity Management: Emerging Opportunities for Health Promotion Professionals for the 21st Century." *American Journal of Health Promotion* 14(5) (2000): 211-214.

84. Golaszewski, T. "Shining Lights: Studies That Have Most Influenced the Understanding of Health Promotion's Financial Impact." *American Journal of Health Promotion* 15(5) (2001): 332-340.

85. Gomaa, W., P. Muntendam, and T. Morrow. "Technology-based Disease Management, a Low-Cost, High-Value Solution for the Management of Chronic Disease." *Disease Management Health Outcomes.* 9(10) (2001): 577-588.

86. Gordon, N.F., et al., "Effectiveness of Three Models for Comprehensive Cardiovascular Disease Risk Reduction." *American Journal of Cardiology* 89(11) (2002): 1263-68.

87. Gorski, L.A. and K.A. Johnson. "Disease Management Program for Heart Failure." *Lippincott's Case Management* 8(6) (2003): 265-73.

88. Gruber W., et al., "The Economics of Diabetes and Diabetes Care." Brussels: *International Diabetes Federation*, 1998.

89. "Health Improvement: Comprehensive Guide to Designing, Implementing and Evaluating Worksite Programs." Washington, D.C.: The National Business Group on Health. (2003) www.businessgrouphealth.org.

90. "Health Improvement: Comprehensive Guide to Designing, Implementing and Evaluating Worksite Programs." Washington, D.C.: The National Business Group on Health. (2004) www.businessgrouphealth.org.

91. Heaney, C. and R.Z. Goetzel. "A Review of Health-related Outcomes of Multicomponent Worksite Health Promotion Programs." *American Journal of Health Promotion.* 11(4) (1997): 290-308.

92. "HEDIS 2003 Technical Specifications," National Council on Quality Assessment, 2004. Ian Duncan, ed: *Dictionary of Disease Management Terminology*. Washington, D.C.: Disease Management Association of America, 2004.

93. Heffler, S., et al., "U.S. Health Spending Projections for 2004-2014." *Health Affairs.* Web Exclusive, 2005.

94. Heidenreich, P.A, C.M. Ruggiero and B.M. Massie. "Effect of a Home Monitoring System on Hospitalization and Resource Use for Patients with Heart Failure." *American Heart Journal.* (1999): 138(4).

95. Hemp, P. "Presenteeism: At Work – But Out of It." *Harvard Business Review.* (2004): 1-9.

96. Hocking, R.R. "The Analysis and Selection of Variables in Linear Regression," *Biometrics.* (1976): 32.

97. Hoffman C., D. Rice and H.Y. Sung. "Persons with Chronic Conditions. Their Prevalence and Costs." *Journal of the American Medical Association* 276(18) (November 1996): 1473-9.

98. Hoffman, J. "Broad Disease Management Interventions: Reducing Health Care Costs for Plan Members with Congestive Heart Failure." *Disease Management Health Outcomes* 9(10) (2001): 527-29.

99. Hogan, Paul (for the American Diabetes Association). "Economic Costs of Diabetes in the U.S.," *Diabetes Care,* 2003.

100. "Industry Report Card. U.S. Corporate Health Care – Issuers Looking To Benefit From Aging Population Should Proceed With Caution." New York: Standard & Poor's, 2006.

101. Jolly, K., et al., "Randomized Controlled Trial of Follow-up Care in General Practice of Patient with Myocardial Infarction and Angina." *British Medical Journal.* 318 (1999): 706-11.

102. ___. "Follow-up Care in General Practice of Patient with Myocardial Infarction and Angina." *Family Practice.* 15(6) (1998): 548-55.

103. Kahn, K.L., et al., "Comparing Outcomes of Care Before and After Implementation of the DRG-based Prospective Payment System." *Journal of the American Medical Association*, 264 (15) (October 17, 1990): 1984-8.

104. Kauppinen, R., et al., "Long-Term Economic Evaluation of Intensive Patient Education During the First Treatment Year in Newly Diagnosed Adult Asthma." *Respiratory Medicine* 95(1) (2001): 56-63.

105. Ketner, L. "Population Management Takes Disease Management to the Next Level." *Health Financial Management* 53(8) (1999): 36-39.

106. Khandker, R.K. and W.G. Manning. "The Impact of Utilization Review on Costs and Utilization." *Developments in Health Economics and Public Policy* 1 (1992): 47-62.

107. Khandker, R.K., W.G. Manning, and T. Ahmed. "Utilization Review Savings at the Micro Level." *Medical Care.* 30(11) (1992): 1043-52.

108. Kilian, R., et al., "A Comparison of Methods to Handle Skewcost Variables in the Analysis of the Resource Consumption in Schizophrenia Treatment." *Journal of Mental Health Policy and Economics* 5 (200): 21-31.

109. Kinmonth, A. et al., "Randomized Controlled Trial of Patient-Centered Care of Diabetes in General Practice. *British Medical Journal.* 317 (1998): 1202-08.

110. Klonoff, D.C. and D.M. Schwartz. "An Economic Analysis of Interventions for Diabetes." *Diabetes Care* 23(3) (2000): 390-404.

110a. Kongstvedt, P.R., *The Managed Health Care Handbook*, 4th ed. Aspen Publishers (2001).

111. Krause, David S., "Review of the Literature: The Financial Effectiveness of Disease Management, unpublished manuscript. Presented to the Conference Maximizing." San Francisco.: *Disease Management.* ROI, November 10, 2003.

112. Laramee, A.S., et al., "Case Management in a Heterogeneous Congestive Heart Failure Population: A Randomized Controlled Trial." *Archives of Internal Medicine.* 163(7) (2003): 809-17.

113. Lattimer, V., et al., "Cost Analysis of Nurse Telephone Consultation In Out of Hours Primary Care: Evidence from a Randomized Controlled Trial." *British Medical Journal.* 320(7421) (2000): 1053-57.

114. Leatherman, S., et al., "The Business Case for Quality: Case Studies and an Analysis." *Health Affairs.* 22(2) (2003): 17-30.

115. Lessler, D.S. and T.M. Wickizer. "The Impact of Utilization Management on Readmissions among Patients with Cardiovascular Disease." *Health Services Resource.* 34(6) (2000): 1315-29.

116. Leutzinger, J., et al., "Projecting Future Medical Care Costs Using Four Scenarios of Lifestyle Risk Rates." *American Journal of Health Promotion.* 15(1) (2000): 35-44.

117. Levin-Scherz, J. "Disease Management Will Suffer if Providers Remain on the Sidelines." *Disease Management.* 8(4) (2005): 199-204.

118. Lewis, A. "Mild Cases of Disease Throw off ROI Numbers, But New Calculations Balance Out Regression to the Mean. Managed Healthcare Executive." (2007) www.managedhealthcareexecutive.com/mhe/content/printContent Popup.jsp?id=415870.

119. Linden, A. "What Will It Take for Disease Management to Demonstrate a Return on Investment? New Perspectives on an Old Theme." *American Journal/Managed Care* 12(4) (2006): 217-222.

120. Linden, A., J.L. Adams, and N. Roberts "An Assessment of the Total Population Approach for Evaluating Disease Management Program Effectiveness." *Disease Management.* 6(2) Summer 2003.

120a. ___. "Evaluating Disease Management Programme Effectiveness: An Introduction to the Regression Discontinuity Design," *Journal of Evaluation in Clinical Pradctice*, 10 (2004)

121. ___. "Using Propensity Scores to Construct Comparable Control Groups for Disease Management Program Evaluation." *Disease Management and Health Outcomes* 13(2) (2005): 107-127.

122. Litzelman, D.K., et al., "Reduction of Lower Extremity Clinical Abnormalities in Patients with Non-Insulin-Dependent Diabetes Mellitus." *Annals of Internal Medicine.* 119(1) (1993): 36-41.

123. Liu, X., R. Sturm, and B.J. Cuffel. "The Impact of prior Authorization on Outpatient Utilization in Managed Behavioral Health Plans." *Medical Care Research Review.* 57(2) (2000):182-95.

124. Loeppke, R. "The Business Impact of Health and Health-Related Productivity." American Occupational Health Conference Joint Seminar No. 905. Atlanta: 2003.

125. Lucas, D.O., et al., "Two-Year Results from the Asthma Self-Management Program: Long-Term Impact on Health Care Services, Costs, Functional Status, and Productivity." *Journal of Asthma* 38(4): (2001) 321-33.

126. Lucas, F.L., D.E. Wennberg and D.J Malenka. "Variation in the Use of Echocardiography." Effective Clinical Practice. 2 (2) (March-April 1999): 71-5.

127. Lukacs, S.L., et al., "Effectiveness of an Asthma Management Program for Pediatric Members of a Large HMO." A*rchives of Pediatric and Adolescent Medicine* 156(9) (2002): 872-76.

128. Lynch, J.P., et al., "High-Risk Population Health Management: Achieving Improved Outcomes and Near-term Financial Results." *American Journal of Managed Care.* (6) (2000): 781-791

129. Lynne, D. "Diabetes Disease Management in Managed Care Organizations." *Disease Management* 7(1) (2004).

130. Mattke, S. MD, et al., "Evidence for the Effect of Disease Management: Is $1 Billion a Year a Good Investment?" *American. Journal of Managed Care* 13 (2007): 670-676.

131. Mattke, S., et al., "A Review of Methods to Measure Health-related Productivity Loss." *American Journal of Managed Care.* 13(4) (2007): 211-217.

132. Mattke, S., "Measuring and Reporting the Performance of Disease Management Programs," *RAND Health*, 2006.

133. McAlister, F.A., et al., "Randomized Trials of Secondary Prevention Programmes in Coronary Heart Disease: Systematic Review." *British Medical Journal.* 323 (2001): 957-62.

134. ___. "A Systematic Review of Randomized Trials of Disease Management Programs in Heart Failure." *American Journal of Medicine.* 110 (2001): 378-84.

135. McGinnis, J.M. and W.H. Foege. "The Immediate vs the Important." *Journal of the American Medical Association.* 291 (2004): 1263-1264.

136. "Medicaid Program General Information. U.S. Department of Health and Human Services." Available at www.cms.hhs.gov/ MedicaidGenInfo/. Accessed November, 2007.

137. Mokdad, A.H. "Actual Causes of Death in the United States, 2000." *Journal of the American Medical Association.* 291(10) (2004): 1238-1245.

138. Moeller, J.F., et al., "Projecting National Medical Expenditure Survey data: a framework for MEPS projections." MEPS Methodology Report No. 13, AHRQ Pub. No. 02-0009. Rockville, MD: Agency for Healthcare Research and Quality, 2002.

139. Mood, A., and F. Graybill: *Introduction to the Theory of Statistics*. 2nd ed. New York: McGraw-Hill, 1963.

140. Morgan, M.W., et al., "Randomized, Controlled Trial of an Interactive Videodisc Decision Aid for Patients with Ischemic Heart Disease." *Journal of General Internal Medicine.* 15(10) (2000): 685-93.

141. Mulvihill, M. "The Definition and Core Practices of Wellness." *Journal of Employee Assistance.* (4th Quarter) (2003): 13-15.

142. Murray, M.E. and J.B. Henriques. "An Exploratory Cost Analysis of Performing Hospital-Based Concurrent Utilization Review." *American Journal of Managed Care* 9(7) (2003): 512-18.

143. Musich, S.A., et al., "Examination of Risk Status Transitions Among Active Employees in a Comprehensive Worksite Health Promotion Program." *Journal of Occupational and Environmental Medicine* 45(4) (2003): 393-399.

144. Naji, S. "Integrated Care for Diabetes: Clinical, Psychosocial, and Economic Evaluation." *British Medical Journal.* 308 (1994): 1208-12.

145. Naylor, M.D., et al., "Comprehensive Discharge Planning and Home Follow-up of Hospitalized Elders." *Journal of the American Medical Association* 281(7) (1999): 613-20.

146. ___. "Comprehensive Discharge Planning for the Hospitalized Elderly." *Annals of internal Medicine* 120(12) (1994): 999-1006.

147. Nicholson, S., "How to Present the Business Case for Healthcare Quality to Employers." *Applied Health Economics and Health Policy* 4(4) (2005): 209-218.

148. Nicholson, S., et al., "Measuring the Effects of Work Loss on Productivity with Team Production." *Health Economics* 15 (2006): 111-123.

149. Norris, S.L., et al., and the Task Force on Community Preventive Services. "The Effectiveness of Disease and Case Management for People with Diabetes." *American Journal of Preventive Medicine.* 2002: 15-38.

150. O'Connell, J.M., et al., "Satisfaction and Return-on-Investment Study of a Nurse Triage Service." *American Journal of Managed Care.* 7(2) (2001): 159-69.

151. O'Connor, P.J., et al., "Continuous Quality Improvement Can Improve Glycemic Control for HMO Patients with Diabetes." *Archives of Family Medicine.* 5(9) (1996): 502-506.

152. Olsen, J. and J. Richardson "Production Gains from Health Care: What Should be Included in Cost-effectiveness Analyses?" *Social Science & Medicine.* 49 (1999).

153. Onsite Healthcare webpage. downloaded 04/07,
www.onsitehealthcare.com/presenteeism.html
http://wfnetwork.bc.edu/glossary_entry.php?term=Presenteeism,%20Definition(s)%20of.

154. "Outcome Guidelines Report." 1st ed. Washington, D.C: Disease Management Association of America. 2006.

155. "Outcome Guidelines Report." 2nd ed. Washington, D.C: Disease Management Association of America. 2007.

155a. "Outcome Guidelines Report." 3rd ed. Washington, D.C: Disease Management Association of America. 2008.

156. Ozminkowski, R. and R. Goetzel. "Getting Closer to the Truth: Overcoming Research Challenges when Estimating the Financial Impact of Worksite Health Promotion Programs." *American Journal of Health Promotion.* 15(5) (2001): 289-295.

157. Ozminkowski, R.J. "The Impact of the Citibank, NA, Health Management Program on Changes in Employee Health Risks Over Time." *Journal of Occupational and Environmental Medicine.* 42(5) (2000): 502-511.

158. Parry, T., "The Business Case for Managing Health and Productivity." San Francisco: Integrated Benefits Institute. 2004. www.ibiweb.org

159. Parry, T. and B. Auerbach. "Linking Medical Care to Productivity." San Francisco: Integrated Benefits Institute. 2001. www.ibiweb.org

160. Parry, T., et al., "The Impact of Integrating Health and Disability Data." San Francisco: Integrated Benefits Institute. 2006. www.ibiweb.org

161. Pauly, M., et al., "A General Model of the Impact of Absenteeism on Employers and Employees." *Health Economics.* 11 (2002): 221-231.

162. Pelletier, K. "A Review and Analysis of the Clinical and Cost-Effectiveness Studies of Comprehensive Health Promotion and Disease Management Programs at the Worksite: 1998-2000 Update." *American Journal of Health Promotion.* 16(2) (2001): 107-116.

163. Philbin, E.F. "Comprehensive Multi-Disciplinary Programs for the Management of Patients with Congestive Heart Failure." *Journal of General and Internal Medicine.* 14 (1999): 130-35.

164. Phillips, C.O., et al., "Comprehensive Discharge Planning with Postdischarge Support for Older Patients with Congestive Heart Failure, A Meta-Analysis." *Journal of the American Medical Association.* 291 (2004):1358-67.

165. Piette, J.D., et al., "Do Automated Calls with Nurse Follow-up Improve Self-Care and Glycemic Control among Vulnerable Patients with Diabetes?" *American Journal of Medicine.* 108(1) (2000): 20-27.

166. Porter, M. "*Competitive Advantage: Creating and Sustaining Superior Performance.*" New York, NY: Free Press, 1985.

167. "Preventing Chronic Diseases: A Vital Investment." Geneva: World Health Organization, 2005.

168. Pronk, N.P., et al., "Relationship Between Modifiable Health Risks and Short-term Health Care Charges." *Journal of the American Medical Association* 282(23) (1999): 2235-2239.

169. Ramsay, J. "Integrating Health & Safety: What Might Be ASSE's Role?" CDC-NIOSH Steps to a Healthier U.S. Washington, D.C.: Workforce Symposium, 2004.

170. "Reducing Corporate Health Care Costs 2006 Survey." Deloitte Consulting and Deloitte Center for Health Solutions. Washington, D.C. 2006.

171. Rich, M.W., et al., "Effect of a Multidisciplinary Intervention on Medication Compliance in Elderly Patients with Congestive Heart Failure." *American Journal of Medicine* 101(3) (1996): 270-76.

172. ___. "A Multidisciplinary Intervention to Prevent the Readmission of Elderly Patients with Congestive Heart Failure." *New England Journal of Medicine.* 333(18) (1995): 1190-95.

173. Riedel, J., et al., "The Effect of Disease Prevention and Health Promotion on Workplace Productivity: A Literature Review." *American Journal of Health Promotion.* 15(3) (2001): 167-191.

174. Riegel, B., et al., "Effect of a Standardized Nurse Case-Management Telephone Intervention on Resource Use in Patients with Chronic Heart Failure. *Archives of Internal Medicine.*162(6) (2002): 705-12.

175. Rosenberg, S.N., et al., "Effect of Utilization Review in a Fee-for-Service Health Insurance Plan." *New England Journal of Medicine* November 333(20) (November 1995): 1326-30.

176. Rubin R.J., et al., "Health care expenditures for people with diabetes mellitus." *Journal of Clinical Endocrinology and Metabolism.* 78: (1992): 809A–809F 1992.

177. ___. "Clinical And Economic Impact of Implementing a Comprehensive Diabetes Management Program in Managed Care." *Journal of Clinical Endocrinology Metabolism* 83(8) (1998): 2635-41.

178. Sabin, M. "Telephone Triage Improves Demand Management Effectiveness." *Healthcare Financial Management* 52(8) (1998): 49-52.

179. Sadur, C.N., et al., "Diabetes Management in a Health Maintenance Organization. Efficacy of Care Management Using Cluster Visits." *Diabetes Care.* 22(12) (1999): 2011-17.

180. Scheffler, R., et al., "The Impact of Blue Cross and Blue Shield Plan Utilization Management Programs 1980-1988." *Inquiry.* 28(3) (1991): 263-75.

181. Schermer, T.R., et al., "Randomized Controlled Economic Evaluation of Asthma Self-management in Primary Health Care." *American Journal of Respiratory Medicine.* 166(8) (2002): 1062-72.

182. Seabury, S., et al., "The Economics of Integrating Injury and Illness Prevention and Health Promotion Programs," RAND Institute for Civil Justice, 2005.

183. Serxner, S., et al., "Guidelines for Analysis of Economic Return from Health Management Programs." *The Art of Health Promotion.* 2006.

184. "Seven Benchmarks of Success," Wellness Council of America (no date). www.welcoa.org/wellworkplace/index.php?category=2 accessed 04/07.

185. Sidorov, J., et al., "Does Diabetes Disease Management Save Money and Improve Outcomes? A Report of Simultaneous Short-Term Savings and Quality Improvement Associated with a Health Maintenance Organization-Sponsored Disease Management Program among Patients Fulfilling Health Employer Data and Information Set Criteria." *Diabetes Care.* 25(4) (2002): 684-89.

186. Snyder, J.W., et al., "Quality Improvement and Cost Reduction Realized by a Purchaser through Diabetes." *Disease Management.* 6(4) (2003): 233-41.

187. Sorensen, G. and E. Barbeau. "Steps to a Healthier US Workforce: Integrating Occupational Health and Safety and Worksite Health Promotion: State of the Science." Washington, D.C.: NIOSH - Steps to a Healthier US Workforce Symposium. 2004. www.cdc.gov/niosh/worklife/steps/pdfs/Sorensen%20plenary.pdf

188. "Standard Outcomes Metrics and Evaluation Methodology for Disease Management Programs." American Healthways, Inc., and Johns Hopkins University: *Disease Management*, 6(3) (Fall 2003) 121-138.

189. Stewart, W., et al., "Lost Productive Time and Cost Due to Common Pain Conditions in the US Workforce." *Journal of the American Medical Association* 290(18) (2003): 2443-2454.

190. Stewart, S., J.E. Marley, and J.D.Horowitz. "Effects of a Multi-Disciplinary Home-based Intervention on Planned Readmissions and Survival among Patients with Chronic Congestive Heart Failure." *Lancet* 354 (1999): 1077-83.

191. Strunk B.C. and Ginsburg P.B. "Tracking health care costs: trends stabilize but remain high in 2002." *Health Affairs*, Millwood (2003) Jan-Jun; Suppl Web Exclusives: W3-266-74.

192. Sullivan, S.D., et al., and National Cooperative Inner-City Asthma Study (NCICAS) Investigators. The Cost-Effectiveness of an Inner-City Asthma Intervention for Children. *Journal of Allergy & Clinical Immunology* 110(4) (2002): 576-81.

193. Testa, M. A. and D. C. Simonson. 1998. Health Economic Benefits and Quality of Life during Improved Glycemic Control in Patients with Type 2 Diabetes Mellitus: A Randomized, Controlled, Double-Blind Trial. *Journal of American Medical Association* 280(17): 1490-96.

194. "The Burden of Chronic Diseases and Their Risk Factors National and State Perspectives." Atlanta, U. S. Department Of Health and Human Services. Centers for Disease Control and Prevention. Atlanta. 2004 www.cdc.gov/nccdphp.

195. "The Power of Prevention. Reducing the Health and Economic Burden of Chronic Disease." U.S. Department of Health and Human Services. Centers for Disease Control and Prevention. Atlanta. 2003 www.cdc.gov/nccdphp.

196. Thorpe KE, et al., "Trends: The Impact Of Obesity On Rising Medical Spending." *Health Affairs* Millwood: (2004a). Oct 20, 2004 (e-published ahead of print).

197. Thorpe KE, C.S. Florence and P. Joski. "Which Medical Conditions Account For The Rise In Health Care Spending?" *Health Affairs* Millwood: (2004b) Aug 25, 2004 (e-published ahead of print).

198. Tompa, E. "The Impact of Health on Productivity: Empirical Evidence and Policy Implications." *The Review of Economic Performance and Social Progress* (2002) 181-202.

198a. Trochim, William M.K., "Research Design for Program Evaluation," Sage, 1984.

199. "Unscheduled Absence Survey." CCH. 2006. www.cch.com/press/ news/2006/20061026h.asp.

200. Vaccaro, J., et al., "Utilization Reduction, Cost Savings and Return on Investment for the Pacificare Chronic Heart Failure Program." *Disease Management.* 4(3) (2001): 131-38.

201. Van Den Eynde, M. "A Sustainable Solution," Americas Health Insurance Plans, 2006 www.deloitte.com/dtt/cda/doc/content/us_l shc_sustainable_solution_oct2006.pdf.

202. Vickery, D.M., et al., "Effect of a Self-Care Education Program on Medical Visits." *Journal of the American Medical Association.* 250(21): (December 2, 1983) 2952-56.

203. Villagra, V.G. "Strategies to control costs and quality: a focus on outcomes research for disease management." *Medical Care.* 42(4 (supp)) (2004): 24-30.

204. ___. "Effectiveness of A Disease Management Program for Patients with Diabetes." *Health Affairs* 23(4) (2004): 255-266.

205. Viner, K.M., et al., "Managed Care Organization Authorization Denials: Lack of Patient Knowledge and Timely Alternative Ambulatory Care." *Annals of Emergency Medicine* 35(3) (2000): 272-76.

206. Vinicor, F., et al., "Diabeds: A Randomized Trial of the Effects of Physician and/or Patient Education on Diabetes Patient Outcomes." *Journal of Chronic Disease.* 40(4) (1987): 345-56.

207. Wachter, R.M. "Hospitalists in the United States- Mission Accomplished or Work in Progress?" *New England Journal of Medicine*, 350(19) May, 2004.

208. Wagner, E. and N. Sandhu. "Effect of Improved Glycemic Control on Health Care Costs and Utilization." *Journal of the American Medical Association.* 285(2) (2001): 182-89.

209. Weingarten, S.R., et al.,. "Interventions Used in Disease Management Programmes for Patients with Chronic Illness—Which Ones Work? Meta-Analysis of Published Reports." *British Medical Journal* 325(7370) (2002): 925.

210. ___. "Practice Guidelines and Reminders to Reduce Duration of Hospital Stay for Patients with Chest Pain. An Interventional Trial." *Ann Internal Medicine* 120(4) (1994): 257-63.

211. Wennberg, D., et al., "The Relationship Between the Supply of Cardiac Catheterization Laboratories, Cardiologists and the Use of Invasive Cardiac Procedures in Northern New England." *Journal of Health Services Research Policy*, 2 (2) (April 1997): 75-80.

212. Wennberg, J.E. "On Patient Need, Equity, Supplier-Induced Demand, and the Need to Assess the Outcome of Common Medical Practices." *Medical Care*, (5) (May 23, 1985): 512-20.

213. Wennberg, J.E., et al., "Use Of Hospitals, Physician Visits, and Hospice Care During Last Six Months of Life Among Cohorts Loyal to Highly Respected Hospitals in the United States." *British Medical Journal*, (7440) (March 12, 2004): 607.

214. Whitmer, R.W., et al., "A Wake Up Call for Corporate America." *Journal of Occupational and Environmental Medicine* 45(9) (2003): 916-925.

215. Wheeler, J. "Can a Disease Self Management Program Reduce Health Care Costs? The Case of Older Women with Heart Disease." *Medical Care.* 41(6) (2003): 706-15.

216. Whellan, D.J., et al., The Benefit of Implementing a Heart Failure Disease Management Program." *Archives of Internal Medicine.* 161(18) (2001): 2223-28.

217. Wickizer, T.M.D. and Lessler. "Utilization Management: Issues, Effects and Future Prospects." *Annual Review of Public Health* 23 (2002): 233-54.

218. Wilson, T.W., et al., "Assessing Return on Investment of Defined-Population Disease Management Interventions." *Joint Commission Journal on Quality and Safety*, 30 (11) November 2004.

219. Wilson, T.W. and M. MacDowell. "Framework for Assessing Causality in Disease Management: Principles." *Disease Management*, 6 (3) Fall 2003.

220. Winkelman, R and S. Mehmud. "*A Comparative Analysis of Claims-Based Tools for Health Risk Assessment.*" Schaumburg, IL. Society of Actuaries, 2007.

221. Wright, D., et al., "Comparing Excess Costs across Multiple Corporate Populations." *Journal of Occupational and Environmental Medicine.* 46(9) (2004): 937-945.

222. Yen, L., A. Schultz, et al., "Financial Costs Due to Excess Health Risks Among Active Employees of a Utility Company." *Journal of Occupational and Environmental Medicine.* 48(9) (2006): 896-905.

223. Yu, W. "Prevalence and Costs of Chronic Conditions in the VA HC System." *Medical Care Research and Review*, 2003.

224. Yu W., et al., "The Relationships among Age, Chronic Conditions, And Healthcare Costs." *American Journal of Managed Care*. 10(12) (December 2004): 909-16.

225. Zhang, P., et al., "Application of Economic Analysis to Diabetes and Diabetes Care." *Annals of Internal Medicine.* 140 (2004): 972-977.

INDEX